Robert T. Dixon

Associate Professor of Astronomy
Riverside City College

DYNAMIC ASTRONOMY

Second edition

Prentice-Hall, Inc., Englewood Cliffs, New Jersey

Library of Congress Cataloging in Publication Data

Dixon, Robert T
    Dynamic astronomy.

    Includes bibliographies and index.
    1. Astronomy.   I. Title.
QB43.2.D58 1975   520   74-19467
ISBN 0-13-221234-X

This book has been composed on film in Bembo, with headings in Bembo Bold. Line illustrations were prepared by Herschel Wartik, Inc. Production by Bert N. Zelman and Norma Karlin. Typographical design by John J. Dunleavy.

10   9   8   7   6   5   4   3   2   1

Prentice-Hall International, Inc., London
Prentice-Hall of Australia, Pty. Ltd., Sydney
Prentice-Hall of Canada, Ltd., Toronto
Prentice-Hall of India Private Ltd., New Delhi
Prentice-Hall of Japan, Inc., Tokyo

Contents

Preface

Like the first edition of this text, which has been used in over 200 colleges and universities in the United States and elsewhere, this revised version is designed to help the liberal arts student and general reader to gain an understanding of how the astronomer studies his subject and to appreciate the grandeur of the universe in which we live. No prior background in science is presumed. Concepts are developed in the light of common experiences, and what little mathematics is needed is developed as the need arises. Relationships that are usually presented only as mathematical expressions are also stated verbally in order to dispel any anxiety on the part of the reader as to the mysteries of mathematics. The real beauty of astronomy lies not only in the facts that surround the subject but also in the development of an understanding of relationships within the universe. The background of thought that has brought us to our present view of the cosmos is presented here in conjunction with the methods whereby we make pertinent observations.

This revision represents not only the updating of information relative to a fast-moving science, but also it represents a move in the direction of a more comprehensive treatment of astronomy. Significant portions of the text have been completely rewritten to reflect the current state of the art. Within the coming years, we in North America will be moving toward almost exclusive use of the International System of Units (*Système International,* SI), and this will be the system adopted for this edition. In the first two chapters, in order to familiarize the reader with this system, the SI units will be followed by English units in parentheses; in subsequent chapters, however, the SI units will be used exclusively. An explanation of this system, together with the conversion factors, may be found in Appendix 2.

While the text is designed primarily for a one-semester course, it lends itself as well to a natural division for the two-quarter or two-semester program. Chapters 1 through 6 emphasize the methods of astronomy and deal with the solar system in particular, while the remaining chapters (7 through 14) treat of the stars and galaxies.

Significant changes which have been made in this second edition include: (1) a unification of the history of astronomy in a single chapter; (2) an extension of the methods of astronomy to include infrared, ultraviolet, X-ray, and gravitational-wave detection; (3) treatment of the earth and moon as a binary system; (4) data and photos from the latest space probes; (5) detection of organic molecules in space; (6) a completely new section on the evolution of stars; and (7) a clear picture of the various cosmological models and the curvature of space. The question of life elsewhere in the universe is a thread that runs throughout the text.

To a large extent, the astronomy student's understanding is dependent upon his ability to visualize the motion of whatever is being discussed in terms of both space and time. To assist the student in visualizing certain rather intricate motions of objects in the universe, a unique kind of illustration is presented in the margins of this text. By flipping the successive pages, the illustrations appear to move. (Complete instructions for the use of these flip pages and interpretations of them are given below.) I am also happy to be able to include spectacular color plates in this new edition.

While many people have had a significant part in the review of this edition, I am particularly indebted to Dr. Roland Carpenter for his generous display of time and interest. William Grimshaw of Prentice-Hall again provided sound advice and steady encouragement. To John J. Dunleavy, the book's designer, I owe much for its dynamic and beautiful format. My gratitude is also due to Bert N. Zelman and Norma Karlin for their aid in all stages of the book's preparation for the press.   R.T.D.

KEY TO FLIP PAGES

Odd-numbered
pages

Right-hand flip pages

Even-numbered
pages

Left-hand flip pages

The eight flip-page sequences that occupy the lower margins of each page of this text are a unique instructional tool dynamically illustrating the basic motions of astronomy. To use the flip pages on the right-hand margins, grasp the desired section with the right hand, bending these pages as illustrated here and allowing the pages to flip, one by one, from beneath your thumb. Left-hand flip pages may be handled in a similar fashion, using the left hand. Remember, flip pages starting on an odd-numbered page (right-hand) are flipped toward higher page numbers; those starting on an even-numbered page (left-hand) are flipped toward lower page numbers. (See the illustrations here in the left margin, which make this clear.)

A brief introduction to each flip sequence follows, together with an indication of its location in the text.

The Ptolemaic system (Right-hand flip pages beginning on page 5) Ptolemy envisioned the earth to be the center of the universe. In order to explain the apparent retrograde (westward) motion of the planets among the stars, he utilized the concept of the epicycle. Each planet was thought to revolve on its epicycle as the epicycle revolved on its primary orbit called the deferent. By assigning the proper speed to each of these motions, he was able to create a retrograde motion. This motion also explains the fact that at certain times a given planet is closer to the earth. Since it had been observed that Mercury and Venus always remained close to the sun, the centers of their epicycles must always align with the earth and the sun. (This sequence of flip pages will be useful in your study of Chapter 1.)

Retrograde motion of Jupiter (Left-hand flip pages beginning on page 94) This sequence shows Jupiter moving first in a direct (eastward) motion among the stars, then apparently stopping and moving in a retrograde (westward) motion among the stars. Later the planet appears to stop again and resume its direct motion. By careful observation over an extended period of time, this apparent retrograde motion of Jupiter or of any other planet may be observed in the real sky. (This sequence will be helpful in your study of Chapters 1 and 5.)

The Copernican system (Right-hand flip pages beginning on page 95) In this sequence, the planets will be seen to move at their proper speeds in relation to the earth's motion. A period of approximately one year is depicted. The period of revolution of Mercury is 88 days, hence it can make four complete revolutions in one year. Within the period of 116 days, it returns to inferior conjunction with the earth. This is called its synodic period. Venus, on the other hand, makes a complete revolution in 225 days but does not return to inferior conjunction in the period shown. This planet requires 584 days for one synodic revolution. Jupiter needs approximately 12 years for one revolution, hence it is seen to move only about 30° during the period shown. Other configurations such as maximum elongation, superior conjunction, conjunction, quadrature, and opposition may be seen on certain pages individually. See if you can find all possible configurations. (This sequence will be helpful in your study of Chapters 1 and 5.)

A binary system (Left-hand flip pages beginning on page 162) This sequence demonstrates the fact that the earth and the moon form a binary (two-body) system and that it is the barycenter of the system which follows a smooth elliptical orbit. The barycenter of the system is located approximately 3000 miles from the center of the earth. As the moon revolves about this barycenter, the earth also deviates up to 3000 miles on either side of the system's orbit. In a very similar way, two binary stars, stars which lie in each other's gravitational field, orbit around a barycenter. The position of the barycenter is determined by the way in which the material (mass) is distributed in the two stars. (This sequence of flip pages should be helpful in your study of Chapters 4 and 9.)

A comet in motion (Right-hand flip pages beginning on page 215) This sequence depicts Halley's comet, moving in its highly elongated elliptical orbit about the sun. This comet returns to the region of the sun every 76 years, its next expected return being in 1986. Halley's comet travels in a retrograde direction that carries it beyond the orbit of Neptune. When a comet is at such a great distance from the sun, it possesses no coma (head) nor tail but exists only as a swarm of frozen gas bodies. As the comet approaches the sun, however, the warmth of the sun vaporizes a portion of the gas, thus producing the coma and tail. The outflow of particles from the sun (the solar wind) continually pushes the gases of the tail in a direction away from the sun. The speed with which the comet travels increases as it approaches the sun, hence only a relatively short time is spent in the vicinity of the sun. (This section of flip pages will be helpful in your study of Chapter 6.)

The proper motion of stars (Left-hand flip pages beginning on page 264) Over a 100,000-year period, the familiar constellation of the Big Dipper will change in appearance until it no longer resembles a dipper. This change results from the fact that stars are in constant motion. The stars that make up this constellation are moving in different directions. The apparent change in the position of a star in 1 year is very small, perhaps in the order of 1 second of arc per year. This is called the proper motion of the star. (This sequence of flip pages will be helpful in your study of Chapter 8.)

Motion of globular clusters (Right-hand flip pages beginning on page 285) The upper view in this series shows the motion of globular clusters that form the halo of the Milky Way galaxy. Each globular moves along an elliptical path which causes it to periodically "dip" into the nucleus of the Galaxy; however, it spends a relatively short time there. (In this sequence, it is best to choose a particular globular and follow its motion, say, the one marked by the double circle.) **Rotation of the Milky Way galaxy** The lower half of the pages shows the revolution of the Galaxy. The sun participates in this revolution and makes a circuit around the center of the Galaxy in 200 million years. From the sun's position, we see one spiral arm beyond and two arms toward the center of the Galaxy. (This sequence of flip pages will be helpful in your study of Chapter 13.)

  An eclipsing binary system (Left-hand flip pages beginning on page 390) The top view in this section shows the motion of a binary system, seen from above. The brighter star (light in color) is about five times as massive as its cooler (darker) component.

  The middle view shows the same system, seen from our position on earth. One star is seen periodically to eclipse the other, for the earth lies very nearly in plane of their orbit.

  The lower view shows the light curve which is generated as these stars move in their orbit. When the cooler star almost completely eclipses the hot star, the lowest light output is apparent. When the hotter (brighter) star is in front, only a slight dip occurs. While you are seeing the motion of these stars and the light curve generated simultaneously, the astronomer usually observes only the light curve and he must infer the actual motion from that curve. (This sequence will be helpful in your study of Chapter 9.)

CHAPTER-OPENING ILLUSTRATIONS

Chapter 1 Stonehenge, in England. (British Tourist Authority)
Chapter 2 The 64-m Goldstone radio antenna, near Barstow, California. (NASA-JPL)
Chapter 3 The earth photographed from Apollo 10 in 1969. (NASA)
Chapter 4 Astronaut James Irwin of Apollo 15 walking on the moon, August 1971. (NASA)
Chapter 5 Surface of the planet Mercury, photographed by Mariner 10 from a range of 86,800 km, March 29, 1974. (NASA-JPL)
Chapter 6 Comet Ikeya-Seki (1965f). (Lick Observatory)
Chapter 7 Solar prominence 64,500 km high, photographed in red light of H_α at Big Bear Solar Observatory, March 31, 1971. (Hale Observatories)
Chapter 8 Region of the Orion Nebula. (Lick Observatory)
Chapter 9 An open cluster in Cancer (M67). (Hale Observatories)
Chapter 10 The Small Magellanic Cloud. (Mount Stromlo and Siding Spring Observatories, The Australian National University)
Chapter 11 The Horsehead Nebula in Orion. (Hale Observatories)
Chapter 12 The Crab Nebula, the remains of a supernova first seen in 1054 A.D. (Hale Observatories)
Chapter 13 Portion of the Milky Way. (Hale Observatories)
Chapter 14 Spiral galaxy (NGC 628; M74). (Hale Observatories)

DYNAMIC
ASTRONOMY

HISTORY
OF
ASTRONOMY

1

The history of astronomy is characterized by man's ever-expanding

concept of the universe. Your own study of astronomy will no doubt

expand your awareness of the cosmos. Through astronomy, man has

been able to synchronize certain of his own activities with the motions

of celestial objects. This has permitted him to measure the passage of

time, to make sundials, clocks, calendars, and almanacs, and to relate

the rhythms of his life to that of nature around him. In order that

you may understand the events which have led to this harmonious

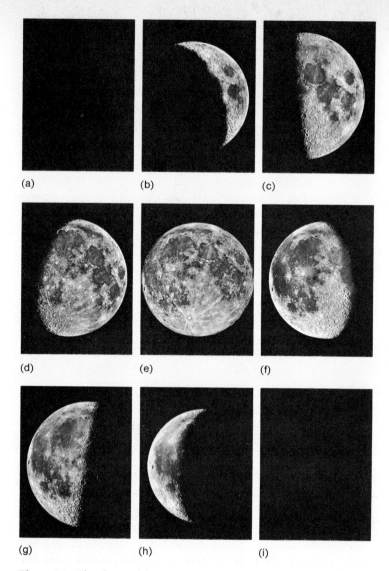

Figure 1.1 The phases of the moon: (a) "new moon"; (b) waxing crescent, 4 days old; (c) first quarter, 7 days old; (d) waxing gibbous, 10 days old; (e) full moon; (f) waning gibbous; (g) last quarter; (h) waning crescent; (i) "new moon" again. (Lick Observatory)

relationship, place yourself backward in time about 6000 years and try to imagine what was taking place then—what concerned men of that day. We have few written records; it is possible to make some assumptions, however, based on various clues that reveal something of ancient man's interest in the heavens.

We may assume that prehistoric man's basic needs were the same as ours are today. For instance, he required food. As he learned to meet that need by planting and harvesting, he soon realized that cycles exist, not only within his own body but within the world around him. What are some of the cycles which he would recognize most easily? Probably the cycle of day and night was the most obvious. The sun was the dominant celestial object in man's life: it provided warmth and light for his daytime activities; its absence at night allowed for a period of inactivity and rest.

Another cycle which he must surely have recognized was that of the phases of the moon. Prehistoric man saw the same changes in the appearance of the moon that we see today (Figure 1.1): The moon is first recognized as a thin crescent, seen in the west just after sunset. The next night it is seen in a slightly different part of the sky and appears a little more fully lighted. Similar changes occur night after night until the moon is full, and then each night its lighted portion begins to shrink until it appears as only a thin crescent again. Finally it is lost from view, in the sun's glare, for several days. If Stone Age men kept count of the days from when they first saw the moon as a thin crescent just after sunset until they again saw it in a similar phase (say, by scratching lines on a rock), they would have counted off either 29 or 30 days. No doubt they eventually came to recognize that cycle which we call the *lunar month*.

Early man must also have noticed the cycle of seasons, which influenced so drastically the growth of plants, with the long warm days of summer and the short cool days of winter.

How can we be so sure that man recognized these cycles at least 4000 years ago? The answer lies in the calendars which he left. The people of Mesopotamia created a calendar based upon a 30-day month and a 12-month year, thus a 360-day year. After some time, however, they realized that their year of 360 days did not fit the year of seasonal changes ($365\frac{1}{4}$ days), so they simply added a month to every sixth year and this very nearly corrected the discrepancy.

The people of China, often thought to be the world's oldest continuous civilization, produced one of the more accurate determinations of the length of a year. It was recorded by means of a number of circular objects divided into 365.25 parts. What kind of an experiment could they have performed in order to determine the number of days in a year so accurately? Visualize yourself standing under the imaginary dome of the sky, facing south. Let an imaginary curved line run on that dome directly north and south over your head. This line is called your *local meridian*. The point directly over your head is called your *zenith* (Figure 1.2).

The Ptolemaic system

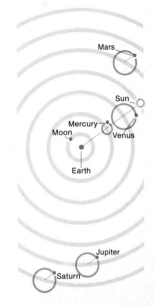

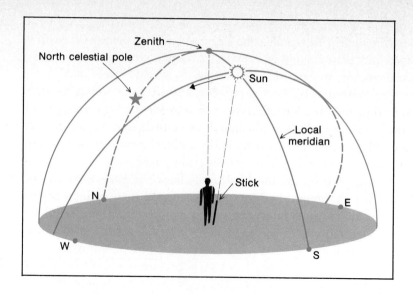

Figure 1.2 A stick is placed in the ground so as to cast no shadow when the sun appears highest in the sky.

Choose a time of year when the sun passes closest to your zenith, and place a stick in the ground so that it points directly toward the sun and therefore has no shadow. Note that if the sun were located east or west of the meridian, the stick would cast a shadow. It will then be easy to tell when a day has passed because then the stick will cast no shadow again. As the days go by, however, it will become evident that even when the sun crosses your meridian, it crosses lower in the sky and as a consequence the stick will cast a shadow even at noon. But count the number of days until the sun again passes close to your zenith and the stick casts no shadow at noon and you will have determined that a year is approximately 365 days. After several years of counting a more accurate determination may be made by averaging the counts for those years, revealing that a year contains 365.25 days. (Even this is not exact and must be corrected periodically. We will consider this further adjustment later.)

The Egyptians accomplished essentially the same feat by observing that the sun appears to move against the background of stars and moves completely through the twelve "houses" (constellations) of the zodiac in a period of exactly one year. They observed that in the springtime the sun was in the same part of the sky as was a certain bright star, Sirius, and that its nearness to Sirius was a predictor of the overflow of the Nile. Priests were assigned the task of making careful observations of the heavens so that crops might be ready for planting in the fertile silt brought down with the flooding. Again we see that man had recognized the harmonious association of the cycle of food production with the seasonal passage of the sun through the constellations of the zodiac.

The brightness of the sun prevents anyone from seeing the stars with which the sun aligns directly, so it may seem absurd to speak of the sun as being "in" a certain house, or constellation, of the zodiac; it is possible, however, to make an indirect observation as to its position. One might observe what house of the zodiac appears on his meridian at midnight, then by his knowledge of all twelve houses, determine the one directly opposite in the sky. That would then be the constellation which would be on his meridian at noon the next day, along with the sun, and would be the house in which the sun resides at that time.

As the sun appears to move among the constellations of the zodiac and the earth progresses through the seasons, new groups of stars dominate our evening skies. Surely ancient man noticed these seasonal changes (depicted in Figure 1.3).

The science of astronomy was thus born of necessity and had its roots in very practical social needs. However, the need to tell time and to predict seasonal changes was not the only motivation for man's interest in the heavens. He has typically sensed a cosmic force or power, a universal order, far greater than his own. This sense has been expressed in many ways—through magic and superstition, through astrology, and through religion. Babylonian sorcerers believed that the relative positions of the sun, moon, and planets directly influenced events on earth and controlled the thoughts and activities of mankind. They thus charted the movements of these bodies in the sky, and the pseudoscience of astrology was born. While astrologers and astronomers each make similar types of observations and predictions regarding the motion of celestial objects, each is motivated by a different purpose. The astronomer is attempting to describe the various properties of objects in the universe, such as position, motion, size, appearance, composition, origin, and evolution; but, unlike the astrologer, he does not believe that the events and circumstances of his life are influenced by some mysterious force emanating from these objects.

In many ancient cultures the people were highly superstitious, and the unannounced appearance of a comet or an eclipse was taken as a bad omen, often interpreted as a sign of the failure of a king or emperor to rule justly. Generally, the priestly class was assigned the task of predicting such "ominous" events, and this led to more diligent observations and to more accurate record keeping. Thus the regularity of motion of objects in the sky came to be recognized in many lands, and the person who could predict such awesome happenings as the

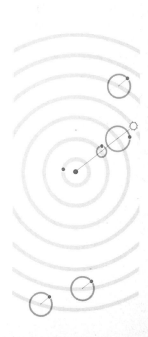

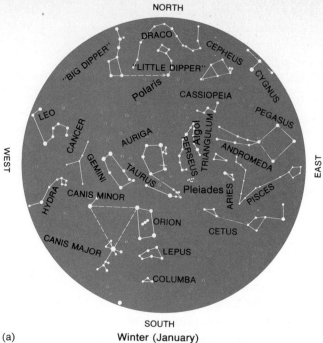

(a)   **Winter (January)**

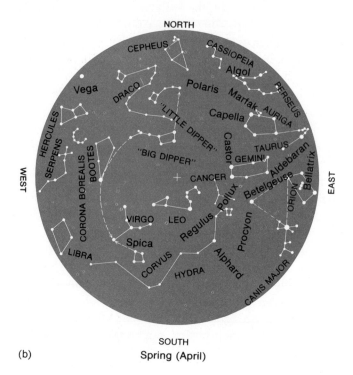

(b)   **Spring (April)**

Figure 1.3 Evening constellations of winter, spring, summer, and fall. (Griffith Observatory)

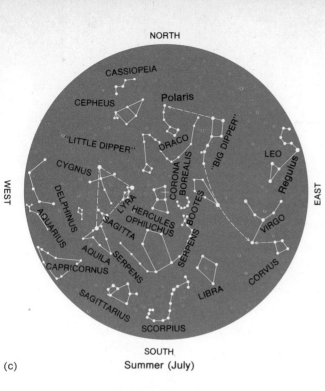

(c) Summer (July)

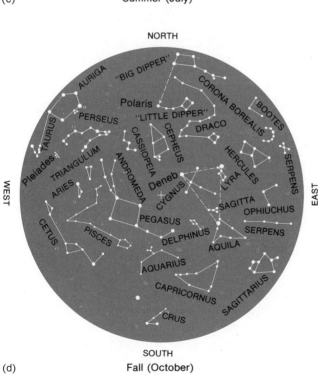

(d) Fall (October)

(a)

(b)

Figure 1.4 Megaliths possibly used by early man for celestial observations: (a,b) Stonehenge, in England; (c,d) Carnac, in Brittany. (e) On the Nasca Plateau in Peru, mysterious ancient sightlines have been discovered from the air that may have served the same function as the European megaliths. (f) Sketch of an enormous figure of a flying bird, about 400 feet long, at Nasca; line parallel to the wings is a solsticial sightline. (a,b, British Tourist Authority; c,d, French Government Tourist Office; e,f, Servicio Aerofotográfico National, Peru; from Paul Kosok, *Life, land, and water in ancient Peru,* Chap. 6. New York: Long Island University Press, 1965; reprinted by permission)

appearance of a comet or an eclipse gained great power among the people.

Stonehenge, a spectacular monument to prehistoric man's attempt to observe seasonal changes in the heavens (some 4000 years ago), stands today on Salisbury Plain in southern England (Figure 1.4). Here massive stones were aligned so as to point to the extreme rising or setting positions of the sun at the summer and winter *solstices;* that is, they were the means whereby the shortest and longest days of the year could be noted and the length of the year accurately determined. There are also a number of other sites in England and Brittany, in northwestern France, where similar megalithic structures were erected, however of somewhat less massive stones. It is interesting to contemplate the degree of intelligence and sophistication which the builders of such monuments possessed. If we were to pursue the subject further we would find that in many other parts of the world, massive structures (temples, pyramids, obelisks, and the like) have been oriented toward objects in the sky.

10

(c)

(d)

(e)

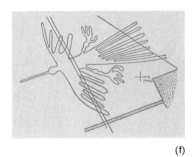

(f)

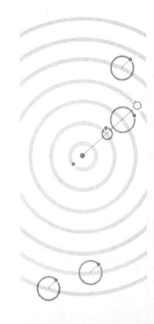

EARLY CONCEPTS
OF THE UNIVERSE

Man's concept of the earth on which he abides appears to influence greatly his concept of the universe, and logically so. Can you imagine your own interpretation of the earth if you had never traveled farther than you were able to walk in a day? Undoubtedly you would be convinced that the earth was flat and that the stars simply form a tent or canopy overhead. It almost appears as though the sky were a huge brass shield stretching over your head with a fire on the outside and hundreds of small holes punched for the light to shine through—an idea of the ancient Greeks.

To explain the apparent motion of the sun, the Greeks held that Helios, the sun god, drove his chariot across the sky each day from east to west and sailed round the northerly stream of Ocean each night to arise in the east again at dawn. The Egyptians favored a scheme in which the sun god (Ra) sailed in his barge up over the back of his mother, Nut (the sky), who arched her body over the earth [Figure 1.5(a)]. As you can see, the flat-earth concept caused men to create explanations for the motion of the sun which might appear absurd to us today but which reflect their personal feeling for objects in the sky.

While Figure 1.5(b) depicts the early Greek concept of the universe in general terms, let us examine the various ideas set forth by major schools of Greek philosophers. Thales of Miletus (636–546 B.C.) said that water was the first principle of all things, and he visualized the earth as a flat disk, floating on water; Anaximander (611–547 B.C.) thought of the world as infinite and viewed the earth as a cylinder floating free in space; and Anaximenes (585–526 B.C.) pictured the earth as a disk supported by air.

It is interesting to note that from the same school of training which produced these imaginative schemes came a man who's ideas were so advanced for his day that they were branded as sacreligious and he was exiled for his teachings. This was Anaxagoras (499–428 B.C.), who more accurately pictured the moon and planets as earthlike in nature—having a solid, crusty surface and shining by reflected sunlight. Furthermore he rightly explained lunar eclipses as the result of the moon moving into the earth's shadow.

Another school was established about the same time in southern Italy by the philosopher-mathematician Pythagoras of Samos (about 582–507 B.C.) and his followers. It is thought that Pythagoras first recognized the shape of the earth to be spherical (ball-like). Perhaps

(a)

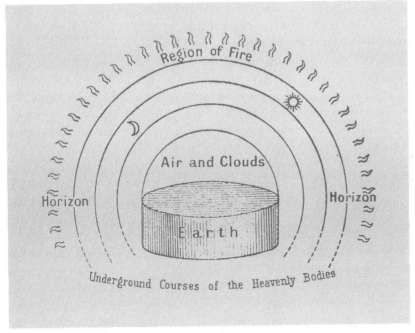

(b)

Figure 1.5 (a) An Egyptian concept of the sun god traveling in his barge over the back of a starry goddess and down into the underworld. (b) An early Greek concept of the universe. (Yerkes Observatory)

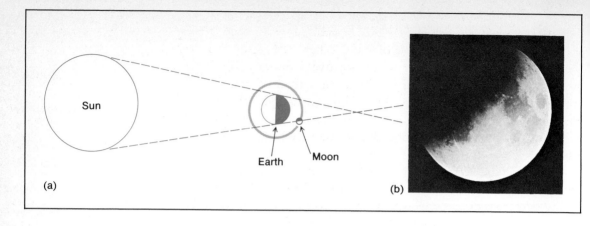

Figure 1.6 (a) The moon passing into the shadow of the earth. (b) A partially eclipsed moon.

it was the fact that he had witnessed boats sailing away from him that led him to this conclusion. A boat appears to "sink" into the water as it sails away from an observer and appears to "rise" from the water as it sails toward an observer, indicating the curvature of the earth's surface. He may also have noticed that, at the time of a lunar eclipse, as the moon passes into the earth's shadow the curvature of the edge of that shadow is suggestive of the curved nature of the earth itself (Figure 1.6).

The concept of a spherical earth was a great step forward, for it changed man's entire concept of the universe. In place of a canopy of stars, he could now view the stars as surrounding the earth in all directions. Some thought of them as fixed to a vast crystal sphere. Now the sun could be visualized as moving in a smooth orbital motion around the earth.

This is an example of how a single discovery may topple an entire conceptual structure that is based upon a false premise. Such discoveries serve to produce a scientific revolution. As you progress through this book, see if you can identify other such discoveries that produced major revolutions of thought.

In the sixth century B.C. there were still no indications that the earth is in motion (*rotating* on its axis or *revolving* around the sun). If the earth does not move in space, then all apparent movement of objects in the sky must be explained in terms of their own motion. It was not until about 450 B.C. that another Greek scholar, Philolaus, made an attempt to loosen the earth from its fixed position in the minds of his contemporaries by suggesting that there existed a "central fire" (not the sun) around which revolved the earth, the moon, the sun, and the planets. The earth was supposed to make one trip around this

14

central fire each day, producing the apparent motion of all objects around the earth in that period of time. When asked if he had ever seen the central fire, he replied in the negative, indicating that Greece was always turned away from it. While the system of Philolaus did not find many adherents, it served the significant purpose of suggesting that the earth is in motion. Today we realize that the apparent daily motion of all objects in the sky is due to the rotation of the earth on its axis.

Also of the Pythagorean school, Democritus (about 450 B.C.) recognized that the fuzzy band of light we call the Milky Way is in reality numerous distant stars which appear close together. It is interesting to compare the wildly imaginative scheme of Philolaus, on the one hand, and the very keen insight of Democritus, on the other. Perhaps it is only our advantage of hindsight that allows us to judge between these ideas.

Plato's Academy, the world's first university, was founded in Athens in the fourth century B.C., and one of its most famous pupils was Aristotle (384–322 B.C.). Aristotle, who became the predominant philosopher of his age and tutor to the young Alexander of Macedon (Alexander the Great), was to influence astronomical thinking for approximately 2000 years, having firmly established the idea that the spherical earth was the center of the universe and stood stationary in that position, with the sun, moon, and planets moving around it in circular orbits. Aristotle's contemporary, Heraclides (388–315 B.C.), suggested that the apparent daily motion of these objects was due to the rotation of the earth, a very logical idea, but because it went counter to the thinking of the dominant academic group, it was cast aside.

In 332 B.C., Alexander the Great founded the city of Alexandria on the Mediterranean coast of Egypt. This city was established as a cultural center, a place where theoreticians and practical observers alike could find a level of support unheard of in other lands. Here Aristarchus (about 270 B.C.) challenged the teachings of Aristotle by asserting that the sun is the center of the solar system and that the earth and other planets revolve around the sun. He explained the apparent daily motion of all objects to be the result of the earth's rotation, and he believed the stars to be very distant. These ideas were far too radical for his contemporaries. Because the erroneous theory of Aristotle had become so deeply ingrained by that time, the challenge failed. It might have been argued by the Aristotelians that if the earth traveled around the sun, then nearby stars should appear to shift in their alignment with more distant stars. No such shift could be seen with the naked eye. The distances are too great. But had observers of that day been able to measure (as we can with our modern instruments) the very slight shift in the apparent position of nearby stars against the background

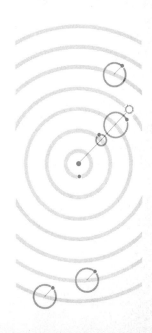

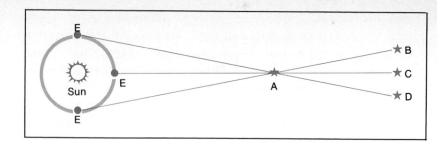

Figure 1.7 The apparent shift of a nearby star (A) against the background of more distant stars, due to the revolution of the earth, as suggested by Aristarchus.

of distant stars, as the earth revolves around the sun, the validity of Aristarchus's *heliocentric* (sun-centered) model would have been apparent. One can visualize this shift in the alignment of a star (A) with respect to more distant stars (B, C, or D) as the earth moves to various positions shown in Figure 1.7. Even in the case of the nearest star, α (Alpha) Centauri, the apparent shift is only 1/4800 of one degree (1°), to either side of its apparent central position.

Hipparchus, also of the Alexandrian school, made several very significant contributions to astronomy toward the end of the second century B.C. His methods of observation were very advanced for his time. He is often called the father of positional astronomy, for he constructed one of the first systematic catalogues of stars. He accurately stated the position of more than 1000 stars and ranked them according to their apparent brightness. He placed them into six categories: the brightest were called *first magnitude stars;* the dimmest (to the naked eye) were called *sixth magnitude stars.* This cataloguing project appears most remarkable when we realize that Hipparchus had no telescope or other optical aids with which to work. Hipparchus had observed that the sun appeared to move faster through the stars during one part of the year and slower during the other part. He reasoned that when it moved more slowly the sun must be farther from the earth and when it moved more quickly the sun must be nearer the earth. He concluded that its orbit could not be circular and devised the model depicted in Figure 1.8. The sun moves on a

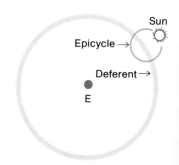

Figure 1.8 The epicycle of Hipparchus.

second smaller orbit called an epicycle. His model, you might say, is a wheel turning on a wheel. By choosing the proper speed of turning for the epicycle and for the larger orbit upon which it moves, the *deferent,* the apparent variations in the sun's rate of motion and distance from earth, could be explained.

PLANETS IN MOTION

The model conceived by Hipparchus for motion of the sun could also be applied to the moon with only minor adjustments, but the apparent motions of the sun and moon were really quite simple compared to those of the planets. Not only did planets vary in their rate of travel against the background of stars, but they even appeared to stop and reverse their direction among the stars at certain intervals. The casual observer would not recognize this reversal, for he only notices the daily westward motion of the sky. However, if he were to plot the position of a planet on a map of the sky, night after night, he would discover that planets usually move eastward among the stars but sometimes appear to stop, move westward for a number of nights, then again stop and proceed in an easterly direction (Figure 1.9). The astronomer speaks of the westerly motion of planets, among the stars, as being their *retrograde* (backward) motion. The flip pages beginning on page 94 show the retrograde motion of Jupiter, seen among the stars in the constellation Leo, in a very dynamic way. Hipparchus not only recognized this motion of a planet but made detailed observations and kept accurate records of planetary positions that were invaluable in later years.

In 140 A.D. Ptolemy (Claudius Ptolemeus), the last great astronomer of the Alexandrian school, gathered together all the accumulated astronomical knowledge of the ancient world and published his *Almagest.* This series of 13 volumes reflected the thinking of such men as Aristotle, Pythagoras, and Hipparchus, in combination with a few of Ptolemy's own ideas, and this combined picture of the universe is

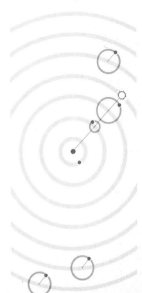

Figure 1.9   The apparent retrograde motion of a planet (as seen by an observer facing south).

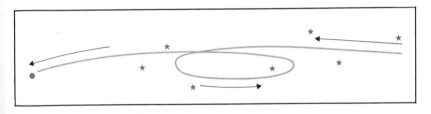

called the *Ptolemaic system*. Remember that Aristotle viewed the earth as standing still in space at the center of the cosmos, Pythagoras had proposed a spherical earth, and Hipparchus had introduced the concept of the epicycle, as applied to the sun. However, the observation which demanded Ptolemy's main attention, and that of his immediate predecessors, was the fact that planets sometimes appear to *retrograde* (back up) against the background of stars. In an attempt to preserve the concept of uniform circular motion, thought to be an absolute necessity, Ptolemy assigned each planet its own epicycle, the center of which moved along the larger orbit called the *deferent* (Figure 1.10). As the sun moved about the earth, so the outer planets (Mars, Jupiter, and Saturn) moved on their respective epicycles. This motion produced two desired effects; the planets appeared to retrograde at the proper time, and they sometimes appeared closer to the earth and therefore brighter at that time. The right-hand flip pages beginning on page 5 show Ptolemy's model of planetary motion.

It should be particularly noted that Mercury and Venus move so that the centers of their respective epicycles always lie on an imaginary line joining the earth and the sun. This is consistent with the fact that Mercury is always seen within 28° of the sun. From our point of view on earth, Mercury would appear to flit back and forth on either side of the sun. Likewise Venus, while it has a much slower apparent motion among the stars than Mercury, also moves from one side of the sun to the other, and never more than 47° from it. The epicycle of the sun has been omitted in the drawing for the sake of simplicity. Of course, the sun never appears to retrograde among the stars, and the turning of its epicycle had to be synchronized with its motion on the deferent to explain its lack of retrograde motion.

HOW GOOD WAS
PTOLEMY'S MODEL?

We should now ask ourselves some interesting questions: Just how good is the Ptolemaic system? How well does it work as a model of the universe? Does it seem to agree with the observations of Ptolemy's time? Can one use this model to predict the location of any planet at some prescribed time in the future? Yes, within fairly good accuracy, and to that degree the Ptolemaic system was a good model. There were no observations at that time which seemed to invalidate the model. As time passed, however, it became evident that the accuracy with which the position of a planet could be predicted was not good enough. Small corrections were frequently necessary, and these multiplied until the model became quite cumbersome.

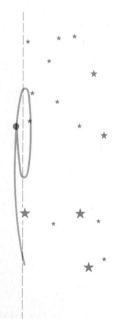

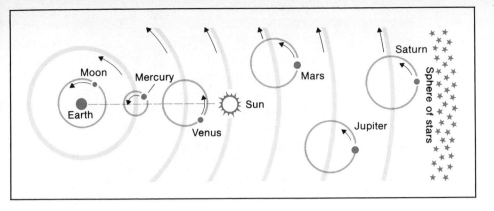

Figure 1.10 The Ptolemaic system.

In spite of these difficulties Ptolemy's picture of the universe was destined to remain the principal model for more than 1300 years. How is it that a theory based upon so many erroneous ideas stood unchallenged for such a long period? Ptolemy's model was one of the last to emerge from the classic age of philosophy and natural science. Successor to the Greek power, the once mighty Roman Empire had already begun its gradual decline in Ptolemy's time. By the middle of the fifth century A.D., Rome had fallen prey to barbarian hordes from the north, the Vandals, Visigoths, and other tribes. Alexandria, now a provincial city of the Eastern (Byzantine) Empire, fell to Arab invaders in 642 A.D. With the plundering that ensued, much of the classical culture that had been preserved by the Roman world, along with many fine works of art and literature, were destroyed. In these times of turmoil, the spirit of science and philosophy found little opportunity for expression. However, the works of Ptolemy were preserved by the Arabs. His *Almagest,* translated into Arabic, found numerous readers among scholars of Baghdad, Cairo, Morocco, and Spain from the ninth through the fourteenth centuries. This same period has been called the "Dark Ages" of Europe, where Roman Catholic monasteries became the main repositories of classical ideas of Greece and Rome.

Perhaps a new awakening may be traced to Alphonso X, king of Castile (northern Spain), who in 1222 commissioned the preparation of new tables describing the motion of the sun, moon, and planets. These were known as the Alphonsine Tables. Within these tables we see the Greek influence transmitted through Ptolemy's *Almagest;* however, certain improvements had been made by both Arab and Jewish astronomers, working in the observatory of Toledo, Spain. (Study of the errors that remained in the Alphonsine Tables was destined to be a prime motivating force for the major discoveries of the sixteenth century.)

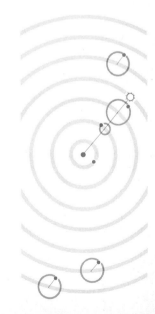

Figure 1.11   Nicolaus Copernicus. (Yerkes Observatory)

In the thirteenth century St. Thomas Aquinas, a prominent Dominican educator, philosopher, and theologian, had succeeded in elevating the Aristotelian model, which placed the earth at the center of the universe, to the level of religious dogma. From then on, when any person taught a contrary view he might be tried before the Inquisition as a heretic and, if found guilty, be put to death. It is within this atmosphere that we witness the work of Nicolaus Copernicus, Tycho Brahe, Johannes Kepler, and Galileo Galilei. As late as 1600, Giordano Bruno, an opponent of Aristotelianism and champion of the new Copernican cosmology, was burned at the stake by the Inquisition.

Renewed interest in science had been evident in Europe as early as the fourteenth century, but that interest really blossomed in the fifteenth and sixteenth centuries, especially in the universities of Italy and Germany. With the successful voyages of exploration around Africa to India and East Asia, discovery of the Americas, and circumnavigation of the globe (in 1522), there was renewed interest in astronomy and mathematics as aids to ocean mariners. The astronomical-philosophical classics of ancient Greece were examined in their original form, and the study of these works produced a flood of reactions. Many of the concepts of Aristotle, Philolaus, Aristarchus, Ptolemy, together with the writings of the Arab world, were now scrutinized very critically. It is at this juncture that we turn to the life and work of the great Polish astronomer Nicolaus Copernicus (1473–1543).

NICOLAUS COPERNICUS, FOUNDER OF MODERN ASTRONOMY

Under the influence of a learned uncle who had adopted him at the age of 10, Nicolaus Copernicus attended the University of Cracow to study the classics, philosophy, theology, law, medicine, and mathematics (Figure 1.11). Continuing his education in Italy, he acquired a doctoral degree in canon law and also became competent in medical practices of the time, but his contact with a noted astronomer at the University of Bologna sparked a lasting interest in astronomy. In 1500 he lectured in that subject at the Vatican in Rome. His training in the Greek language allowed him to pursue a first-hand study of the classics. Along with these factors, the errors he had found in the Alphonsine Tables spurred him to spend approximately 30 years in the development of a model of the solar system (Figure 1.12), published in a six-volume work called *De Revolutionibus Orbium Coelestium*. Although the manuscript of this great work was virtually completed in 1530, Copernicus delayed publication until the final years of his life because of political and religious considerations. The final volume only reached him at his deathbed.

The essence of his scheme is expressed by his own words:

> *At rest in the middle of everything is the sun. For in this most beautiful temple, who would put this lamp in another or better position than from which it can illuminate the whole thing at the same time? Thus, indeed, as though seated on a royal throne, the sun governs the family of planets revolving around it.*

Copernicus had thus displaced the earth from its favored position at the center of the universe and had relegated it to the position of one of several planets which orbit the sun. Obviously he might well have

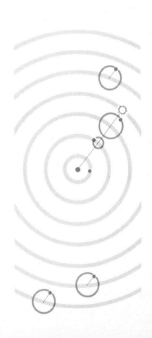

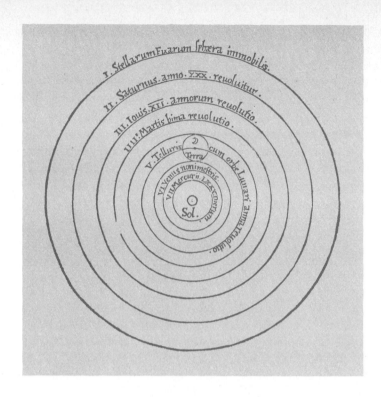

Figure 1.12 The Copernican system, as shown in *De Revolutionibus Orbium Coelestium,* 1566. (Yerkes Observatory)

incurred the wrath of the Inquisition for such a heretical idea if he had not died within a few days of the publication of his theory.

Copernicus believed that the earth both rotated on its axis and revolved around the sun, as did all the other planets. He viewed the stars as being very distant and fixed in place. It was their great distance, he argued, that explained the lack of any apparent shifting in the position of nearby stars as the earth moves in its orbit around the sun. Copernicus explained that the daily "rising" and "setting" of all objects in the sky could easily be explained by the daily rotation of the earth on its axis. The apparent yearly motion of the sun among the stars could be explained by the revolution of the earth around the sun. But what about the retrograde motion of the planets? Could Copernicus explain why planets sometimes appear to move backwards among the stars?

The right-hand flip pages, starting on page 95, illustrate the motions of the planets in the Copernican model. As you flip these pages you will see that Mercury and Venus periodically pass the earth in its orbit and likewise the earth passes the outer planets of Mars, Jupiter, and Saturn periodically in their orbits. It is this phenomenon of passing which produces the apparent retrograde motion of the planets. Consider the earth and Mars as seen in Figure 1.13. Note that as the earth moves from positions A through K, Mars also moves through the corresponding positions on its orbit; however, the earth moves at a faster rate. At any one position the stars with which Mars appears to align vary. Moving from A to E, Mars seems to move eastward among the stars, but while moving from E to G it seems to move westward. Finally, moving from G to H, it appears to move eastward again. A similar explanation applies to the apparent retrograde motion of the other planets.

It is also easy to see from the flip pages that planets are much closer to the earth on some occasions and farther from it at others. This explains their apparent changes in brightness. While Copernicus no longer needed the epicycle to explain the retrograde motion of planets, he retained the idea for other reasons. He believed that all objects move in a uniform way (at the same rate), on circular orbits or on combinations of circular orbits. Yet Copernicus saw planets sometimes moving rapidly against the background of stars and sometimes slowly; he

Figure 1.13 The apparent retrograde motion of Mars (shown at the right).

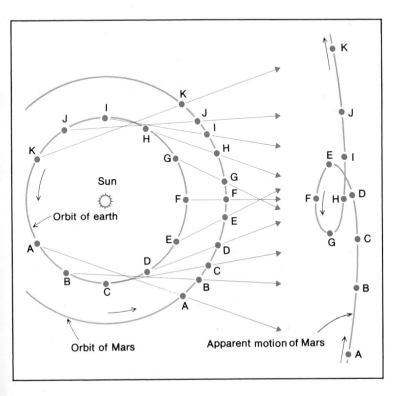

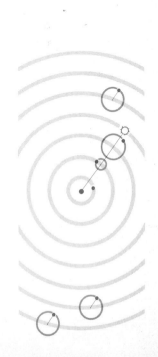

thought that through a set of epicycles which were assigned the proper uniform motion, the complex motion of the planet could be explained. Some of his earlier works contained epicycles upon epicycles. The model of Copernicus appears to explain the observations of the time, but the model of Ptolemy did so as well. Although there was not yet any substantial evidence as to which model most closely represented reality, the publication of the Copernican theory created a furor which was to last more than 200 years. The daring of Copernicus encouraged others to devise better means for observation so that his theory might be put to the test. Typical of this new spirit of observation was the work of Tycho Brahe.

TYCHO BRAHE, THE DILIGENT OBSERVER

Tycho Brahe (1546–1601), a Danish nobleman, was trained as an astronomer and, under the sponsorship of the king of Denmark, he devoted himself to a systematic observational approach to the subject. He was granted the tiny Baltic island of Hven (Figures 1.14 and 1.15), where he established an observatory and constructed instruments capable of measuring angles between stars quite accurately (Figure 1.16). Tycho made literally thousands of observations of star positions, averaging his readings to produce a catalogue of approximately 800 stars. The positions of many stars were accurate to within 1/100 of a degree. Tycho's catalogue was far more accurate than that of Hipparchus or Ptolemy, and it stood as a reliable reference source for more than a century. Tycho also kept precise records of the changing positions of planets, believing that only through an understanding of the orderliness and unity of the universe might man better order his own affairs. In a lecture presented at the University of Copenhagen in 1574, Tycho said:

> To deny the forces and influence of the stars is to undervalue firstly the divine wisdom and providence and moreover to contradict evident experience. For what could be thought more unjust and foolish about God than that He should have made this large and admirable scenery of the skies and so many brilliant stars to no use or purpose—whereas no man makes even his least work without a certain aim.

Tycho's labors epitomized an important aspect of the scientist's work that is often overlooked, that of keeping absolutely honest and careful records, which are often valuable regardless of the correctness of conclusions drawn at the time. Tycho's observational records were his greatest contribution to astronomy, for they were to assist those who

Figure 1.14 Tycho Brahe, the observer. (Yerkes Observatory)

Figure 1.15 Uraniborg, Tycho Brahe's observatory. (Yerkes Observatory)

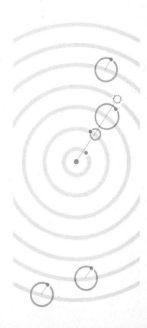

followed him to present a clearer picture of the solar system. He could not accept Copernicus's premise that the earth is in motion, so he devised a very interesting scheme that pictured Venus and Mercury as circling the sun but had the sun and the other planets orbiting around the earth (Figure 1.17).

In his later years, Tycho fell out of favor with the new king of Denmark and lost his island sanctuary. He sought and found the support of Rudolf II, the scholarly Holy Roman emperor, and built a new observatory near Prague, in Bohemia. Here the master astronomer took as his aide a young German philosopher and mathematician, Johannes Kepler (1571–1630), who at the time of Tycho's death fell heir to his voluminous observational records.

JOHANNES KEPLER, THE INVENTIVE MATHEMATICIAN

Kepler was educated at Tübingen University and taught at the University of Graz in Austria (Figure 1.18). When he was relieved of this professorship for religious reasons, he received an invitation from Tycho Brahe to become his assistant. Joining Tycho, Kepler soon acquired a

Figure 1.16 Tycho Brahe at Uraniborg: (a) Tycho observing with his great mural quadrant; (b) sextant used to measure angles between celestial objects. (Rare Book Division, The New York Public Library, Astor, Lenox and Tilden Foundations)

(a)   (b)

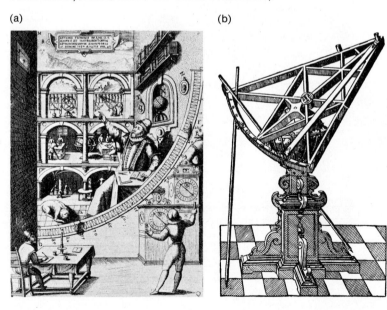

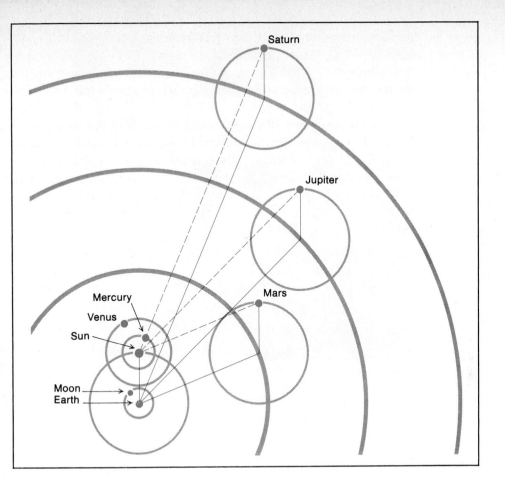

Figure 1.17 Hypothetical planetary system devised by Tycho Brahe in 1578: here Venus and Mercury circle the sun, the sun and moon circle the earth, and Mars, Jupiter, and Saturn move in epicycles, with their deferents centered on the earth.

keen respect for the high degree of accuracy with which Tycho observed the positions of stars and planets.

Kepler immediately recognized that Mars did not move against the background of stars at a constant rate but moved faster during one part of its orbit and then slowed down during another part. This fact alone must have suggested to him that the planet did not move around the sun in a circular orbit as Copernicus had proposed, for if the orbit were circular a constant rate of motion would have been expected. Kepler attempted to fit various orbital shapes to the observed motion of Mars, shapes which would provide for the variation in speeds he had witnessed. He eventually concluded that the best fit was that of an *ellipse*.

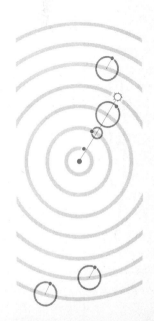

Figure 1.18 Johannes Kepler. (Yerkes Observatory)

A device for drawing ellipses can be fashioned using two thumb-tacks and a string of fixed length. By attaching each end of the string to a thumbtack and by stretching the string taut with a pencil, it is possible to draw an ellipse (Figure 1.19). By varying the spacing of the thumbtacks, one may draw ellipses of varying eccentricity. Figure 1.20 shows a number of terms associated with an ellipse. The two points

Table 1.1 Planetary data

PLANET	SEMIMAJOR AXIS (r), A.U.	r^3	PERIOD (p), YEARS	p^2
Mercury	0.39	0.058	0.24	0.058
Venus	0.72	0.378	0.62	0.378
Earth	1.00	1.000	1.00	1.000
Mars	1.52	3.54	1.88	3.54
Jupiter	5.20	140.7	11.86	140.8
Saturn	9.54	867.7	29.46	867.9

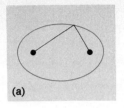
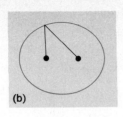
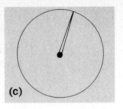

Figure 1.19 Drawing ellipses of different eccentricities.

(thumbtacks) are called the *foci* (plural of *focus*), and a line drawn through these points and extending to the curve itself is called the *major axis* of the ellipse. One half that distance is called the *semimajor axis,* and this is equivalent to the average distance (radius) from one focus to any point on the ellipse. In Table 1.1 the semimajor axis for each planet is given, thus expressing its average distance from the sun. The *eccentricity* of an ellipse is found by dividing the distance between the foci by the length of the major axis. A circle has an eccentricity of zero, and the eccentricities of the planetary orbits range from 0.007 (Venus) to 0.25 (Pluto), with that of the earth being 0.017, not very much different than a circle.

Figure 1.20 Axis and radius of an ellipse.

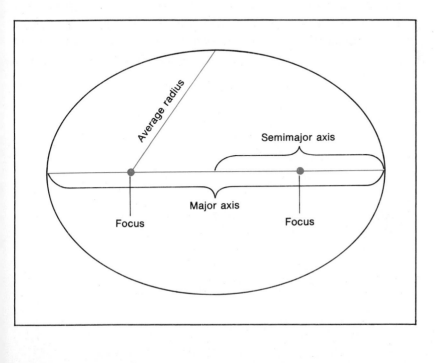

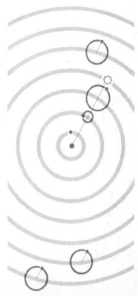

Kepler found that he could best fit the observed motions of Mars to an elliptical orbit, with the sun at one focus, the other focus being only an imaginary point in space. He generalized this idea to include all planets, and this statement is now known as Kepler's first law of planetary motion:

> *Each planet moves around the sun in an orbit whose shape is that of an ellipse, with the sun at one focal point.*

Kepler also observed that the planet Mars speeds up when it is approaching the sun and slows down as it moves away from the sun. After some calculations, Kepler determined that this phenomenon could be expressed thus:

> *A straight line joining the planet and the sun sweeps out equal areas in space in equal intervals of time.*

This is called Kepler's second law of planetary motion.

As an illustration of Kepler's second law (Figure 1.21), let us suppose that Mars moves from points A to B in a month. Some time later it also moves from C to D in a month: but this is a greater distance, requiring that Mars be moving faster in order to sweep out an equal area in the same time. Likewise when the planet travels from E to F it must move still faster to sweep out an equal area in a month; however, as it moves from G to H it is moving more slowly, and as it passes from A to B it has returned to the speed that it had at the start of this illustration. Thus Kepler's second law provides a mathematical model whereby the speed of a planet may be computed for any given position on its orbit.

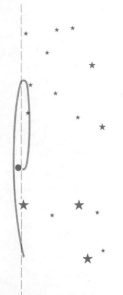

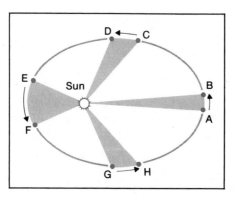

Figure 1.21 Illustration of Kepler's law of equal areas in equal time.

The third basic relationship that Kepler recognized came only after several years of effort on his part. Of course, it was obvious to him that the farther a planet was from the sun, the longer it took to complete one revolution around the sun. But Kepler sought to find the exact mathematical relationship between its period of revolution and its average distance from the sun (the semimajor axis of its orbit), if such a relationship did indeed exist. Although the actual distances between the sun and the planets were then not known in miles, it was possible to calculate the ratio between a planet's distance from the sun and that of the earth's distance from the sun. For example, Kepler knew that the semimajor axis of Mars's orbit was equal to approximately one and one-half times the semimajor axis of the earth. If we let the semimajor axis of the earth's orbit be called 1 A.U. (astronomical unit), then the semimajor axis of Mars's orbit can be specified as 1.5 A.U. In Table 1.1 (on p. 28) are listed the semimajor axes for each planet, as measured in astronomical units. This table also shows the period of revolution for each planet, measured in years. Note that for any planet if the semimajor axis (r) is cubed and the period of revolution (p) is squared, the two numbers produced are the same, with only minor discrepancies for Jupiter and Saturn. This fact may be expressed by the simple equation $p^2 = r^3$, where p is measured in years and r is measured in astronomical units. Should we choose to measure the period of the planet in days or the distance in miles, then we would not expect $p^2 = r^3$; however, we can allow for this possibility by writing $p^2 = kr^3$, where k is a constant whose value is determined by the units of measure used. Still another equation may be written to specify Kepler's third law:

$$\frac{(p_1)^2}{(p_2)^2} = \frac{(r_1)^3}{(r_2)^3}$$

which may be stated as

The squares of the periods of any two planets have the same ratio as the cubes of their semimajor axes.

Assuming that this relationship would hold true for any planet in our solar system, let us suppose that an imaginary planet X has a period of 8 years. Can we find its average distance from the sun in astronomical units? Let the period and semimajor axis of planet X replace p_1 and r_1 in the equation, and let the period and semimajor axis of the earth replace p_2 and r_2. For the earth, we know that $p_2 = 1$ year and $r_2 = 1$

A.U. (see Table 1.1). The period of planet X has been given as 8 years, so $p_1 = 8$. If we make these replacements in the equation and solve for r_1, we have:

$$\frac{(p_1)^2}{(p_2)^2} = \frac{(r_1)^3}{(r_2)^3}$$

$$\frac{(8)^2}{(1)^2} = \frac{(r_1)^3}{(1)^3}$$

$$\frac{64}{1} = \frac{(r_1)^3}{1}$$

$$4 = r_1$$

Therefore the imaginary planet X would have a semimajor axis of 4 A.U.

A warning   All of Kepler's laws are highly idealized, for they neglect the fact that each planet influences every other so that the orbits are never smooth ellipses, nor are the areas swept out exactly the same. Furthermore, Kepler's third law is limited to a restricted set of conditions, namely, to very small (low-mass) objects going around very large (high-mass) objects, like planets around the sun, or moons around a large planet. However Kepler's discoveries were remarkable approximations that were later confirmed and generalized by Sir Isaac Newton, whose astronomical knowledge and mathematical techniques were more advanced. Although Kepler was a mystic, his work served as the foundation for the removal of astronomy from the realm of mysticism and the establishment of its cause-and-effect nature.

GALILEO GALILEI, FATHER OF EXPERIMENTAL SCIENCE

The seventeenth century can be called a century of discovery, experimentation, and invention. The particular invention that had the largest impact on astronomy was that of the telescope. While the exact history of this invention is unclear, the Dutch spectacle maker Hans Lippershey is usually credited with having combined several lenses to produce an enlarged image of a distant object. Although he made this discovery in 1608, Lippershey apparently did not fully grasp the enormous practical importance of such an instrument. The following year in Padua, Italy, Galileo Galilei (1564–1642) heard of this invention and, without any detailed knowledge of how the task had been accomplished, set

Figure 1.22 Galileo Galilei. (Yerkes Observatory)

out to produce a telescope of his own (Figure 1.22). Galileo's first success resulted in an instrument that enlarged objects three times, a *three-power* telescope. Later refinements resulted in a 30-power instrument. These instruments he put into immediate use. By directing them skyward, Galileo soon discovered four moons circling the planet Jupiter, each moving around the planet in its own particular period (Figure 1.23). This sight reminded Galileo of the solar system itself, as Copernicus had described it, and it surely demonstrated that centers of revolution exist elsewhere in the system.

Using the telescope, Galileo also found that what had appeared as a fuzzy patch in the sky, a nebula, could now be seen as a group of separate stars. In fact, in all regions of the sky the instrument revealed many stars that were too faint to be seen with the naked eye. Concerning a familiar constellation (Figure 1.24), Galileo wrote:

> I had determined to depict the entire constellation of Orion, but I was overwhelmed by the vast quantity of stars and by want of time, and so I have deferred attempting this to another occasion, for there are adjacent to, or scattered among, the old stars more than five hundred new stars.

Galileo also observed that the planet Venus goes through phases (see Figure 5.8, page 175), sometimes appearing as a thin crescent and at other times as a disk almost fully lighted. This was a startling observation;

it provided evidence, for the first time, that the Ptolemaic system could not represent reality. Remember that in the Ptolemaic system, the center of Venus's epicycle must always remain on an imaginary line joining the earth and the sun. Under this restriction, the planet Venus could never appear any fuller than a mere crescent (see Figure 1.25). However Galileo observed that Venus sometimes appears almost full. Could this fact be better explained by the Copernican system? Yes, as you can see in Figure 1.26. Venus may be seen in all possible phases, except when it is closely aligned with the sun.

The revelation that Venus goes through phases dealt the death blow to the Ptolemaic system. Confident in his new-found proof, Galileo tried to convince the leadership of the Roman Catholic church that its interpretation of the Holy Scriptures was inconsistent with observed facts. He failed in this attempt. In fact, the church hierarchy pronounced his findings to be false and heretical and forbade anyone to teach them. So blind are the eyes of men when they do not want to see!

Figure 1.23 Galileo's drawings showing the motions of the moons of Jupiter. (Yerkes Observatory)

Galileo also observed sunspots and identified them as being on the surface of the sun itself. By charting their movement, he determined the rotation period of the sun (Figure 1.27). To the philosophers of

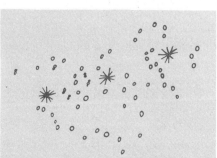

Figure 1.24 The stars in the Belt of Orion as represented by Galileo.

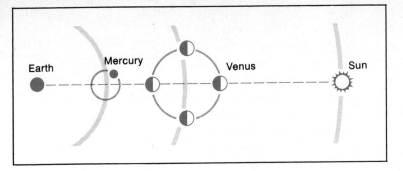

Figure 1.25 The phases of Venus—Ptolemaic system.

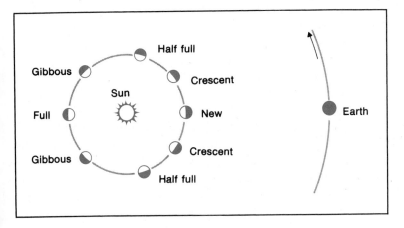

Figure 1.26 The phases of Venus—Copernican system.

that time, however, any "imperfection" on a celestial body was unthinkable; and so his report was again ridiculed.

Yet despite all these obstructions, Galileo opened up a new era of scientific experimentation. For example, he wondered about Aristotle's claim that when two objects of different weight are dropped from a high place the heavier object hits the ground first. According to legend, Galileo climbed the Leaning Tower of Pisa (in the city of his birth) and dropped two round stones from the top, one of which was much heavier than the other. To the amazement of the crowd that gathered, the stones fell side by side—hitting the ground together. In order to measure the effect of gravity more accurately, Galileo caused a ball to roll down an inclined ramp and timed its acceleration. He caused an object to slide along different surfaces and observed that when friction was least the object would travel farther. He may have come

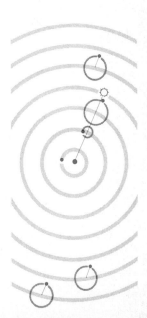

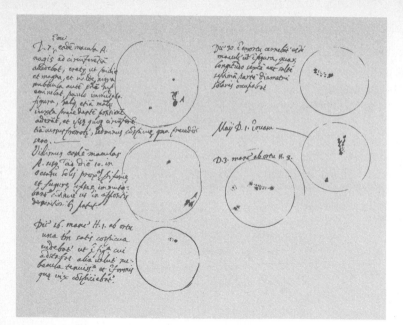

Figure 1.27 Galileo's drawings of sunspots. (Yerkes Observatory)

to the realization that an object which is moving through space, where no friction exists, will travel onward at its given speed forever; this concept is now credited to Sir Isaac Newton. That great British scientist surely was recognizing the work of Galileo, as well as of Kepler, Tycho, and Copernicus, when he said, "If I have been able to see farther than other men, it is because I was standing on the shoulders of giants."

ISAAC NEWTON, THE YOUNG GENIUS

Newton (1642–1727) entered Cambridge at 19. Four years later, in 1665, the year of the great London plague, the university was closed during the epidemic and he returned home (Figure 1.28). It was at this time that he made lasting contributions in three areas: in mathematics, by inventing the calculus; in optics, by demonstrating that ordinary white light is composed of various colors that can be separated upon refraction; and in astronomy, by precisely formulating the idea of gravitation and the laws of motion that govern bodies that are in each other's gravitational field. The idea of the mutual attraction of objects had earlier been suggested by Copernicus in his explanation of the earth's spherical shape. Newton recognized this force as being responsible for the tides, for the fact that objects fall toward the center of the earth when released, and for the fact that the planets remain

36

in orbit around the sun. Realizing that circular motion is not the natural motion of an object, he stated his first law—the law of *inertia:*

> *Every body perseveres in its state of rest, or of uniform motion in a right (straight) line, unless it is compelled to change that state by force impressed thereon.*

This is to say that a body will, if it is at rest, remain at rest unless acted upon by an external force. It also says that a body will, if it is moving, continue to move in a straight line forever—unless acted upon by an external force. It follows that the natural motion of an object moving in space is not circular but in a straight line (assuming that no other force is acting upon that object).

Newton's second law says:

> *The alteration of motion is ever proportional to the motive force impressed; and is made in the direction of the right (straight) line in which it is impressed.*

He explained this law further by saying,

> *If any force generates a motion, a double force will generate a double motion, a triple force triple the motion.*

This second law also expresses the idea that if a force is applied that opposes a motion, the object will slow down, but if the force is applied

Figure 1.28 Sir Isaac Newton. (Yerkes Observatory)

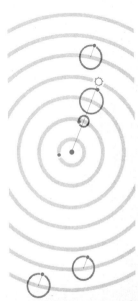

partially or entirely in line with the motion, the object will speed up. Newton's second law also embodies the idea that the amount by which an object is speeded up or slowed down by a given force is dependent on the mass of the object. For a given force (f), the greater the mass (m), the less the acceleration (a): $F = ma$.

Newton further stated, in his third law:

> *To every action there is always opposed an equal reaction; or the mutual actions of two bodies upon each other are always equal, and directed to contrary parts.*

To illustrate this law, imagine jumping from the stern of a boat into the water. While your body is propelled in one direction, the boat moves in the other direction. It is exactly this law that explains the force that propels a rocketship (Figure 1.29). As particles of gas are expelled from the rear of the rocket, the equal but opposite reactive force propels the ship forward. The action and reaction forces always act on different bodies (*action*—force on gas; *reaction*—force on rocketship).

Let us apply Newton's laws to the planets and their orbits around the sun. His first law says that the natural tendency is for the planet to move in a straight line, thus "flying off" the tangent (A) to the circle (see Figure 1.30). However, the force of gravitation between the planet and the sun is acting in a direction (B) toward the sun. The effect of this force of gravity is such that the planet continually falls away from its natural path (A) by an amount which just maintains it in an elliptical orbit.

Kepler had already described the motions of the planets, based on what he had observed. Now it was possible for Newton to deduce these same motions from his universal laws of gravitation. He realized

Figure 1.29 Newton's third law in action.

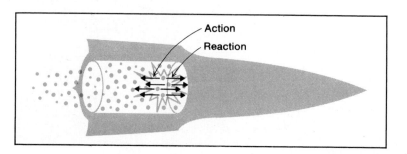

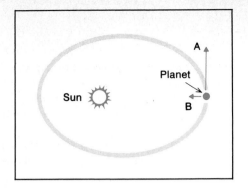

Figure 1.30 The orbit of a planet.

that the total mass of the objects in question also entered into the relationship, as shown in the following equation:

$$(m_{\text{sun}} + m_{\text{planet}})\, p^2 = kr^3$$

Since the mass of the sun (m_{sun}) is so much greater than the mass of any one of its planets, we may say that ($m_{\text{sun}} + m_{\text{planet}}$) is approximately the same as the mass of the sun alone; therefore

$$(m_{\text{sun}})\, p^2 = kr^3$$
$$m_{\text{sun}} = \frac{kr^3}{p^2}$$

This shows that the mass of the sun can be found with only the knowledge of the period of any planet and its average distance from the sun. Furthermore, Newton's law of planetary motion reduces to that of Kepler when we permit the approximation:

$$m_{\text{sun}} + m_{\text{planet}} = m_{\text{sun}}$$
$$(m_{\text{sun}})\, p^2 = kr^3$$
$$p^2 = \frac{kr^3}{m_{\text{sun}}}$$

Let k/m_{sun} be set equal to a new constant K; then

$$p^2 = Kr^3$$

Thus Newton was able to confirm Kepler's laws in essence and to refine them in detail. Using the refined statements, it is possible not only accurately to describe the motions of natural bodies but also to predict to a high degree of accuracy the orbits of today's artificial satellites.

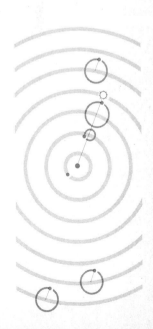

QUESTIONS

1. List several facts that serve as evidence that man made astronomical observations prior to 1000 B.C.
2. What are some of the ways in which early man lived more harmoniously with nature as a result of observing cycles in nature?
3. What object in the sky appears to have determined the length of a month?
4. Of what practical value were astronomical observations in Egypt?
5. Why did the Mesopotamian calendar of 12 equal months, with 30 days each, fail to record the length of a year accurately?
6. What are several similarities and differences between astronomy and astrology?
7. What evidence led Pythagoras to conclude that the earth was shaped like a ball?
8. While Philolaus's model of the planetary system did not represent reality, it did contribute an important true concept. What was that concept?
9. In what sense was Aristarchus's model many years ahead of his time?
10. List the principal points of Aristotle's picture of the sun, earth, planets, and universe.
11. By what scheme did Hipparchus explain that the sun was not always the same distance from the earth?
12. How did Ptolemy explain the apparent retrograde (backward) motion of the planets?
13. How can the apparent retrograde motion of the planets be explained in terms of the Copernican system?
14. Why did the fact that the Aristotelian model became part of church dogma tend to delay man's gaining a more accurate picture of the solar system?
15. How was Tycho Brahe able to make a catalogue of accurate star positions when the telescope had not yet been invented?
16. What do you think was Tycho's motivation for studying the planets and stars?
17. What is the shape of the orbits of the planets?
18. Express Kepler's second law in common language.
19. Explain the significance of Galileo's discovery that Venus goes through phases like the moon.
20. What did Newton view as the most natural tendency for a body moving in empty space?
21. Design a calendar which would make the new moon fall on the first day of each month. Would your calendar make the shortest day of the year fall at the same date (give or take one day) each year? Why?

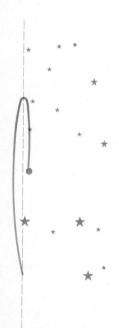

22. If at noon of the shortest day of the year you placed a stick in the ground so that it had no shadow, how could you use that stick to tell when a year had passed?

SUGGESTED READINGS

de Vaucouleurs, Gerard, *Discovery of the universe*. London: Faber and Faber, 1957.

Gingerich, Owen, Johannes Kepler and the Rudolphine Tables. *Sky and Telescope* **42** (6), 328–333 (1971).

Gingerich, Owen, Copernicus and Tycho. *Scientific American* **229** (6), 86–101 (1973).

Lockyer, J. Norman, *The dawn of astronomy*. Cambridge, Mass: M.I.T. Press, 1964.

Pannekoek, A., *A history of astronomy*. New York: Wiley (Interscience), 1961.

Rosen, Edward, Copernicus' place in the history of astronomy. *Sky and Telescope* **45** (2), 72–75 (1973).

Shapley, Harlow, *A source book in astronomy: 1900–1950*. Cambridge, Mass.: Harvard University Press, 1960.

Shapley, Harlow, and Howarth, Helen E., *A source book in astronomy*. New York: McGraw-Hill, 1929.

Stillman, Drake, Galileo's discovery of the law of free fall. *Scientific American* **228** (5), 84–92 (1973).

Wilson, Curtis, How did Kepler discover his first two laws? *Scientific American* **226** (3), 92–106 (1972).

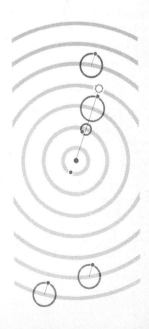

METHODS
OF
ASTRONOMY

2

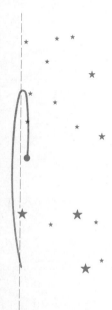

Unlike the physicist, the chemist, and the geologist, the astronomer literally cannot get his hands on much of what he studies. While man has now walked on the moon and brought home samples, and while he may soon sample the surface of a planet like Mars, for the most part the astronomer is restricted to working with the one thing which almost every celestial object sends to him, namely, radiation. Light is perhaps the most familiar form of radiation received from stars and galaxies, but it is only one of many forms; others are radio, infrared,

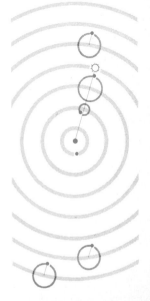

Figure 2.1 Galileo's telescopes. (Yerkes Observatory)

ultraviolet, X rays, and gamma rays. All these forms of radiation have certain aspects in common with light, so as we study the various properties of light, most of these properties will apply to the other forms as well. The important thing is to learn how to extract as much information as is possible from the radiation that reaches us.

In 1610 Galileo constructed one of the earliest telescopes (Figure 2.1), by which he could observe some of the moons of the planet Jupiter. He recorded the times when these moons were eclipsed by the planet, that is, when they went behind the planet and then reappeared on the other side. By 1675 the Danish astronomer Ole Roemer became interested in the possibility that the motion of these moons might be so regular as to form a natural clock that could be used for purposes of navigation (Figure 2.2). First he observed the length of time between eclipses of Io when the earth was at position E_0 (Figure 2.3) and the time intervals seemed to be the same, but as the earth moved on to position E_1, E_2, E_3, E_4, and E_5, the length of time between eclipses was not the same; it became a bit longer after each eclipse. As the earth reached E_6, Roemer could not see Jupiter because of the sun's glare, but when he saw Jupiter again from position E_7 and began his timing once again, a strange thing occurred. Now the intervals of time between eclipses had decreased and this continued until he again re-

Figure 2.2 Roemer's telescope.
(Yerkes Observatory)

Figure 2.3 Roemer's determination of the velocity of light.

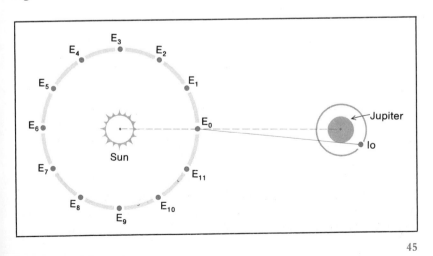

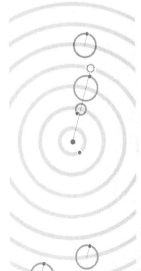

turned to E_0. While Roemer had failed to find a regular clock, he had discovered something more important—the velocity of light (Figure 2.4). He reasoned that as the earth moves farther from Jupiter it should take longer for the light that signals Io's eclipse to reach the earth. He was then able to determine the speed with which light travels. It took approximately 1000 sec (seconds) more time to reach the earth at position E_6 than at E_0. The best estimate for the major axis of the earth's orbit at that time was 196,000,000 miles, and so the velocity of light was computed as:

$$\frac{196,000,000 \text{ miles}}{1000 \text{ sec}} = 196,000 \text{ miles/sec}$$

Today we know that the value of the major axis is closer to 186,000,000 miles, yielding:

$$\frac{186,000,000 \text{ miles}}{1000 \text{ sec}} = 186,000 \text{ miles/sec}$$

To appreciate how fast that really is, suppose you had the privilege of climbing into a jet which had unlimited speed capabilities and flying over the equator of the earth you attained a speed of 186,000 miles/sec. At that speed it would be possible to make more than seven complete trips around the earth in 1 sec. If you can comprehend such speed, it will help you to relate to the size of the universe in later sections of the book, because the unit of length used to measure the distances to stars and galaxies depends directly on the speed of light. If light travels 186,000 miles in a second, and there are 60 sec in a minute, then light travels 186,000 × 60 miles in a minute. Since there are 60 minutes in an hour, then it travels 186,000 × 60 × 60 miles in an hour, 186,000 × 60 × 60 × 24 miles in a day, and 186,000 × 60 × 60 × 24 × 365¼ miles in a year. By multiplying this set of numbers, we have the distance light travels in a year—a *light-year*. Perform this arithmetic yourself and your answer will be just under 6 trillion (6,000,000,000,000) miles/year. The closest star, α (Alpha) Centauri, is 4.3 light-years away: thus its distance from the earth is 4.3 × 6,000,000,000,000 miles, or roughly 26 trillion miles.

In 1924, Albert A. Michelson, an American physicist, developed an experiment by which he could more accurately determine the velocity of light. There were two things he had to know in order to determine velocity: the distance traveled and the time required. He set up part of his apparatus on Mt. Wilson, in California, and part on Mt. San Antonio, approximately 22 miles away. It is not an easy task to measure the distance from one mountain peak to another; however, by carefully using standard surveying techniques, a Coastal Geodetic Survey team was able to measure the distance accurately to a fraction of an inch. The device whereby he might measure the time for light to travel from one mountain top to the other and return consisted of a rotating mirror set on a motor which would turn it at any desired speed. A bright source of light was directed onto mirror face A, one of eight mirrors on the eight-sided wheel (Figure 2.5), and mirror A reflected the light to a flat mirror on Mt. San Antonio. When the wheel

Figure 2.5 Michelson's rotating mirror experiment.

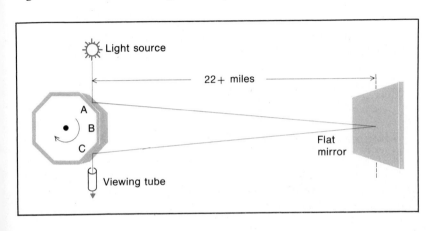

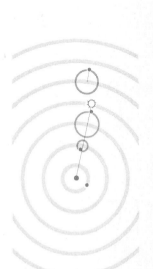

was standing still, the flat mirror returned the light to mirror face C and into the viewing tube. Once adjusted to the correct speed, the wheel was rotated so that the flash of light sent by face A would be caught by face B—which had turned to the position that face C had occupied by the time the flash traveled to Mt. San Antonio and back—a distance of 43.978 miles. If the wheel turned at the rate of 529.37 rps (revolutions per second), the computation would look like this:

$$529.37 \text{ rps} \times 8 \text{ flashes/revolution} \times 43.978 \text{ miles/flash}$$
$$= 186,250 \text{ miles/sec}$$

Expressed in metric units this velocity is 299,729 km/sec, or almost 300,000 km/sec. Of course this experiment was not performed in a vacuum, and so this result represents the velocity of light in air. Modern

Figure 2.6 Relationships between units of the International System (*Système International*—SI) and the English system are shown in graphic form.

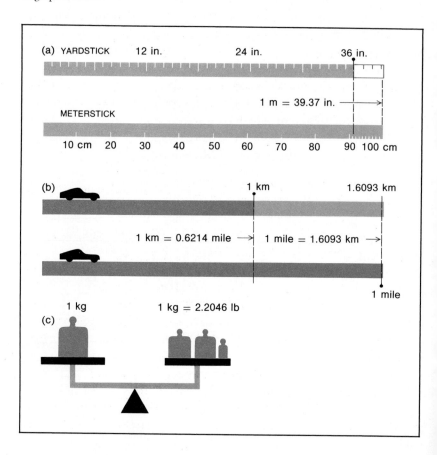

determination in a vacuum produces only a slightly faster velocity of 299,793 km/sec (186,288 miles/sec). This is the accepted value for the velocity of light in empty space. Light travels considerably slower than that in media such as water or glass.

INTERNATIONAL SYSTEM
OF UNITS (SI)

While the English system of weights and measures has long been used for everyday transactions in the United States and certain other countries, we are now gradually moving toward a conversion to the International System (SI), already in use by scientists around the world. This system is essentially the same as the metric system. The fundamental unit of length is the *meter* (m), which was originally defined as one ten-millionth of the distance from the north pole to the equator, as measured on the earth's surface. A more reasonable way to determine the length of a meter is presented in Appendix 2, where the International System is more completely discussed and conversion units are given. The fundamental unit of mass is the *kilogram* (kg), and the unit of time is the *second* (sec). It will be very helpful to you if you can visualize distances in terms of meters and kilometers (km), where 1 km = 1000 m. Figure 2.6 will help you to do this.

In the remainder of this chapter, we will use the SI units and give the English equivalents in parentheses; however, in the chapters that follow, the SI units will be used exclusively. (Refer to Appendix 2 for a more detailed explanation.)

THE WAVE NATURE OF LIGHT

We are all familiar with the expanding wave pattern that is set up when a pebble is dropped into a quiet pond. Molecules of the water will rise and fall periodically in a very definite and predictable manner. While light may be created by the oscillation (up-and-down motion) of a charged particle, it is not transferred from one place to another by causing particles to move up and down. We know this to be true because light travels through empty space, where no particles exist. Therefore when we speak of the wave nature of light we are speaking of something that appears to be both electrical and magnetic in nature, changing in a wavelike manner.

Perhaps you have experienced the phenomenon of becoming charged electrically by scuffing your feet on a nylon rug. Picture a small object that is charged and standing still. The space around the charged particle can be thought of as a "field," and if another charged (test)

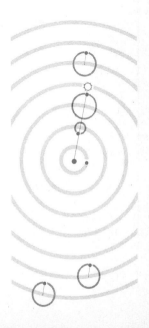

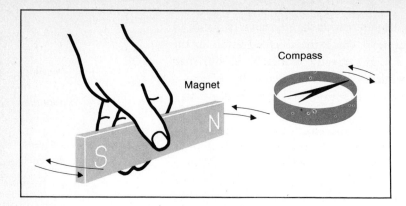

Figure 2.7 A changing magnetic field.

particle is brought into the field, the test particle will experience a constant force. If the test charge is like that of the fixed charge, the test particle will experience a force that repels. If the test particle is charged in a manner opposite to the fixed charge, it will experience a force of attraction. If the first particle is set into oscillation, then the test particle will experience a changing field and will respond by oscillating also.

Thus, the oscillation of one particle can be transferred to another without there being any material in between the two. This is a partial model of how light travels through empty space, but to complete the model we should recognize the fact that whenever a changing electrical field occurs, a changing magnetic field also accompanies it. To picture a changing magnetic field, hold a bar magnet in one hand and set a compass nearby. Now rotate the magnet back and forth. You are creating a changing magnetic field, which is evidenced by the action of the compass needle (see Figure 2.7). Again the effect of the oscillating magnet will travel to the compass even if no material exists between the two. Now we have a more complete picture of light, as an electro-

Figure 2.8 A graphic representation of electrical and magnetic disturbances.

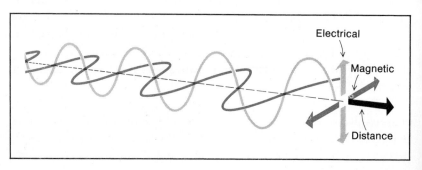

magnetic disturbance, produced by an oscillating charge that creates a changing electrical and magnetic field simultaneously. A graphic representation is shown in Figure 2.8. Because the electric component of the wave is responsible for all optical effects, and because the magnetic component will always accompany a changing magnetic field, we will henceforth speak only of the electrical component.

Light is only a small portion of the electromagnetic spectrum, which includes radio, radiant heat (infrared), ultraviolet radiation, X rays, and gamma rays. What is it that makes these forms of radiation different from one another? It is their wavelength. We may picture one *wavelength* in a changing electrical field as the distance the disturbance travels as it goes through one complete oscillation, say, from the crest of one wave to the crest of the next (Figure 2.9). Remember that all forms of electromagnetic disturbances travel through empty space at approximately 300,000 km/sec; thus, if a radio wave travels 1000 m while going through one wave cycle, we speak of its wavelength as 1000 m. It should be apparent, at this point, that if a wave travels 1000 m in one cycle and it travels 300,000,000 m in 1 sec, then it must go through $300,000,000/1000 = 300,000$ cycles/sec. This is the frequency of the disturbance. While we will continue to emphasize wavelength, it will always be possible for you to obtain the frequency of the disturbance by dividing the velocity of light by the wavelength, using the same units, of course. The wavelengths of radio signals which we receive on AM radio fall within the range of 200 to 500 m, whereas the amateur radio operator typically uses wavelengths in the range of 2 to 160 m. Radio astronomers are particularly interested in radio wavelengths between 0.01 m (1 centimeter) and 1 m. The wavelengths of these and other forms of electromagnetic radiation are shown in Figure 2.10. Note that an expression like 10^{-2} m means 0.01 m, 10^{-3} m means 0.001 m, and so on. (Appendix 3 provides a full explanation of powers of ten.) As you can see, the wavelength of visible light is very short, namely, between 0.0000004 and 0.0000007 m, with ultraviolet, X rays, and gamma rays possessing even shorter wavelengths.

Figure 2.9 The waveform, showing one complete oscillation.

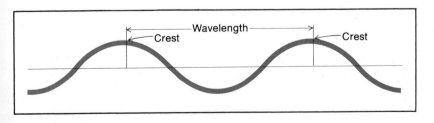

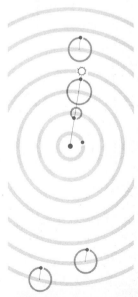

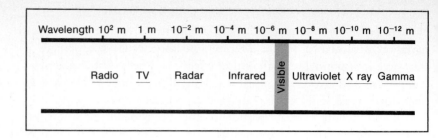

Figure 2.10   The electromagnetic spectrum.

Rather than measuring such small lengths with a unit called the meter, we use a much smaller unit called the *angstrom,* denoted by the symbol Å:

$$1 \text{ Å} = 10^{-10} \text{ m} = 0.0000000001 \text{ m}$$

The range of visible light, measured in angstroms, is thus 4000 to 7000 Å.

POLARIZATION OF LIGHT

Light is typically emitted by atoms oscillating in many different orientations, and we refer to such light as being unpolarized. If unpolarized light is passed through certain filters that have been manufactured by laying down many long needlelike crystals in the same direction, then only that portion of the oscillations which are parallel to the length of the crystals will be transmitted—thus polarizing the light. Analogous to such a filter is a common picket gate. The long narrow spaces between the pickets will permit a wave motion to be transmitted only in one plane, and so we say that the first gate polarizes the wave. If the second gate is oriented in the same direction, then the polarized wave is transmitted [Figure 2.11(a)]; however, if the second gate is turned 90°, then the polarized wave is blocked [Figure 2.11(b)].

When sunlight strikes a flat surface, such as a lake or the hood of a car, the reflected rays tend to be horizontally polarized because the surface absorbs oscillations that are perpendicular to it but reflects oscillations parallel to it. The reflected light is called "glare," and because it is polarized, it may be prevented from reaching the eye by use of polarized sunglasses with vertical "gates" (Figure 2.12).

The astronomer is particularly interested in the polarization of starlight because it provides clues to the material through which it has passed in reaching the observer. For instance, dust is thought to polarize starlight. This topic will be more fully discussed in Chapter 11.

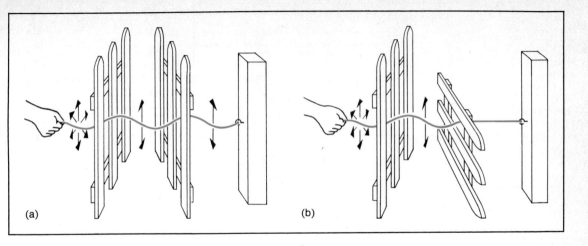

Figure 2.11 An analogy for the polarization of light: (a) both vertical gates; (b) vertical and horizontal gates.

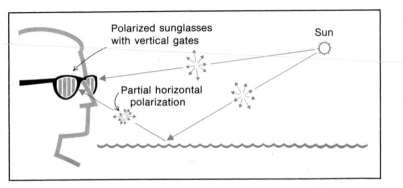

Figure 2.12 Sunlight which is reflected from the surface of the water is partially polarized in a horizontal orientation, and the vertical "gates" of the polarized sunglasses prevent its entry into the eyes.

REFLECTION OF LIGHT

Does light travel in a straight line? We assume that it does in space that is free of all matter; however, in our own environment light is subject to many influences, one of which is *reflection*. In order to describe the reflection phenomenon more accurately, we must first understand what is meant by the expression "a normal to the surface." The *normal* is a line that is perpendicular to the surface at a given point. A vertical flagpole erected on level ground is an example of a normal to a surface.

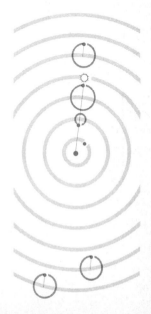

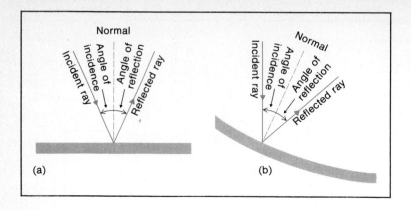

Figure 2.13 The angle of reflection always equals the angle of incidence (a), even for a curved mirror (b).

The angle between the *incident* (incoming) ray of light and the normal is called the *angle of incidence,* and the angle between the reflected ray of light and the normal is called the *angle of reflection.* The law of reflection may thus be stated: *The angle of reflection is equal to the angle of incidence.* This law forms the basis for design of the reflecting telescope, for it is true for every point on the surface of a mirror, even if that mirror is curved (Figure 2.13).

REFRACTION OF LIGHT

Another way in which light is influenced by its environment is that of *refraction.* Light travels at different velocities in different materials. We have shown that light travels at 299,793 km/sec (186,288 miles/sec) in a vacuum. It travels at about 224,000 km/sec (140,000 miles/sec) in water, and at still different velocities in glass or other transparent materials. The refraction (bending) of light results from this fact—that light travels at different velocities in different materials. For light of a given wavelength, the ratio of its velocity in a vacuum to its velocity in a given medium is called the *index of refraction* for that medium.

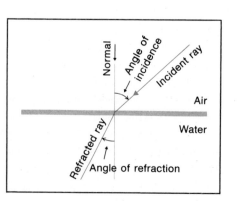

Figure 2.14 Refraction of light.

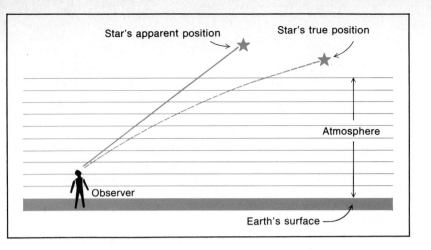

Figure 2.15 Refraction by the earth's atmosphere.

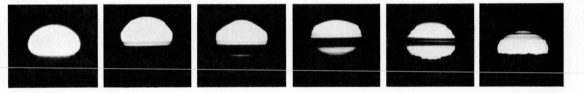

Figure 2.16 Photographs of the setting sun, showing effects of atmospheric refraction. (Lick Observatory)

In Figure 2.14 you can see that the angle that the refracted ray makes with the normal is called the *angle of refraction*. As the light passes from air into water the angle of refraction is smaller than the angle of incidence; this is true because the velocity of light is less in water than in air. This illustrates the basic relationship between the angle that a ray makes with the normal and the velocity of light in that medium. Perhaps you have noticed that a spoon, when placed in a glass of water and viewed from an angle, appears to be bent. This is due to refraction. A less obvious result of refraction occurs in the atmosphere of the earth. As light from a star enters the atmosphere it passes through "layers" of increasing density and thus is refracted, causing the star to appear higher in the sky than its true position (Figure 2.15).

The effects of atmospheric refraction are quite obvious when the sun is seen setting over the ocean: as it approaches the horizon, its bottom part is refracted more than the top part, and so the sun appears flattened (Figure 2.16).

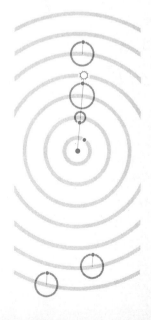

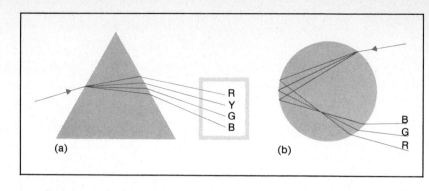

Figure 2.17 Dispersion of white light by (a) a prism and (b) a raindrop.

DISPERSION BY REFRACTION

A phenomenon that occurs simultaneously with refraction is that of *dispersion*. White light is composed of all colors, and each color represents a different wavelength. Since the angle of refraction also depends upon the wavelength of the light, each color is bent at slightly different angles when refracted by a transparent medium. Blue light has the shortest wavelength among visible colors and is bent more than red light, which has a longer wavelength. By use of the prism, white light may be separated into the full range of colors, an array called the *spectrum* [Figure 2.17(a)]. Reflection and dispersion also takes place in rain drops, producing a rainbow [Figure 2.17(b)]. See Plate 6.

As we shall see, the phenomenon of dispersion creates a serious problem in the simple refracting telescope, yet it also serves as the basis for one of the most useful tools of astronomy, the spectrograph.

DIFFRACTION OF LIGHT

As light passes the edge of an object or through a small opening, it spreads out in all directions as though the edge were a new source of light. This is called diffraction, and it is illustrated in water waves in Figure 2.18(a). Diffraction may be useful in certain applications but is somewhat detrimental in astronomical instruments, for as light enters the telescope it must travel past numerous edges. A telescope generally has a round opening at the front and braces to support parts of the telescope, as in the case of the secondary mirror of a reflector (see Figure 2.36, page 66). Each of these parts acts as a new source of light. Figure 2.19 reveals the pattern of diffraction spikes (cross shape) and circle. Diffraction prevents any telescope from forming perfect images of stars.

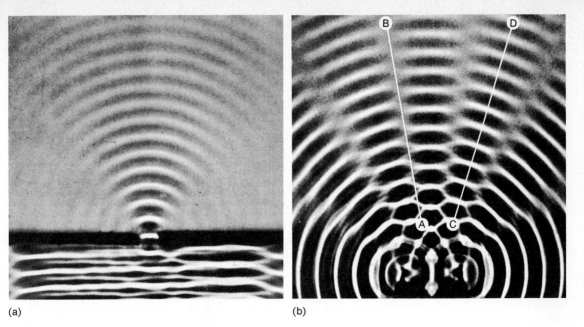

(a)   (b)

Figure 2.18 (a) Diffraction in water waves. (b) Interference in water waves. Destructive interference occurs along line AB; constructive interference, along line CD. (Ealing Films, Inc., and Educational Development Corp.)

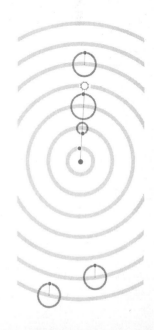

Figure 2.19 Diffraction spikes are produced by the structure which supports the secondary mirror of the telescope. (Hale Observatories)

INTERFERENCE OF LIGHT

When two (or more) small openings act as new sources of waves, a pattern of interference is seen, as in Figure 2.18(b). Along the line AB no wave motion is evident, which indicates that the waves from the two sources have canceled each other. This is called *destructive interference.* We visualize this as resulting from the *crest* (high point) of one wave meeting the *trough* (low point) of the other, as in Figure 2.20.

On the other hand, along line CD in Figure 2.18(b), the wave action is distinct. This is *constructive interference,* resulting from the fact that the two waves interact with crest meeting crest and trough meeting trough, as shown in Figure 2.21.

Both diffraction and interference are easily seen in water waves. What evidence do we have that similar phenomena occur in light? Suppose that many fine lines are ruled (scratched) on a sheet of glass, in effect providing many edges. Such a device is called a *diffraction grating.* When the light from a single source passes these edges, they act as many new sources. Consider the light that passes two adjacent edges, lines A and B in Figure 2.22. The wave nature of light tells us that at certain angles the light waves from adjacent lines will interfere with each other destructively, thereby producing dark bands, and that at other angles the light waves will interfere constructively, producing bright bands on the screen. The spacing between the bright and dark regions will depend on the spacing of the lines and on the wavelength

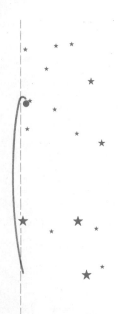

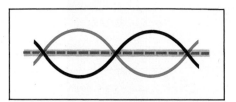

Figure 2.20 Crest of one wave meets trough of another wave, resulting in destructive interference.

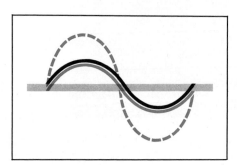

Figure 2.21 Crest of one wave meets crest of another wave, resulting in constructive interference.

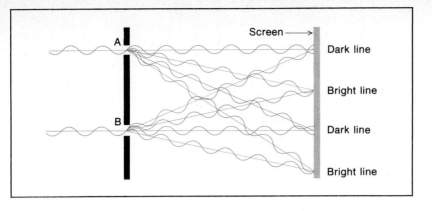

Figure 2.22 The diffraction grating.

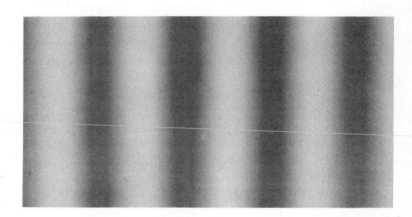

Figure 2.23 The interference of light. The light bands represent constructive interference; the dark bands destructive interference. (Don Jenkins)

of the light that is being considered (Figure 2.23). Furthermore, could these bright bands be seen in color, the full spectrum would be evident in each band because different colors (different wavelengths) interfere constructively at slightly different places on the screen. Thus, the diffraction grating becomes an important device whereby the light of a given source may be dispersed into its spectrum. Often the diffraction grating is used in place of a prism in a spectrograph.

THE DUAL NATURE OF LIGHT

We have noted several experiments demonstrating that light behaves like waves. Some experiments require another kind of explanation. Such an experiment may be performed using an electroscope with a clean zinc plate attached to its knob. An electroscope is a device that is capable of detecting the presence of charged particles. When there is

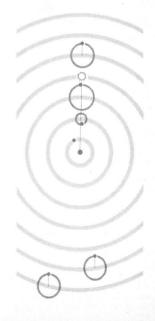

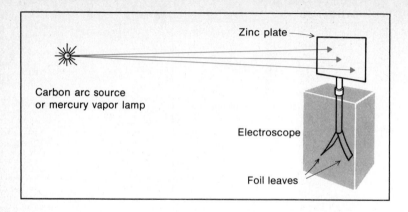

Figure 2.24 The photoelectric effect.

no charge on the zinc plate, the foil leaves hang downward together, but if the zinc plate becomes charged, that charge is conducted to the foil leaves and they experience a like charge on each leaf, causing them to be repelled—to separate.

Suppose that a negative charge (a surplus of electrons) is placed on the plate, causing the foil leaves to separate, then ultraviolet light is allowed to fall onto the plate. The leaves will be seen to fall back together, indicating that electrons have been knocked free of the plate, leaving it neutralized. To explain this phenomenon, called the *photoelectric effect* (Figure 2.24), imagine that light behaves like particles, called *photons,* which are capable of knocking the electrons free of the plate. Photons are capable of knocking electrons free because they represent energy; but unlike ordinary particles, photons can not be placed on a scale and weighed—that is to say, they have zero rest mass. Their energy is inversely proportional to their wavelength: thus electromagnetic energy that is characterized by short wavelengths, such as ultraviolet light, carries more energy per photon than does blue light. Blue light of any desired intensity can be directed onto the plate of the electroscope and no electrons will be freed, but when ultraviolet light falls onto the plate, electrons are ejected instantaneously. Evidently the ultraviolet photon carries enough energy to free the electron, whereas no collection of blue light photons could accomplish the task. If light behaved only like a wave (with its energy distributed uniformly over a wave front), and not as particles, then the photoelectric effect could not be explained.

Could it be possible that all matter exhibits a dual nature—that of a wave and that of a particle? The following experiment suggests that it does. When electrons (particles) are shot through the very small opening of a crystal lattice, a diffraction pattern is formed [Figure 2.25(a)] that closely resembles the diffraction pattern created when X rays (usually thought of as a wave phenomenon) are passed through the small openings within the structure of aluminum foil [Figure 2.25(b)].

60

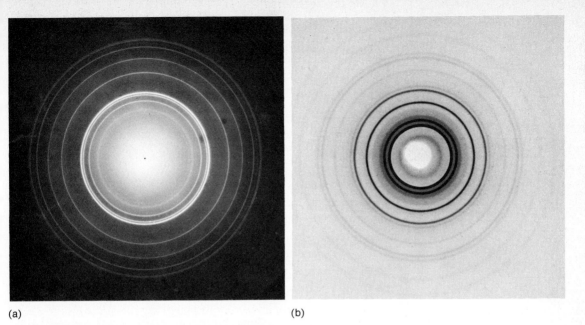

(a)   (b)

Figure 2.25 (a) An electron diffraction pattern created by passing a beam of electrons through a crystal lattice, in this case beryllium. (b) The diffraction pattern created by X rays directed through polycrystalline aluminum. (a, RCA Laboratories, Princeton, New Jersey; b, courtesy of Mrs. M. H. Read, Bell Telephone Laboratories, Murray Hill, New Jersey)

TELESCOPE DESIGN

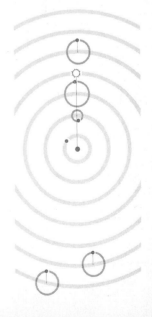

When Galileo viewed the sky with his telescope, he realized that he could see stars which were too faint to be seen with the naked eye. This fact illustrates the real purpose for assembling either lenses or mirrors to make a telescope, that is, to gather light over a large surface and concentrate its energy into a small area so as to produce an image which is brighter than the object appears to the naked eye. The effects of refraction were known before the time of Galileo, but mere refraction, say, into water or a flat piece of glass, would not concentrate the light energy at one point; Galileo's important contribution was the discovery that when he gave a piece of glass the proper curvature, light rays from a distant star that passed through the glass near its edge would be bent (refracted) more than those which passed near its center, causing the rays of light from a given source to bend toward a focal point (Figure 2.26). The distance between the lens and the focal point is called the *focal length* of the lens.

Were we to view an object like the moon, it would present many points from which light travels to our telescope. Each point on the object is brought to a focus at a different point, and the collection of all such

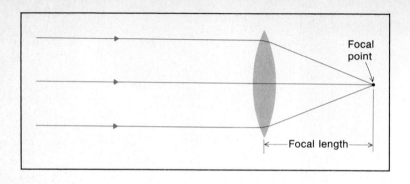

Figure 2.26 A simple convex lens.

focal points forms the image of the moon on the *focal plane* of the telescope (Figure 2.27).

Today, a piece of film can be placed at the focal plane and a picture of the moon may be made in which every point is said to be in focus. To use such a telescope for visual observations, it is necessary to place an eyepiece just behind the focal plane (Figure 2.28). The eyepiece serves as a magnifying glass, making the image of the moon appear larger.

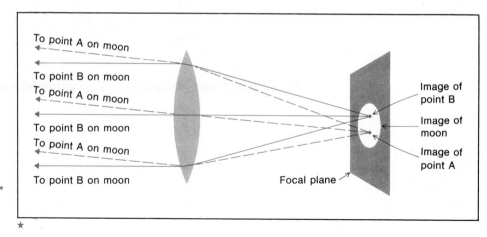

Figure 2.27 Formation of the extended image.

Figure 2.28 The refracting telescope.

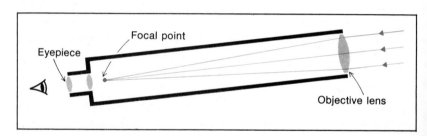

Figure 2.29 The 1-m (40-in.) refractor at Yerkes Observatory in Wisconsin. (Yerkes Observatory)

For a given focal length, the larger the objective (first) lens is made, the more light will be collected and the brighter the image will be. In an attempt to see fainter objects, opticians have constructed several large objective lenses, the largest of which is approximately 1 m (40 in.) in diameter and is located at Yerkes Observatory in Wisconsin (Figure 2.29).

LIMITATIONS IN REFRACTORS

Refractor telescopes are limited in size because large objective lenses are difficult to support without sagging, which changes their shape. The glass from which the objective is ground must be of high quality, free of bubbles and other imperfections. Still further limitations occur owing to the design of the lens itself.

Chromatic aberration Since white light is composed of all colors and blue light is refracted more than red light, blue light is brought to a focus ahead of red light; similarly, all colors between red and blue

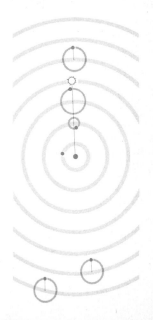

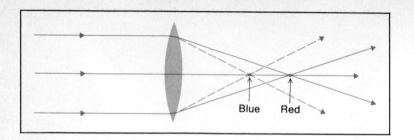

Figure 2.30 Chromatic aberration (see text).

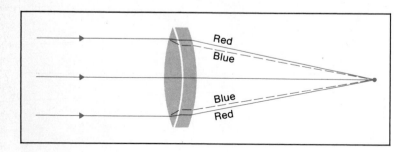

Figure 2.31 The achromatic lens (see text).

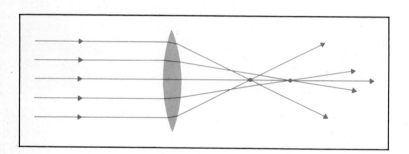

Figure 2.32 Spherical aberration (see text).

are brought to slightly different focal points by a single lens, resulting in the formation of a blurred image. This produces a color defect and is called *chromatic aberration* (Figure 2.30). This defect may be corrected by the addition of a second lens, which, because of its shape and a slightly different index of refraction, will deflect the rays and bring all colors back to the same focal point, producing a sharp image. A compound lens of this type is called an *achromatic lens* (Figure 2.31).

Spherical aberration While it is much easier to grind a lens of spherical shape, a simple lens of this design suffers a defect called *spherical aberration* (Figure 2.32): The rays of light from a distant object are not brought to the same focal point. Those rays passing through the lens near its outer edge are brought to a focus closer than those passing nearer the center of the lens. This defect may also be corrected by the addition of a second element in the lens system.

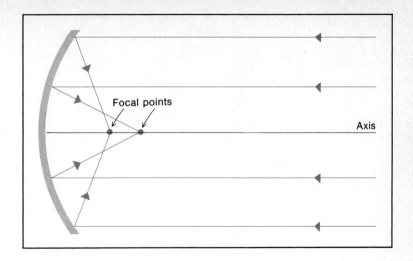

Figure 2.33 Spherical aberration in a mirror.

Focal points

Axis

THE REFLECTING TELESCOPE

Sir Isaac Newton was the first to fully recognize that whenever light is refracted it is also dispersed, causing the phenomenon of chromatic aberration in refractors. He also recognized the fact that light is not dispersed when it is reflected, hence that a telescope depending only upon reflection will not be plagued by chromatic aberration. Obviously a flat mirror would not concentrate the light. He may have tried a spherical mirror—only to find that it possessed spherical aberration because rays of light (from a star) which struck the outside portions of the mirror did not reflect to the same focal point as those which struck the mirror toward its center (Figure 2.33). Newton deduced that if he were to give the mirror a parabolic shape by hollowing out the center of the spherical mirror (Figure 2.34), he could cause all rays from a given star to converge on a point, the focal point. As you can see in Figure 2.35(c), the parabola is one of the distinctive curves which may be obtained by cutting a cone parallel to one edge. Other curves

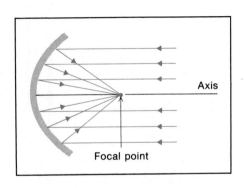

Figure 2.34 The parabolic reflector.

Axis

Focal point

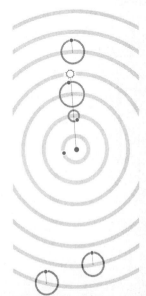

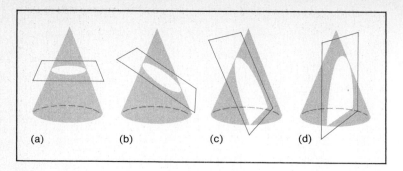

Figure 2.35 Sections of a cone: (a) circle; (b) ellipse; (c) parabola; (d) hyperbola.

which are useful in our discussion of astronomy may also be obtained by cutting the cone in various ways, as is demonstrated in Figure 2.35(a,b,d).

Reflecting telescopes are usually of one of the following designs, differing primarily in the placement of the eyepiece (Figure 2.36). The *prime focus* is used only on larger instruments like the 5-m (200-in.) Hale telescope at Mt. Palomar Observatory, since placement of the observer's head at that position on a small instrument would obscure all incoming rays of light. The *Newtonian focus* was the original design used by Sir Isaac Newton and is still the most popular among amateur astronomers. The *Cassegrain focus* allows the light to make one additional trip through the tube. This fact together with the curvature of the secondary mirror allows the design of a long effective focal length in a short tube, thus increasing the portability of the instrument. The *Coudé focus* is used to direct light to a stationary point, usually for the

Figure 2.36 Four reflecting telescopes, utilizing different focal points: (a) prime focus; (b) Newtonian focus; (c) Cassegrain focus; (d) Coudé focus.

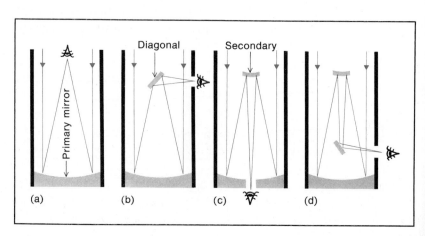

Figure 2.37 The 3-m (120-in.) parabolic mirror of Lick Observatory. (Lick Observatory)

purpose of spectroscopic analysis. The Hale (5-m) telescope utilizes the prime focus, the Cassegrain focus, and the Coudé focus in the same instrument by moving the proper secondary mirror into place. The focal length of the primary mirror is 16.8-m (55 ft), thus the prime focus position is 16.8 m from the mirror. At this position the astronomer moves with the telescope while making long exposures on film. An astronomer may also ride at the Cassegrain focus while the telescope is in motion (Figures 2.39 and 2.40).

THE SCHMIDT CAMERA

We speak of this design as a camera because it is used exclusively for photographic work and has no provision for visual observation. All guiding is done through an auxiliary scope mounted on the exterior of the camera. The principles of refraction and reflection are both employed in the Schmidt camera. Light enters the system through a weak lens called a corrector plate, where it is refracted slightly, and

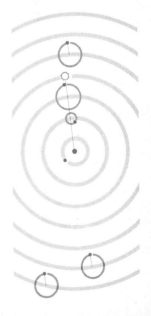

Figure 2.38 The 4-m Nicholas U. Mayall telescope at Kitt Peak National Observatory in Tucson, Arizona. (Kitt Peak National Observatory)

then the rays of light are reflected by the spherical primary mirror to the focal point. A piece of film, 35.6 cm × 35.6 cm (14 in. × 14 in.), exposed at this point, will record a wide-angle view of the sky. The 1.22-m (48-in.) Schmidt camera at Mt. Palomar records a square portion of the sky 6° on a side, covering 36 square degrees in a single exposure. The 5-m (200-in.) telescope covers only about one square degree per exposure. The Schmidt camera is very well suited to a survey of the visible sky, a program that has required 7 years (over 1800 photographs) to complete (Figure 2.41).

TELESCOPE PERFORMANCE

The factors that ultimately affect the size, brightness, and quality of an image formed in a telescope include the aperture (diameter of lens or mirror), the focal length, and the quality of the objective lens or

68

Figure 2.39 (a) Looking down the tube of the 200-in. (5.1-m) Palomar telescope, past the observer at the prime focus position, to the mirror at the far end. (b) A drawing of the Palomar telescope. (Mount Wilson and Palomar Observatories)

(a)

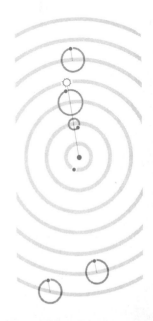

(b)

mirror and of the eyepiece used. Of first importance is the quality of the lens or mirror. This basically refers to its shape. We have already stressed the fact that there is a correct shape for a lens or a mirror, so the degree to which this shape is achieved determines the quality of the telescope. If the mirror is ground so that its surface is like that of a parabola with no variations larger than one-tenth of the wavelength of blue light [no more than 0.00000004 m, that is, 40 nanometers (nm)], then its quality is specified as being "tenth wave," considered to be very adequate for an amateur telescope. Some mirrors have a superior "twentieth-wave" quality, with no deviations greater than one-twentieth the wavelength of blue light.

Before we can specify the factors which determine size, brightness, and sharpness of the image, we must realize that there are two classes of objects that the astronomer views: those which have an apparent size, like the sun, moon, planets, clusters, nebulae, and galaxies, called *extended objects;* and those which have no apparent size, like stars, called *point sources.* While overmagnification sometimes blurs images to produce an apparent size in stars, no amount of magnification will actually produce a real size in a star image. Stars are simply too far away to be seen as disks, other than those produced by atmospheric effects and optical effects in the telescope.

Size For a given extended object, the size of the image formed at the prime focus depends upon the focal length of the lens or mirror. The longer the focal length, the larger the image formed. If f is the

70

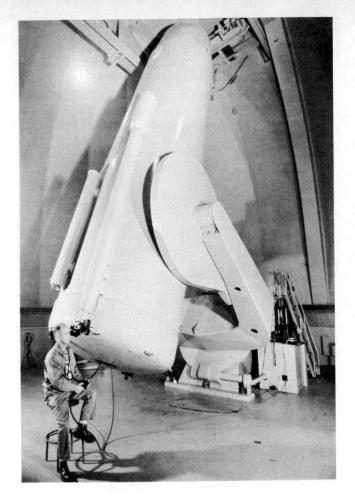

Figure 2.41 The 48-in. (1.2-m) Schmidt telescope of the Palomar Observatory. (Mount Wilson and Palomar Observatories)

focal length of the lens or mirror expressed in inches, then the size of the image (s), expressed in inches, that will be produced by an object 1° in diameter is given by the formula $s = 0.01744\,f$. The scale of a typical amateur telescope—for example, one of 152-cm (60-in.) focal length—would be

$$s = 0.01744 \times 152 \text{ cm} = 2.67 \text{ cm/degree}$$

Using the full moon as an object that has a diameter of 0.5°, we would expect its image to be one-half the figure computed above, that is, 1.33 cm (0.5 in.) in diameter. This would be the size of the image that could be recorded on film without the aid of an eyepiece. A telescope of twice the focal length would produce an image twice as large on a piece of film, without the aid of an eyepiece. Thus the longer focal lengths are particularly useful in observing the planets.

71

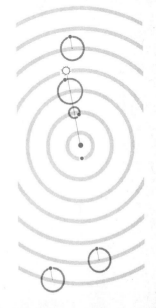

Brightness In the case of a point source (a star), the *brightness* of the image depends only upon the aperture (diameter) of the mirror or lens. The larger the aperture, the brighter the image. For an extended source, the brightness of the image produced by various telescopes of equal focal length depends upon the diameter of the mirror or lens. The brightness of the image increases with the square of the aperture, meaning that if the size of the mirror or lens is doubled, the total light concentrated in the image will be multiplied by four. On the other hand, if the aperture of several telescopes is the same and they differ only in focal length, the one with the longer focal length will produce the dimmer image. This is an inverse relationship. The combined effect of aperture and focal length upon the brightness of the extended image is expressed by the formula

$$B = C\left(\frac{a}{f}\right)^2$$

where B represents brightness, a represents aperture, f represents the focal length of the telescope, and C is a constant. The ratio of focal length to aperture (f/a) is called the focal ratio or f-stop, as when used in connection with a camera. A focal ratio of $f/10$ means that the focal length of the lens or mirror is ten times the aperture. A telescope in which the focal ratio is $f/5$ will provide images which are approximately four times as bright as with the $f/10$ ratio.

We have been referring to the brightness of the image as viewed by the human eye. The effectiveness of this brightness may be increased manyfold by photographic and/or electronic devices. Imagine an object so dim that it could not be seen visually in the telescope. If the light from that object is allowed to fall on a sensitive photographic plate for a prolonged period of time, an image will be "built up" on the plate itself. When developed, the plate will reveal the presence of that object. Dim objects that normally require hours to expose on film may now be intensified by means of an electronic device that senses their presence and builds the photographic image at a much faster rate. Thus the effective aperture of the telescope has been increased (Figure 2.42).

Resolution The *resolution* of a telescope measures its ability to show detail in an image, that is, to separate objects that appear to be close together. The resolving power of a telescope is expressed in terms of the smallest angle between two stars that can be distinguished as separate objects. The resolving power of an optical telescope depends primarily upon its aperture and is expressed by the formula $\alpha = 11.58/d$, measured in seconds of arc, where d is the diameter of the lens or mirror measured in centimeters. A telescope with a 15.24–cm

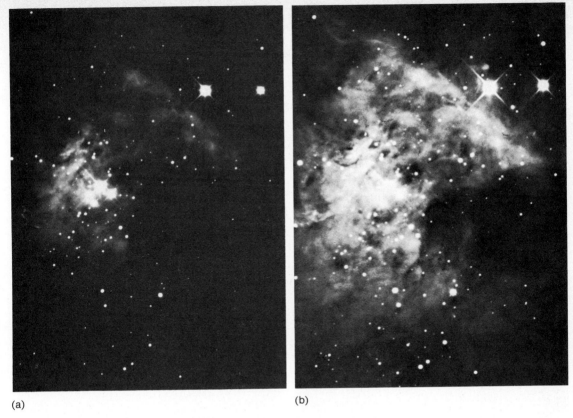

(a)   (b)

Figure 2.42 Region of the Orion Nebula, showing the effect of aperture and time exposure on the formation of star images: (a) small aperture and/or short exposure time; (b) large aperture and/or long exposure time. (Lick Observatory)

(6-in.) lens can separate star images that are at least 0.76 second of arc apart. (In angular measures, $1° = 60$ minutes and 1 minute = 60 seconds.) A 25.4-cm (10-in.) telescope can separate stars that are at least 0.5 seconds of arc apart under ideal atmospheric conditions. Figure 2.43 indicates how two images might appear in telescopes of the indicated aperture.

Figure 2.43 Resolution of star images using different apertures (shown in inches).

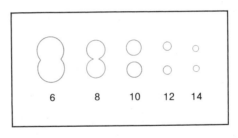

6   8   10   12   14

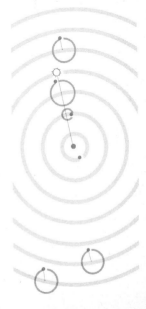

MAGNIFICATION

While the size of an extended image, formed at the prime focus, is determined by the focal length of the objective lens or mirror, the *power* (magnification) of the telescope is determined by both the focal length of the objective and the focal length of the eyepiece used. This is expressed in the following equation:

$$\text{Power} = \frac{\text{focal length of the objective}}{\text{focal length of the eyepiece}} = \frac{f_o}{f_e}$$

Suppose that, for a given telescope, $f_o = 2$ m, and that we choose an eyepiece of 10 mm (millimeters) focal length (f_e). We must first express the focal length of the objective in millimeters:

2 m = 2000 mm

The effective power of this combination is then found:

$$\text{Power} = \frac{f_o}{f_e} = \frac{2000 \text{ mm}}{10 \text{ mm}} = 200$$

Using this telescope with the 10-mm eyepiece, an extended object will appear 200 times as large as with the naked eye. Frequently, the useful power of a telescope is limited by the object being viewed and/or the atmospheric conditions. If an eyepiece with a focal length of 20 mm is chosen, the power will be 100:

$$\text{Power} = \frac{f_o}{f_e} = \frac{2000}{20} = 100$$

As a general rule, the useful limit of power for any telescope is 20 times its aperture in centimeters.

THE SPECTROGRAPH

Spectroscopy is one of the most important areas in astronomy. Its operations depend upon the same phenomenon that was shown to be the cause of chromatic aberration in the simple refractor, that is, the fact that light of different colors is bent by differing amounts when it is refracted by glass or by some other transparent medium. Thus white light, which is composed of all colors, may be separated into these

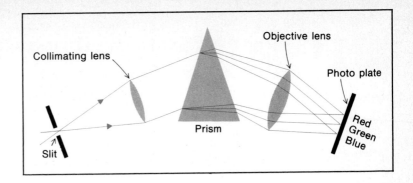

Figure 2.44   The spectrograph.

various colors by refraction, thereby producing a full spectrum of colors (Figure 2.44; see also Plate 6).

Light from a star is passed through a narrow slit, then through a collimating lens, which bends the rays so that they will be parallel as they pass through the prism. The light, which has been broken into its various colors, is then focused onto a photographic plate.

The picture of the spectrum, called a *spectrogram,* consists of a series of adjacent images of the slit, each representing a slightly different wavelength. When sunlight is viewed through such an instrument it will be noticed that dark lines appear at certain places in the spectrum. While at first these were not recognized as being significant, in 1814 the German optician Joseph Fraunhofer recorded the position of several hundred of these dark lines, which are still referred to as *Fraunhofer lines.* In 1859 Gustav Kirchhoff, a German physicist, discovered that this same phenomenon could be produced in the laboratory by passing white light through various gases and then through the spectrograph. He particularly noticed two close lines in the yellow portion of the spectrum and found that he could produce these same dark lines by passing white light through sodium vapors. To date more than 30,000 *absorption* (dark) *lines* have been found in the visible portion of the solar spectrum, and more than half of these have been identified with elements known on earth (Figure 2.45).

Kirchhoff also observed that a *glowing* (excited) gas produced a spectrum consisting of a series of bright lines on a dark background (Figure 2.46). As a result of this observation he stated the following three basic laws:

Continuous spectrum   *A heated liquid or solid, or a gas under high pressure, emits light of all wavelengths, producing a continuous spectrum consisting of all colors.*

Bright-line spectrum   *A low-pressure gas that has been excited (say, by electrical current or heat) produces a bright-line spectrum, consisting of only certain colors.*

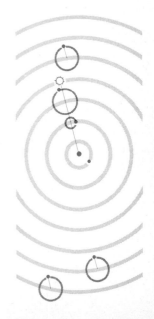

75

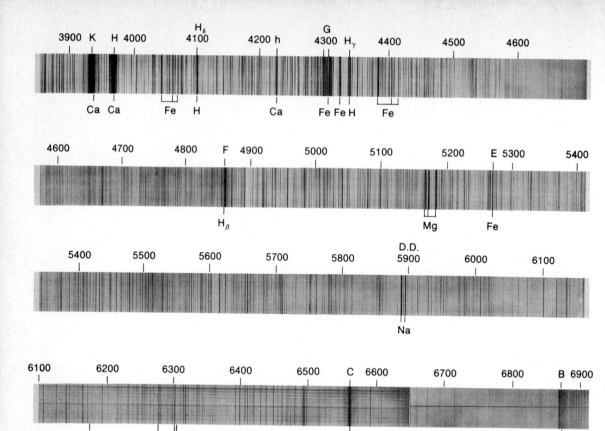

Figure 2.45 The solar spectrum, with certain lines identified with known elements. (Mount Wilson and Palomar Observatories)

Absorption spectrum *If light of a continuous nature is passed through a gas, the gas may absorb certain wavelengths, producing an absorption spectrum consisting of dark lines on a continuous background.*

One might suspect that the wavelengths absorbed by the gas would be reemitted as bright lines and simply fill in the dark lines immediately. It is true that they are reemitted, but they are reemitted in all directions and only a small fraction of their energy continues in the original direction of the light ray, and so the lines appear dark.

THE ATOM SIGNS ITS NAME

Suppose we place some hydrogen gas in a tube from which the air has been removed. Then we pass an electric current through this low-pressure gas by means of electrodes sealed at either end of the tube.

Light will be radiated by the gas, and if that light is passed through a spectroscope, only four dominant bright lines in its spectrum are visible (Figure 2.45). Each line represents one wavelength: the red line has a wavelength of 6563 Å; the blue line, a wavelength of 4861 Å; one violet line, of 4341 Å; and the other violet line, of 4102 Å. But why are these four lines produced in the hydrogen atom?

We visualize the atom, the simplest form of a given element, as being composed of a central nucleus around which electrons move, not in a completely predictable manner but at least in a fashion such that we may predict their most probable levels of energy. These energy levels are represented in rather oversimplified terms as circles surrounding the nucleus in Figure 2.47. Circle number 1 represents the lowest energy the electron may possess, circle number 2 represents the second energy level, and so on. No intermediate levels are possible in this model of the hydrogen atom proposed by the prominent Danish physicist Niels Bohr (1885–1962). The single electron of a hydrogen atom would normally be at the lowest energy level; if an electric current were passed through the tube of gas, however, the electrons of some of the atoms

Figure 2.46 Spectra: (a) continuous; (b) bright-line; (c) absorption.

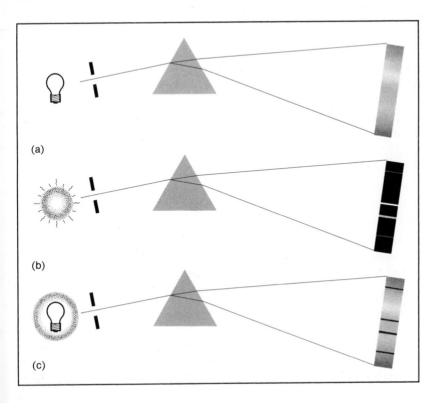

(a)

(b)

(c)

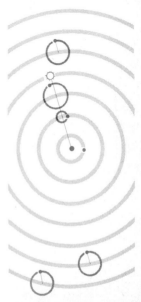

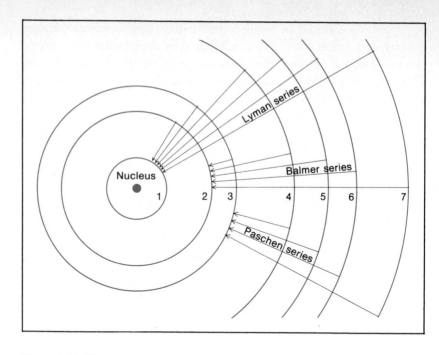

Figure 2.47 Electron transitions in the hydrogen atom.

would receive energy from the electric current, permitting them to move to a higher energy level. An electron would not remain at that higher level but would return to the lowest energy level. In the process of making such a downward transition, the electron may stop temporarily at any level, releasing energy as it makes the downward transition. In other words, the atom has absorbed energy initially to make the upward transition, and now it emits energy as it makes a downward transition. If the electron stops at energy level number 2, even temporarily, it will produce visible light, but only those colors of visible light which correspond to the amount of energy the electron lost in making the downward transition. In other words, corresponding to each possible change in energy level is a definite amount of energy and a definite wavelength.

In the hydrogen atom, when the electron makes a transition from the third to the second energy level (a "3 to 2" transition), it produces the red line (6563 Å), called the *hydrogen-alpha* (H_α) line. A "4 to 2" transition produces the blue line (4861 Å, called the *hydrogen-beta* (H_β) *line;* a "5 to 2" transition produces the first violet line (4341 Å), called the *hydrogen-gamma* (H_γ) *line;* and a "6 to 2" transition produces the second violet line (4102 Å), called the *hydrogen-delta* (H_δ) *line.* Other transitions from still higher energy levels that stop temporarily at level number 2 produce numerous faint violet lines near the end of the visible spectrum. Only these specific lines are possible for the neutral hydrogen atom at low pressure; no partial transitions are possible between energy levels—for example, the electron can not move from number 4 to $2\frac{1}{2}$ or from number 5 to $3\frac{1}{4}$, for only whole-number transitions are possible. The series of visible lines produced by the hydrogen atom is called the Balmer series. Of course, some downward transitions stop temporarily at energy level number 3, and these produce a series of lines in the infrared portion of the spectrum called the Paschen series. Those transitions to the lowest level produce lines in the ultraviolet portion, and these are called the Lyman series.

Whereas downward transitions *emit* light of definite wavelengths, upward transitions *absorb* light of certain wavelengths. Suppose we caused white light, which is a mixture of all visible wavelengths, to pass through hydrogen gas at low pressure. The photons which have wavelengths corresponding to transitions from level number 2 to 3 (or from 2 to 4, or from 2 to 5, and so on), would be absorbed, causing such upward transitions in the atoms. We would see the same dominant four lines of hydrogen, but now they would be dark lines on the full rainbow background of white light. The spectrum of white light is called a continuous spectrum because it contains all colors, but when certain colors (wavelengths) are removed by absorption, it is called an *absorption spectrum* (also called a *dark-line spectrum*). Since the lines occur in an absorption spectrum at the same position as the bright lines of an emission spectrum, either type is equally useful to the astronomer. Both types occur in stars, nebulae, galaxies, and the like.

Now suppose we look at the spectrum of helium, which consists of an entirely different set of lines from that of hydrogen. While the model of the helium atom or of other heavier elements is more complex, it is evident from experimentation that each kind of atom has its own characteristic set of spectral lines. Thus the atom "signs its name" in its spectrum. One of the great values of spectroscopy to the astronomer now becomes clear. He can identify the atoms which compose a distant object by recording its spectrum and comparing that to the spectra of different elements produced in the laboratory. For example, some of the lines of calcium (Ca), iron (Fe), hydrogen (H), magnesium (Mg), and argon (A) have been identified in the solar spectrum (see Figure 2.45).

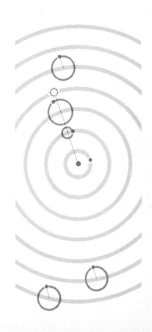

DOPPLER SHIFT

The spectrogram can also be used to tell something about the motion of an object which is emitting light, owing to a phenomenon called the *Doppler effect*. The Doppler effect is a change in wavelength due

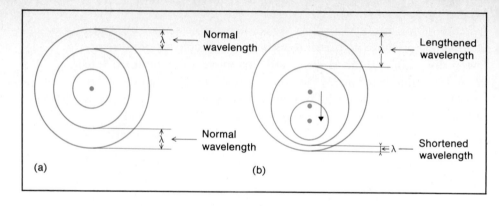

Figure 2.48 The Doppler effect: (a) stationary source; (b) moving source.

to the motion of the source or of the observer or both (Figure 2.48). Imagine that a fire engine is approaching you with its siren operating at a certain note (emitting a certain wavelength of sound). The firemen riding in the truck hear that wavelength, but you hear a higher pitched note (shorter wavelength) than they do as the engine approaches you. Why? Because each time the siren emits a new crest it is closer to you, and therefore the crests occur closer together from your point of view, producing a shortened wavelength. Then as the engine passes and recedes from you, the note you hear is lower (longer in wavelength). This occurs because each time the siren emits a new crest of sound it is farther from you and the crests appear to be farther apart from your point of view. Furthermore the faster the engine is moving, the greater the change in the pitch.

Now while sound is an entirely different kind of wave phenomenon, not an electromagnetic disturbance at all, the Doppler effect also occurs in electromagnetic phenomena. The wavelength of a given line in the spectrum of a star will be lengthened if the star is moving away from the observer, causing the line to appear shifted in position toward the red end of the spectrum. If the star is moving toward the observer, a given line will be shifted in position toward the blue end of the spectrum. The amount by which the wavelength is changed ($\Delta\lambda$) depends only on the relative velocity of the star with respect to the earth, along the observer's line of sight. If c represents the velocity of light and λ represents the laboratory wavelength of the given line, then the change in wavelength due to motion is given by

$$\Delta\lambda = \frac{v}{c} \cdot \lambda$$

This formula, when solved for v, indicates the method by which the *radial velocity* of a star may be determined:

$$v = c\frac{\Delta\lambda}{\lambda}$$

Here v, radial velocity, is that part of the relative velocity which is in the direction of the observer's line of sight.

The first line in the hydrogen spectrum normally has a wavelength of 6563 Å. If in the spectrum of a star this line is observed to have a wavelength of 6565 Å, we may calculate the radial velocity of the star as follows:

$$\Delta\lambda = 6565 \text{ Å} - 6563 \text{ Å} = 2 \text{ Å}$$

$$v = c\frac{\Delta\lambda}{\lambda} = (300,000 \text{ km/sec})\frac{2 \text{ Å}}{6563 \text{ Å}}$$

$$v = 91.4 \text{ km/sec}$$

Since the wavelength of the line from the stellar source appeared longer than that of the laboratory, we know that the star is moving away from us. Thus a shift toward the red end of the spectrum—a "red shift"—indicates that the star is receding from us, whereas a shift toward the blue end of the spectrum—a "blue shift"—would indicate its approach toward the earth. It should be observed that the Doppler shift told us nothing about the distance to the star, only its radial velocity.

A VERY IMPORTANT GENERALIZATION

To this point we have developed concepts around the phenomenon called light, but light is only a very small portion of the electromagnetic spectrum, which includes radio, infrared, ultraviolet, X rays, and gamma rays. These are just different names for various aspects of the same general phenomenon. All forms travel through empty space in a straight line but may be reflected or refracted by the proper materials. They all can be collected or concentrated in some fashion, even as light is concentrated in an optical telescope. Objects in space emit certain wavelengths better than others, creating a spectrum in radio, television, radar, infrared, ultraviolet, X rays, and gamma rays (Figure 2.49), and that spectrum reveals Doppler shifts, even as in the visible spectrum.

Then we might ask why the astronomer has concentrated so much on visual observations and has utilized but a small portion of the

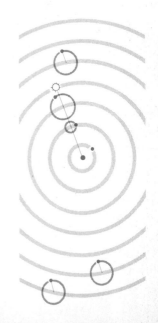

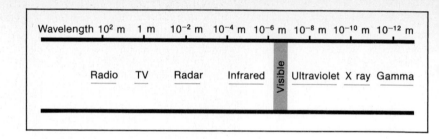

| Wavelength 10² m | 1 m | 10⁻² m | 10⁻⁴ m | 10⁻⁶ m | 10⁻⁸ m | 10⁻¹⁰ m | 10⁻¹² m |

| Radio | TV | Radar | Infrared | Visible | Ultraviolet | X ray | Gamma |

Figure 2.49 The electromagnetic spectrum.

spectrum. There are two very logical reasons. Until the advent of radio receivers, man's only natural "receiver" through which he might perceive the universe was his eye—and his eye only "tunes in" the visible spectrum. With the perfection of the radio telescope, astronomers gained another portion of the spectrum, namely radio wavelengths between 15 and 0.01 m. This gave him two narrow portions of the spectrum in which to work, but what of the remaining portions? With the exception of a small portion in the infrared part of the spectrum, the earth's atmosphere reflects or absorbs most of the energy, leaving only these three small "windows" through which the astronomer may observe the universe. He began to conquer the atmospheric problem by sending balloons high into the atmosphere or rockets above it. Then the real breakthrough came when man was able to place satellites in orbit around the earth. On those satellites he can now install telescopes, some manned (as in the case of Skylab or the Apollo series), but most often unmanned (as in the case of OAO-C and others which will be mentioned later). This capability has opened up the entire spectrum for study, and an explosion of data has taken place in what might be called the new astronomy: infrared astronomy (already begun from earth-based observatories), ultraviolet astronomy, X-ray astronomy, gamma-ray astronomy, and cosmic-ray astronomy.

In order to take advantage of the broadened window to the universe, astronomers are developing new tools and techniques at a rapid pace. With the information gathered, they are beginning to unravel some of the mysteries of the universe. We will consider each of these new techniques briefly. Applications will be treated in pertinent areas of the text.

RADIO ASTRONOMY

The discovery that radio energies are emitted by objects in space came quite unexpectedly when in 1931 Karl Jansky of the Bell Telephone Laboratories noticed a certain kind of interference in his sensitive re-

Figure 2.50 The 210-ft (64-m) Goldstone antenna, located near Barstow, California. This instrument is used primarily to track and communicate with deep space probes. (JPL–NASA)

ceiver. This interference occurred a few minutes earlier each day. He recalled the fact that any given star or galaxy appears to rise 4 min earlier each night, according to our clocks, and he concluded rightly that the source of this radio energy was outside the earth. Now if a device could be constructed to "collect" a very weak radio signal and concentrate its energy at a focal point, and then a sensitive amplifier could strengthen that signal without mixing in its own noise, the astronomer would have a fine tool with which to expand his knowledge of the universe. In view of the similarity in properties of all electromagnetic disturbances, it seemed logical to follow the parabolic design of the optical mirror in planning construction of a *radio telescope*. Owing to the longer wavelengths of radio energy, radio telescopes can be built of steel and simply covered with a wire mesh. It is thus possible to construct very large models such as the 64-m (210-ft) movable antenna at Goldstone, California (Figure 2.50), or the 305-m (1000-ft) fixed antenna at Arecibo, Puerto Rico. At Arecibo, which is in a mountainous area, a natural depression was bulldozed into the shape of a parabolic basin. This was then lined with wire mesh, and a focal point collector was placed on cables overhead (see Figure 2.51). This radio telescope is not fixed as to what it "sees," for as the earth rotates the antenna scans

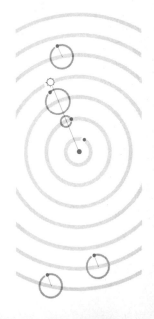

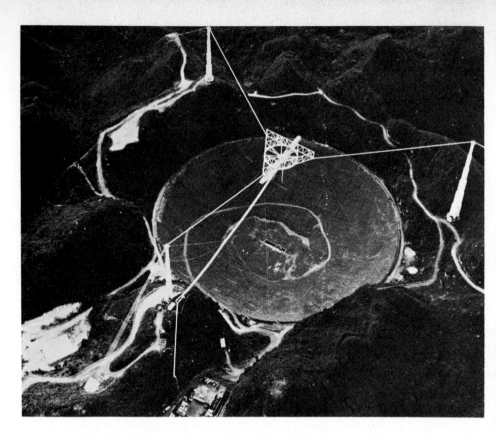

Figure 2.51 The 1000-ft (304.8-m) Arecibo antenna, in Puerto Rico. The focal point for the telescope is suspended by cable from the surrounding elevations and is movable for purposes of scanning the sky. (Cornell University and Air Force Office of Scientific Research)

Figure 2.52 Diagram showing the essential components of a radio telescope: the antenna collects the radio energy and concentrates it at the focal point; the tuner selects the wavelength desired; and the amplifier builds up the signal, which is then plotted as a permanent record.

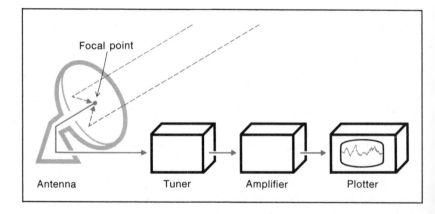

a path through the sky every day. Furthermore the focal collector overhead can be moved north or south, which has the effect of pointing the telescope north or south about 20° from the zenith.

Some objects emit radio energy so efficiently that they can be sensed by a radio telescope when they are too dim to be seen in an optical telescope. Such objects have been dubbed *quasars* (quasi-stellar radio sources) by radio astronomers. Some sources of radio energy are being found that have such large red shifts in their spectra as to suggest that they are receding from us at speeds which approach the speed of light. These may be the most distant objects in the universe. A radio telescope (Figure 2.52) can be used day and night, on cloudy or clear days, and it can penetrate many regions of our galaxy which were previously hidden from us by clouds of dust through which optical telescopes could not see. Also, whereas the optical astronomer is plagued by a background of light radiation that obscures the fainter stars, the radio astronomer has virtually no background radiation to worry about. His biggest problem is how to amplify (build up) the weak radio signal coming from a distant source without introducing man–made noise that will obscure the signal, which itself is in the form of noise. To solve this problem, the scientist uses a device (called a *maser**) submerged in liquid helium, which cools it to approximately $-270°C$ (almost absolute zero). In the maser the weak radio signal triggers a series of downward electron transitions in atoms that are kept in a state of continuous excitation, thus strengthening (amplifying) the original radio signal.

Radio telescopes in general have poor resolution because the wavelengths with which they must deal are much longer than the wavelengths of light. The length of a typical radio wave is 3 cm, compared to the length of a typical light wave of 0.00006 cm. The formula that expresses the resolution of any telescope is given by

$$\alpha = 2.1 \times 10^5 \frac{\lambda}{d} \text{ seconds of arc}$$

The wavelength of the wave received is denoted by the Greek letter λ (lambda); the telescope diameter, by d. For a telescope 30,480 cm (1000 ft) in diameter receiving a 3-cm signal, the resolution is

$$\alpha = 2.1 \times 10^5 \times \frac{3 \text{ cm}}{30,480 \text{ cm}} \text{ seconds of arc}$$

$$\alpha = 21 \text{ seconds of arc}$$

Under the specified conditions, it is impossible to distinguish between two sources of radio emission that are separated by less than 21 seconds of arc. In order to separate two such sources, the same region of the

Maser, acronym for *m*icrowave *a*mplification by *s*timulated *e*mission of *r*adiation.

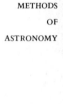
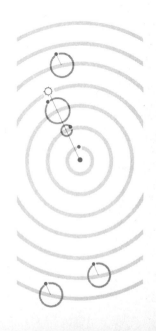

Figure 2.53 Artist's conception of the Very Large Array (VLA) radio telescope system to be constructed in the Plains of Saint Augustin in central New Mexico. The VLA is considered to be the highest priority instrument for astronomical research in the United States during the next decade. When it is completed in the early 1980s, the VLA will permit detailed mapping of radio sources with a resolution equal to or better than any optical telescope and better than our existing radio telescope systems. (National Radio Astronomy Observatory)

sky is photographed with a large optical telescope, and if the radio sources have optical (visual) counterparts it may be possible to separate them.

The advent of the radio telescope has led to the discovery of many distant radio sources, some of which are too faint to be seen visually. We shall return to the subject of quasars in Chapter 14.

RADIO INTERFEROMETRY

The relatively poor resolution of radio telescopes may be improved considerably by interconnecting two or more radio telescopes that have separate locations (Figure 2.53). Since the radio signal from a given source will arrive at the antennas at slightly different times, the received waves will interfere with each other. From these interference patterns it is possible to locate a source much more accurately (Figure 2.54).

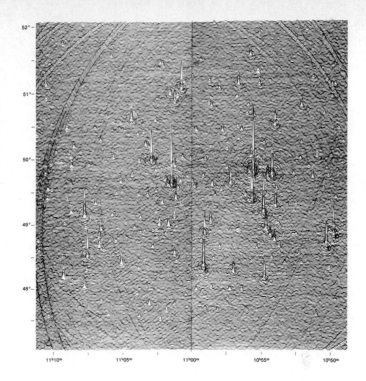

Figure 2.54 A graphical representation of radio sources in a region of the sky 4° in diameter, as recorded by the Cambridge One-Mile Interferometer. (From Pooley and Kenderdine, *Monthly Not. R.A.S.* **139,** 529 (1968); Mullard Radio Observatory, University of Cambridge)

RADAR ASTRONOMY

Many radio telescopes, including those mentioned above, can be used for radar studies as well as for radio astronomy. Radar astronomy involves a two-way communication with relatively nearby objects such as the sun, the moon, and the planets. A radio signal is sent by the antenna toward an object, and then the same antenna is used to listen for the echo or reflection of that signal. Since the velocity of a radio signal is known, the length of time required by the signal to travel to a given planet and back reveals its distance. Other types of information such as the planet's velocity, its rotation, and surface contour may also be ascertained by analyzing the Doppler shifts in the returning signal. Radar astronomy was used to penetrate the clouds of Venus, for instance, to give us our first indication as to its rate and direction of rotation and to its surface features.

INFRARED ASTRONOMY

The development of infrared astronomy lagged behind that of radio astronomy by approximately 20 years. This was true because no one had perfected a detector that would record very small changes in the

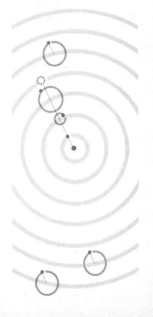

87

amount of infrared energy which fell on it and that would also discriminate as to the direction from which the radiation came. Infrared radiation falls between radio and red light in regard to its range of wavelengths. However, neither the photographic plate used by the optical astronomer nor the antennas used by the radio astronomer will record infrared radiation to any significant degree.

One of the early kinds of detectors consisted of a closed container of gas. It is known that even a small change in temperature causes a corresponding change in the pressure of a confined gas, and it was this change in the pressure of the gas which was recorded to indicate changing amounts of infrared energy that fell on the gas container.

Today a device called a lead sulfide photoconductor is used. This detector relies upon the photoelectric effect; that is, it releases a definite electrical charge for each photon of infrared energy it receives. Thus changing amounts of infrared radiation produce a proportional change in electrical current, and this can easily be recorded. The sensitivity of such a cell is increased by cooling it to $-200°C$ using liquid helium. In order to point the device in only one direction at a given time, a small aperture admits the energy, which may then be restricted to the desired wavelengths by a filter. This apparatus is placed at the focus of an optical telescope. Its design tends to eliminate radiation from stray sources entering the cell (Figure 2.55).

If you could see the sky at a glance through the "eyes" of this detector, you would be surprised to find that you could not recognize familiar constellations, for only a relatively few stars we see with the naked eye would show on a map of bright infrared sources. As we

Figure 2.55 The physical layout of a cooled lead sulfide detector for infrared energy.

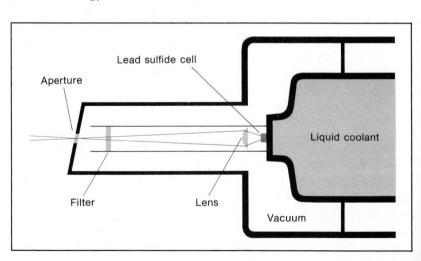

Figure 2.56 The Copernicus satellite (OAO-C) carries a 1-m telescope designed to sense ultraviolet wavelengths and two smaller X-ray telescopes. Also illustrated here are the two solar energy panels and the knoblike star trackers near the base of the satellite. (NASA)

study the characteristics of stars in later chapters, we will see that cooler objects radiate in the infrared range. Astronomers sometimes are able to predict the birth of a star with the aid of infrared detectors.

ULTRAVIOLET ASTRONOMY

The greatest impediment to detection of radiation in the ultraviolet portion of the spectrum has been the earth's atmosphere. Success in this area has come with the use of rockets and orbiting satellites such as the Orbiting Astronomical Observatory named *Copernicus* (OAO-C; Figure 2.56). This observatory carries the largest reflecting telescope ever sent into space. Its 0.8-m mirror, spectrograph, and allied sensors are designed to detect the ultraviolet spectrum of stars and of interstellar molecules with higher resolution than has been achieved previously. The satellite does not actually photograph the spectrum but reads it out as a graph in which the peaks are interpreted as bright spectral lines and the dips as dark (absorption) lines (Figure 2.57). Also on board OAO-C are three small X-ray telescopes.

X-RAY ASTRONOMY

The earth's atmosphere absorbs almost all X-ray radiation directed toward the earth. While this is a fortunate fact for our existence, it limits any effective examination of the universe in wavelengths between 0.1 and 100 Å. The first successful attempts to sense sources of X rays came with the firing of rockets high above the obscuring layers of our atmosphere, and 30 to 40 strong discrete sources of X rays were immediately found within our own galaxy. The launching of a satellite exclusively designed for X-ray observation created a massive amount

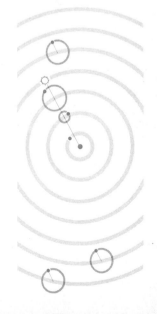

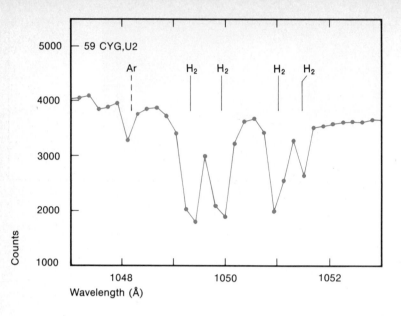

Figure 2.57 A readout of a portion of the ultraviolet spectrum by OAO-C, the Copernicus satellite, showing absorption lines of ionized argon and hydrogen gas (H_2 molecules). [From Rogerson *et al., The Astrophysical Journal* (*Letters*) **181** (3), L97–L102 (1973); courtesy of The American Astronomical Society and University of Chicago Press]

of additional data—the emerging X-ray "picture" of the universe. The satellite was dubbed UHURU, meaning "freedom" in Swahili, and was sent aloft on December 12, 1970, from a location near Kenya in honor of that country's independence (Figure 2.58). The craft spins slowly on its axis, scanning the sky continually for X-ray sources, and

Figure 2.58 Artist's view of UHURU, an X-ray satellite. [From R. Fiacconi, X-ray astronomy. *The Physics Teacher* **11** (3), 135–143 (1973)]

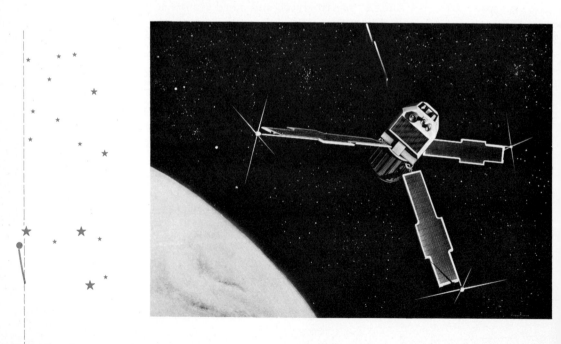

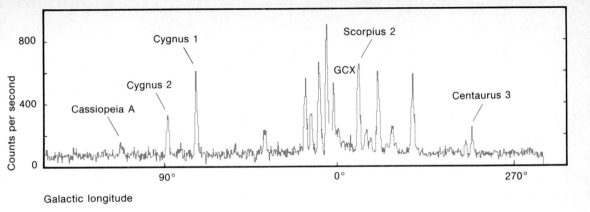

Galactic longitude

Figure 2.59 A readout of X-ray sources from UHURU. Several of the stronger sources are identified and may be compared to the map shown in Figure 2.60, which was constructed from this readout.

its orientation (pointing direction) can be controlled from ground-based control centers. An X-ray source is typically defined as an object that emits at least one thousand times as much energy in the X-ray portion of the spectrum as in the visible portion of the spectrum (Figure 2.59). Several hundred definite X-ray sources are now known, some of which are outside our galaxy (Figure 2.60). In fact the potential for detecting very distant objects is extremely good because X rays do not lose energy as fast as do other forms of radiation in their journey across the vast reaches of intergalactic space. The space between galaxies was once thought to be a perfect vacuum, but X-ray emission studies are now revealing certain amounts of gas in these regions and this fact may significantly increase our estimates of the total mass of the universe. Stars are born, go through a life cycle, and die, some taking the form of neutron stars or black holes. X rays emitted by such dying stars may provide clues as to the reasons for their death. (We will consider these ideas in greater detail later in this text.)

GRAVITATIONAL WAVE ASTRONOMY

We have seen that surrounding every charged particle is an electrical field. If that charged particle is set into *oscillation* (vibration), a changing electrical field results. If another charged particle exists in that field, it will react by oscillating, and this oscillation permits us to detect the existence of that changing electrical field. In 1916 Albert Einstein predicted that a similar thing would happen in the gravitational field of a moving object. First picture an object, say, an uncharged steel ball

91

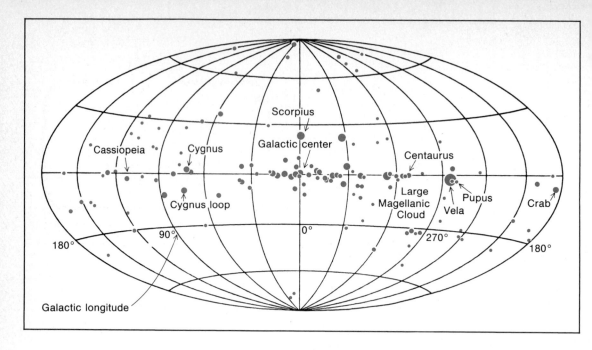

Figure 2.60 A plot of X-ray sources, based on observations by the UHURU satellite. The larger dots indicate the stronger sources; several are identified. (Frederick D. Seward, Lawrence Livermore Laboratory, University of California)

placed in the center of an empty room. We could then say that a certain gravitational field exists in the room because of the presence of the steel ball. We could demonstrate that fact by showing that another steel ball, when brought into the room, would experience a force of attraction toward the original ball. This force is so small in comparison to the electrical and magnetic forces with which we have been dealing that it would be difficult to measure. Suppose that the second ball were hung from a high ceiling by a steel wire so that it was very close to the first ball. The second ball would be deflected slightly toward the first, so that it did not hang vertically from the ceiling. That deflection proves there is gravitational attraction between the two steel balls, an unseen gravitational field, but the field is static (unchanging). Now suppose that the first ball is set into a rapid vibration; then the gravitational field around it would become a changing field, and the second ball would reveal that changing field by vibrating itself.

It was reasoned that if Einstein's prediction that an accelerating mass emits gravitational waves were right, then astronomers might detect the collapse or explosion of gigantic stars or other cataclysmic events by designing a detector for the resulting waves. Such a detector must be free from any other kind of influence, such as earthquakes, changes in electrical or magnetic fields, and air disturbances.

92

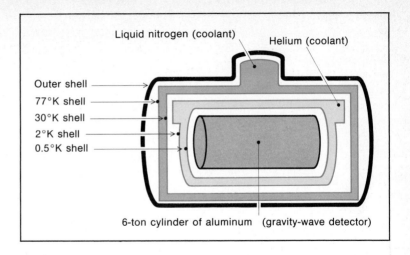

Figure 2.61 Gravitational wave detector.

Liquid nitrogen (coolant)

Helium (coolant)

Outer shell

77°K shell

30°K shell

2°K shell

0.5°K shell

6-ton cylinder of aluminum (gravity-wave detector)

One of the first gravitational wave detectors consisted of a 3000-kg (kilogram) aluminum cylinder suspended from an arch support system. A very sensitive recording device had been placed on the cylinder, and the very small vibrations that gravity waves were thought to produce appeared to be within the detection capability of this instrument. The cylinder could not be isolated completely from its physical surroundings, however, and consequently it recorded man-made vibrations. In order to separate these vibrations from those which might represent gravitational waves, experimenter Joseph Weber installed a second detector 1600 km (1000 miles) away, reasoning that a disturbance originating outside the earth would be recorded almost simultaneously by both detectors, whereas local disturbances would show up only on one. In 1969 Weber detected what he believed to be the first gravitational waves ever recorded.

As is required in science, confirmation of Weber's observations is being sought by other scientists. One such effort centers around the work of William M. Fairbank and William Hamilton at Stanford University. These two men bring their study of *cryogenics* (the branch of physics dealing with the behavior of materials at very low temperatures) to bear upon the problem of isolating the detector from its surroundings in order to reduce the effect of background vibrations. The new detector (Figure 2.61) consists of a 6-ton cylinder of aluminum, encased in several containers that contain coolants to reduce the temperature in the innermost container to within 0.5° of absolute zero. At this temperature (-272.5°C) vibrations due to heat virtually cease. What is more important, the cylinder can be made to "float" in the middle of the innermost cylinder without touching anything. This is possible because when certain metals are supercooled, an electrical current, once started, will flow through them forever. The cylinder can thus be made to float on swirls of electrical current and yet can

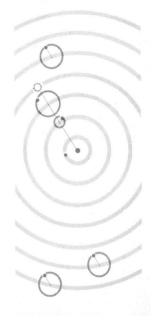

be isolated from any electrical or magnetic disturbances from without. Two such detectors, currently being installed at Stanford University and Louisiana State University, approximately 3200 km apart, are to operate simultaneously in an attempt to confirm vibrations (gravity waves) originating in our galaxy or beyond.

We have briefly surveyed the tools now being used by astronomers to "paint" a clearer picture of the universe than has ever been conceived before, a picture based upon our increasing ability to receive data over the full spectrum of electromagnetic and particle wavelengths.

QUESTIONS

1. Perform the necessary arithmetic to determine the length of a light year in kilometers, based on the fact that light travels at the speed of approximately 300,000 km/sec; then convert this distance to miles.
2. In any experiment to determine the speed of light, what two factors must be known?
3. Albert A. Michelson used a rotating mirror to measure one of the two essential factors mentioned in Question 2. Which factor did he measure with the turning mirror?
4. Other than visible light, in what ways do electromagnetic disturbances exhibit themselves?
5. Why is sound not included among electromagnetic disturbances?
6. The telescope mirror is curved so as to bring light rays from a given source to the same focal point. What basic law or principle is utilized in the design of this curvature?
7. Why do stars near the horizon appear higher in the sky than their true position?
8. The earliest telescopes utilized the principle of ___ (refraction, reflection).
9. List four examples of extended sources.
10. List three defects which may exist in the refracting telescope if it is not correctly designed.
11. Which telescope design is best suited for a sky survey?
12. Discuss the advantage of using film to photograph dim objects over merely observing them with the naked eye.
13. What is the primary reason that radio telescopes have relatively poor resolution in spite of the fact that they are larger than optical telescopes?
14. The functioning of a spectrograph depends upon the fact that whenever light is refracted, it is also ___ .
15. The primary spectrum of the sun, as observed from the earth, is a ___ (dark-line, bright-line, continuous) spectrum.

Retrograde motion of Jupiter

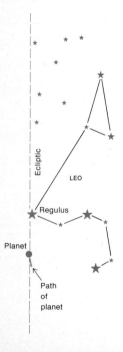

16. A bright-line spectrum is produced by ____ (upward, downward) transitions of the electron.

17. What is indicated by a very large red shift in the spectral lines of a distant galaxy?

18. Find the size of the image of a full moon (0.5° in diameter) photographed at the prime focus of the 5-m (200-in.) telescope; focal length is 16.8 m. (Answer: 14.6 cm.)

19. What advantage does a radio telescope have over its optical counterpart?

20. What advantage does a telescope aboard an orbiting observatory have over a ground-based telescope?

21. Why should the infrared sky look different than the visible sky?

22. What kind of events are expected to produce gravitational waves?

23. If a given star is moving through space at the same speed and direction as the sun, we do not expect to see a Doppler shift in its spectrum; but because the earth is moving around the sun at a velocity of 30 km/sec, the earth's motion creates a periodic blue shift when it approaches the star and a red shift when it recedes from the star. Find the maximum Doppler shift produced by the earth's motion.

24. Given two telescopes having the same focal length, the one with an aperture of 25 cm collects ____ times as much light as the one with an aperture of 12.5 cm.

SUGGESTED READINGS

Giacconi, Riccardo, X-ray astronomy. *The Physics Teacher* **11** (3), 135–143 (1973).

Gingerich, Owen (ed.), *Frontiers of astronomy,* Introduction. San Francisco: Freeman, 1970.

Howard, Neale E., *The telescope handbook and star atlas.* New York: Thomas Y. Crowell, 1967.

Kellerman, K. I., Intercontinental radio astronomy. *Scientific American* **226** (2), 72–83 (1972).

Logan, Jonothan L., Gravitational waves. *The Physics Teacher* **26** (3), 44–52 (1973).

Meyer-Arendt, Jurgen R., *Introduction to classical and modern optics.* Englewood Cliffs, N.J.: Prentice-Hall, 1972.

Neugebauer, G., and Becklin, Eric E., The brightest infrared sources. *Scientific American* **228** (4), 28–40 (1973).

Schawlow, Arthur L. (ed.), *Lasers and light,* Introduction. San Francisco: Freeman, 1969.

Wells, R. A., The "first" Newtonian. *Sky and Telescope* **42** (6), 342–344 (1971).

Wiegand, Clyde E., Exotic atoms. *Scientific American* **227** (5), 102–110 (1972).

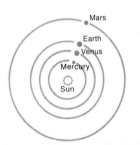

The Copernican system

Jupiter

Mars
Earth
Venus
Mercury
Sun

THE EARTH

3

Although study of the earth is often considered to be the exclusive domain of the geologist, the astronomer is also very much concerned about our planet's origin and properties, such as size, mass, density, layering, atmosphere, magnetic field, and motion. From his knowledge of the earth, he will be better prepared to ask significant questions concerning the other planets and their moons.

Pythagoras had already recognized the shape of the earth as being spherical by the third century B.C. Another Greek astronomer, Eratos-

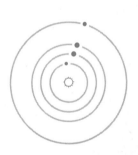

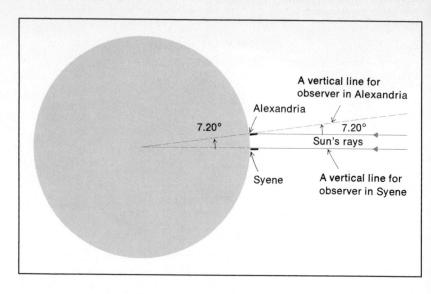

Figure 3.1 The method by which Eratosthenes measured the size of the earth.

thenes, went a step further when, in the second century B.C., he observed that the rays of the noon-time sun illuminated the bottom of a vertical well in Syene (now Aswan), Egypt, indicating that the sun was directly overhead. On the same day in Alexandria, 800 km to the north of Syene, the rays of the sun at noon made an angle of 7.2° with a vertical post (Figure 3.1).

Assuming the earth to be spherical in shape, he then ventured to compute its circumference by the following line of reasoning. The angle formed between the sun's rays and a vertical post at Alexandria must be the same as the angle formed by these lines extended to the center of the earth. This is an application of the geometric theorem which states that if two parallel lines are cut by a transversal (a sloping line), the corresponding angles are equal. If an angle of 7.2° at the center of the earth spans a distance of 800 km on the surface of the earth and 50 such angles will fit in the circle (360°/7.2° = 50), then the total distance around the earth is equal to 50 × 800 km, that is, 40,000 km. This is very nearly the value accepted today. From the circumference, it is possible to find the diameter, remembering that

$$C = \pi d \quad \text{and} \quad d = C/\pi$$

$$d = \frac{40,000 \text{ km}}{3.1416} = 12,732 \text{ km}$$

In 1687 Sir Isaac Newton suggested that the earth was not a perfect sphere, for its rotation tends to flatten it. Today we are able to measure that flattening and find the radius of the earth measured to the north or south pole to be approximately 22.5 km shorter than the radius as measured to the equator. When compared to the radius of the earth, this flattening amounts to only about one-third of 1 percent.

VOLUME OF THE EARTH

The volume of any object is a measure of the space which it occupies. We compute the volume of a room which is 30 m long, 25 m wide, and 10 m high by multiplying length times width times height:

$$30 \text{ m} \times 25 \text{ m} \times 10 \text{ m} = 7500 \text{ m}^3 \text{ (cubic meters)}$$

However the earth is more nearly spherical in shape, so we use the formula for the volume of a sphere

$$V = \tfrac{4}{3}\pi r^3$$

If we were to express the radius of the earth as approximately 6375 km then

$$V = \tfrac{4}{3}(3.1416)(6375 \text{ km})^3$$

and our answer would be a very large number of cubic kilometers. This is not a useful unit of volume to use in the laboratory and so we will not complete the problem in that form but rather will express the radius of the earth in centimeters, yielding an answer of

$$V = 1.08 \times 10^{27} \text{ cm}^3 \text{ (cubic centimeters)}$$

MASS OF THE EARTH

The rest mass of an object is a measure of how much material it contains. Scientists have defined 1 gram (g) as the amount of material in 1 cm³ of pure water at 4°C, and we will use this unit of mass to specify the amount of material in the earth. But how is the mass of the earth determined? If we could apply a certain force (F) to the earth and measure the acceleration (a) which resulted, we could calculate its mass (m) from Newton's second law:

$$F = ma \qquad \text{or} \qquad m = \frac{F}{a}$$

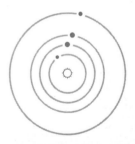

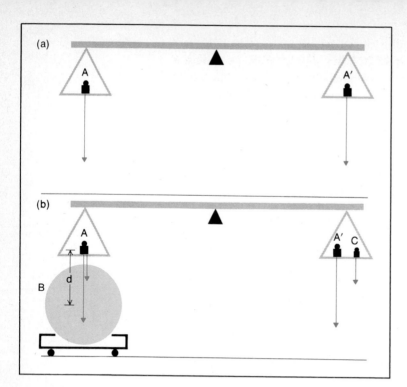

Figure 3.2 Measuring the mass of the earth.

Or if we could place the earth on one side of a balance and some standardized mass on the other, we could determine its mass. However, we are obviously not able to perform either of these experiments, so we must devise an experiment which can be performed.

Suppose that we place equal masses A and A′ on opposite pans of a long-beam balance [Figure 3.2(a)], how much force (F) would the earth exert on each mass? The force on A is found by the formula

$$F = G\frac{M_A M_E}{R^2}$$

and the force on A′ is found by

$$F = G\frac{M_{A'} M_E}{R^2}$$

where M_A, $M_{A'}$, and M_E are the masses of A, A′, and the earth, respectively, and R is the radius of the earth. These forces are obviously equal, because the mass of A is equal to the mass of A′, and so the system is in balance.

Now we roll a large mass B under one pan but not touching it. Mass B exerts an additional force on mass A due to gravitational attraction in the amount of $GM_A M_B/d^2$, where d is the separation of

100

centers of A and B. In order to balance this force, a small mass C is added to the other pan, thus adding the force GM_EM_C/R^2. If a balanced condition is achieved in this way, then

$$G \frac{M_A M_B}{d^2} = G \frac{M_E M_C}{R^2}$$

Since every quantity in this expression is known or can be measured except M_E, M_E may be found and such an experiment would produce a value for the mass of the earth equal to 5.98×10^{27} g.

DENSITY OF THE EARTH

We have looked at the concept of mass (the amount of material in an object) and volume (the amount of space the object occupies). Now we combine these two concepts into one—*density*. Density is a measure of how much material is packed into a given space:

$$\text{density} = \frac{\text{mass}}{\text{volume}} = \frac{\text{the amount of material}}{\text{the amount of space}}$$

Using the values derived for mass (M_E) and volume (V_E) of the earth, we may find its average density by

$$D_E = \frac{M_E}{V_E} = \frac{5.98 \times 10^{27} \text{ g}}{1.08 \times 10^{27} \text{ cm}^3} = 5.5 \text{ g/cm}^3$$

How this density compares to the density of various common materials is shown in Table 3.1.

Material such as ice, the density of which is less than 1 g/cm³, will float in water. The average density of Saturn (0.687 g/cm³) is such that it would float in water if a pond large enough could be found, whereas Mars has an average density of 3.82 g/cm³, more like that of the earth. Thus the density of an object tells us something of its physical nature. Saturn is more like a ball of gas, having a thick atmosphere, perhaps with a liquid center, whereas Mars has only a very thin atmosphere and is characterized by a crusty, solid surface.

The average surface material of the earth has a density of only 2.7 g/cm³, whereas the average density for the entire earth is 5.5 g/cm³. What must the interior of the earth be like in order to make up for this difference? The only logical answer is that the interior must be more dense. The density of the central portion of the earth is thought to range as high as 15 g/cm³ (Figure 3.3). We generally expect increasing density in any body toward its center because of the force of gravity.

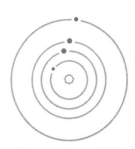

Table 3.1 Densities of some common materials

MATERIAL	DENSITY (g/cm³)
Air	0.00129
Oxygen	0.00143
Cork (average)	0.25
Gasoline	0.69
Ice	0.91
Water	1.00
Sea water	1.02
Blood	1.04
Aluminum	2.70
Granite (average)	2.70
Iron	7.86
Copper	8.89
Lead	11.35
Mercury	13.59
Gold	19.27
Platinum	21.37

All parts of a body experience a mutual attraction that has the effect of pulling these parts toward the center. Material near the center experiences increased pressure that tends to force it into a smaller space, thus increasing its density. Furthermore, elements such as iron and nickel, which are naturally more dense, experience a greater force

Figure 3.3 Layers of the earth.

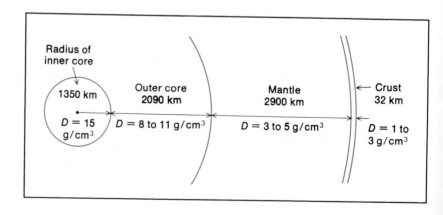

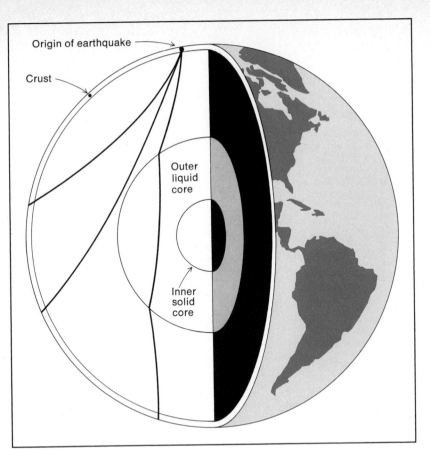

Figure 3.4 Earthquake waves travel at different velocities in various layers of the earth. The refraction which results is an indicator of the density of these layers.

toward the center. When the earth was in a molten state and material was free to distribute itself according to the forces upon it, the more dense material tended to move toward the center of the earth.

How can we verify this change in density with increasing depth? We have studied the fact that light (a wavelike disturbance) slows down in certain materials like glass or water and is thereby refracted. A similar phenomenon happens to earthquake waves as they travel through layers of increasing density within the earth. By timing the arrival of earthquake waves at various points over the surface of the earth, it is possible to detect distinct layers within the earth to a fair degree of accuracy. The density appears to change quite abruptly at the boundaries to these layers, as indicated in Figure 3.4. Earthquakes send out two kinds of waves—those with wavelike motion perpendicular to the line of travel (*transverse*), and those with wavelike motion parallel to the line of travel (*compressional*); the transverse type will not pass through the outer core

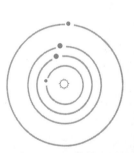

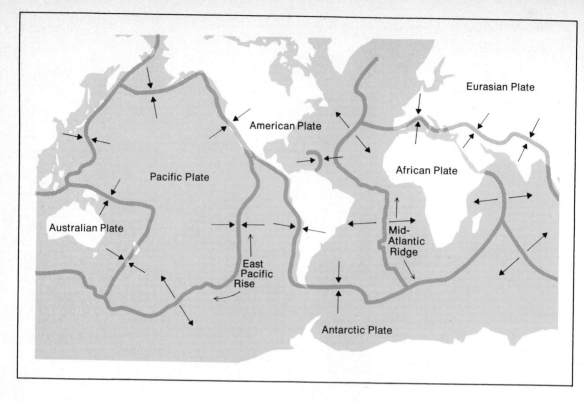

Figure 3.5 The six major plates of the earth's crust with the convergence or separation boundaries indicated.

of the earth, indicating that this layer is most likely molten (a very significant fact in regard to the earth's magnetic field, which we will discuss later).

CRUST OF THE EARTH

As indicated in Figure 3.3, the crust of the earth is relatively thin and, because it is less dense than the mantle, the crust floats on the mantle much as ice floats in water. This is to say that the earth is not static or permanent in its present arrangement of continents, but rather has been rearranging its continents for at least 200 million years. Today six major plates are moving in such a way that compressions ($\rightarrow$ $\leftarrow$) or separations ($\leftarrow$ $\rightarrow$) occur along their boundaries, as indicated in Figure 3.5. Those boundaries where compression occurs are characterized by mountain building and volcanic activity. The entire Pacific Coast of North and South America lies along such a boundary. Where separation occurs, ridges form (such as the mid-Atlantic Ridge; see Figure 3.6). The volcanic activity in the area of the Mediterranean Sea is a further instance of a plate boundary under pressure.

104

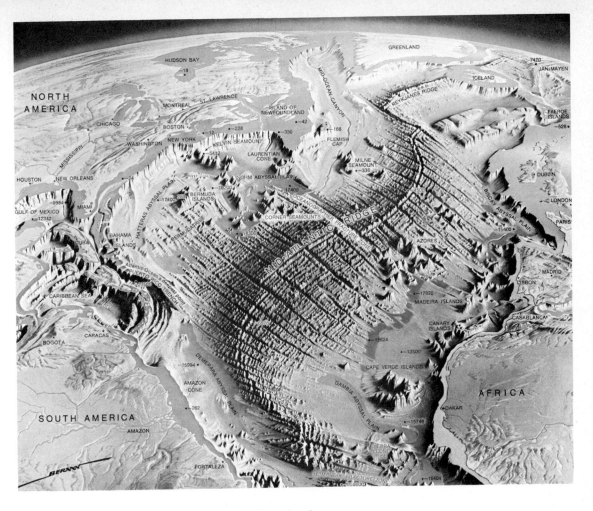

Figure 3.6 The mid–Atlantic ridge, showing the effects of seafloor spreading as the plates drifted apart. Numbers indicate feet above or below sea level. (Photograph courtesy of Alcoa)

AGE OF THE EARTH

The rocks of the earth have a story to tell, for within them lie clues to the age and process of formation of the earth. When compared by weight, the surface material of the earth is approximately 47 percent oxygen, 28 percent silicon, 8 percent aluminum, 5 percent iron, with lesser amounts of magnesium, calcium, potassium, and other elements.

Many rocks contain traces of radioactive elements—elements which tend to break down into lighter elements at a set rate. For instance, suppose we could observe a certain quantity of uranium, say 8 g, over a period of 4.5 billion years. We would find that half of that quantity—4 g—has been spontaneously transformed through several

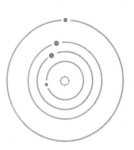

105

intermediate steps into lead. Now a uranium atom contains 238 neutrons and protons, whereas lead contains only 206, hence the uranium atom has rid itself of a total of 32 neutrons and protons in the process. Another 4.5 billion years would reduce the 4 g to 2 g; 4.5 billion years is thus spoken of as the *half-life* of uranium. When a rock crystallizes, the participants in this process are locked in place, and the scientist may estimate the age of the rock by determining the proportion of uranium to lead. There is an element of uncertainty, however, in the fact that some lead may have been present in the rock when the process began. The age of the rock may be confirmed by determination of the presence of elements such as radioactive potassium, which turns into argon gas stored in the crystalline structure of the rock. We may assume that any argon gas formed prior to crystallization of the rock would have been lost into the air.

The oldest earth rocks which have been dated are approximately 3.6 billion years old; however certain meteorites and moon rocks show ages ranging upward to 4.6 billion years. This latter age may more closely represent the age of the earth and perhaps the entire solar system.

ATMOSPHERE
OF THE EARTH

While the atmosphere of the earth is not divided into distinct layers, it will be helpful to think of it in this way. The first layer—that which contacts the earth's surface—is called the *troposphere*. This layer varies 8 to 16 km in thickness and is the location of all weather disturbances. Three-fourths of the total atmosphere is "packed" into this layer due to gravity, creating a normal sea-level pressure of 1 atm (atmosphere; equivalent to the pressure exerted by a column of mercury 76 cm high at $0°C$, or about 15 lb/in.^{2}). This atmospheric pressure is experienced by all objects; however, it is exerted in all directions equally at any given point and so tends to be equalized over a body. We do not normally sense this pressure, but if we dive into a swimming pool to a depth of 2.5 to 3 m, we sense the additional pressure in our ears, due to the overlying layer of water in addition to the normal atmospheric pressure. The troposphere contains all elements necessary to sustain life. It is composed of 78 percent nitrogen, 21 percent oxygen, with water vapor, carbon dioxide, neon, and argon making up most of the remaining 1 percent. Traces of other elements are also found in the atmosphere. The troposphere is characterized by an average temperature that decreases from about $+60°F$ (Fahrenheit)* at sea level to $-60°F$ near

---

*Plus and minus signs are used with degrees of temperature to designate degrees above 0° and below 0°, respectively.

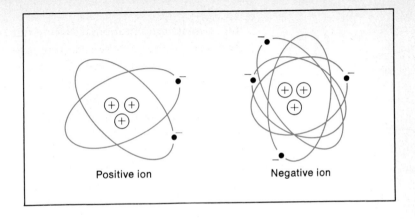

Figure 3.7 Ionized atoms (neutrons not shown).

Positive ion

Negative ion

the top of the layer. The next layer is called the *stratosphere,* extending from about 16 km to a maximum of 80 km and characterized by a temperature increasing from $-60°F$ to $+85°F$. Within this layer there exists a special form of oxygen called *ozone.* Three atoms of oxygen combine to form a molecule of ozone. It has a rather pungent odor that is sometimes noticeable during a lightning storm. The ozone layer absorbs ultraviolet light from the sun, thus protecting us from these dangerous rays. Although it performs this essential function, the ozone layer is nevertheless a handicap to the study of the ultraviolet portion of the spectrum. Observations in this region of the spectrum must be carried out from above the ozone layer with the aid of a balloon or rocket, or from an observatory orbiting in space. All of these methods have been utilized.

Above the stratosphere is the *ionosphere,* a series of layers of *ionized* gases. An *ion* is an atom that has lost or gained one or more electrons, hence is a *charged* atom (Figure 3.7). Ionization is caused by solar radiation, and therefore the degree to which the layers are formed is largely due to activities on the sun. These layers range in elevation between 80 and 320 km; they serve to reflect radio waves that have wavelengths longer than 15 m (Figure 3.8). This function is essential

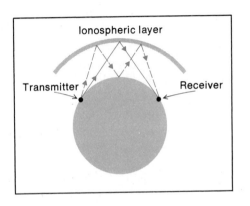

Figure 3.8 The ionosphere reflects certain radio waves.

Ionospheric layer

Transmitter

Receiver

to radio communication, allowing the waves to travel around the curvature of the earth by reflection from the ionospheric layers. Wavelengths shorter than 15 m generally penetrate the ionosphere from the earth or from space; therefore this layer does not have the effect of preventing the study of very short wavelength radio energies in the universe. The atmosphere is usually transparent to radio wavelengths less than 10 m. This is often referred to as the radio "window" into space.

The fact that the earth's atmosphere contains ozone, water vapor, and carbon dioxide causes it to act like a greenhouse. The earth receives many forms of energy from the sun, including some ultraviolet light, visible light, and infrared light. The crust of the earth absorbs this energy and then reemits it, primarily in the form of infrared. The atmosphere tends to absorb this form of radiation quite efficiently, and so the earth retains a large amount of heat; in fact, the earth's surface temperature would probably be 45°C cooler were it not for this "greenhouse" phenomenon.

The earth's atmosphere often puts on a real "show" called the *northern lights (aurora borealis)*. As charged particles, which continually outflow from the sun, approach the earth, they encounter its magnetic field. This field exerts a force on the particles directing them in a circular motion around the earth until they reach the north or south polar region. Here they collide with atoms of the earth's atmosphere, ionizing some of them. When ionized atoms recombine with free electrons, downward transitions occur and light is produced. Such a display of light near the south pole is called the *southern lights (aurora australis)*.

WHY IS THE SKY BLUE?

Because of their very small size, the gas molecules that compose the earth's atmosphere tend to vibrate with a wavelength corresponding to blue light more efficiently than with that of any other color. Scattering refers to the process whereby the molecule absorbs certain colors of light and then reemits that light in all directions. If we viewed a collection of molecules directly in line with the sun, we would see the usual color of the sun; however, if that same collection of molecules were viewed from the side, we would see the light which that collection had scattered (predominantly blue light; Figure 3.9). The red sunset is another result of scattering. As the sun appears to move toward the horizon in the late afternoon, its rays must penetrate an increasing amount of atmosphere. Since molecules in the atmosphere scatter blue light best, the colors that penetrate the atmosphere along our line of sight are predominantly red.

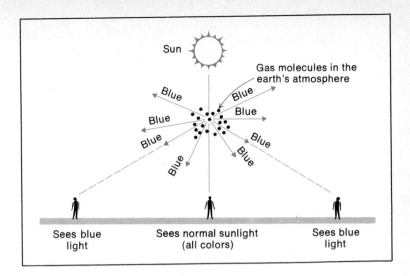

Figure 3.9 The scattering of sunlight produces the blue sky.

Sun

Gas molecules in the earth's atmosphere

Blue Blue Blue Blue Blue Blue Blue Blue

Sees blue light

Sees normal sunlight (all colors)

Sees blue light

The phenomena we call twilight and dawn also result from the scattering of light by molecules in the atmosphere. The moon lacks any atmosphere, and its sky could best be described as black; when the sun "goes down" at any location on the moon, complete darkness immediately comes on, with a severe drop in temperature.

THE EARTH'S MAGNETIC FIELD

It is very evident that the earth possesses a magnetic field. The fact that a compass needle aligns itself in a given direction on every occasion demonstrates this fact. If we travel in a northerly direction, as indicated by the compass, we should eventually arrive at a point called the *north magnetic pole,* and yet we would find ourselves approximately 1600 km from the *geographic north pole,* which is determined by the rotation of the earth. It is a point on the surface of the earth that remains stationary as the earth rotates. These ideas apply equally to the southern polar region.

The north magnetic pole is situated in northeastern Canada at the present time; however, it has not always been at that location, for it appears to wander from time to time. This fact seems to indicate that the magnetic field of the earth is not a result of deposits of magnetic materials (loadstone), as was once thought, but is instead more likely due to charged particles in the earth that are set into a rotational motion by the rotation of the earth itself. It is known that charged particles, when set into circular motion, create a magnetic field much like that of the earth.

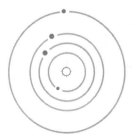

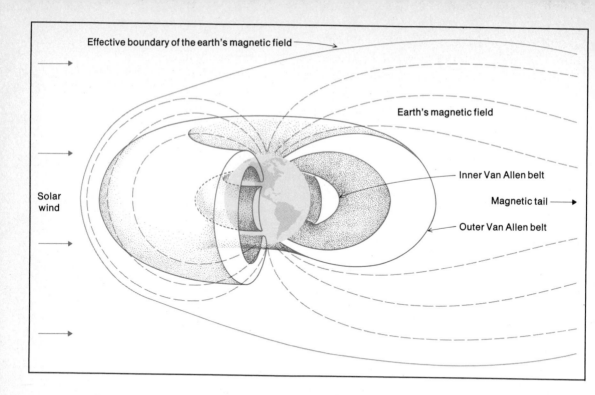

Figure 3.10 The earth's magnetic field, distorted by the solar wind. The two Van Allen belts, somewhat doughnut-shaped, are regions of high-energy charged particles trapped by the earth's magnetic field.

The magnetic field of the earth may be visualized by lines that seem to emerge from the north magnetic pole and return to the south magnetic pole. The lines are of course imaginary, but they indicate the direction that a compass would point if placed at a given location on a line; furthermore, a charged particle that moves into this magnetic field experiences a force that acts at right angles to the magnetic line and causes the charged particle to move in a circular path around the earth. Thus the earth seems to trap some of the rapidly moving charged particles (electrons, protons, and others) that flow from the sun. Two doughnut-shaped regions of these highly energized particles, called the *Van Allen belts,* are located at elevations of 3200 km and 16,000 km above the equator; regions over the poles are relatively free of these trapped particles (Figure 3.10).

The magnetic field of the earth is sometimes greatly disturbed by activities on the sun. Associated with a solar flare, for instance, is a tremendous release of energy that often disrupts radio communications and produces changes in the magnetic field of the earth. Even when the sun is relatively quiet, there is a constant outflow of charged particles

110

called the *solar wind*. This solar wind distorts the magnetic field of the earth. The records of satellites that have orbited the earth, passing in and out of the various regions of the magnetic field many times, show that this field is somewhat flattened on the side toward the sun, and that a magnetic "tail" exists on the opposite side. Figure 3.10 reveals the approximate configuration of the magnetic lines and also shows a cutaway view of the Van Allen belts.

ROTATION
OF THE EARTH

Early observers saw almost all objects—sun, moon, planets, and stars— rise in the east and set in the west and concluded that they all moved around a stationary earth. This idea persisted as late as the sixteenth century. Even when theories regarding a rotating earth were introduced, no conclusive proof was available until the nineteenth century (1852), when Jean Foucault, a French physicist, demonstrated the fact of rotation. He suspended from the dome of the Pantheon in Paris a weighted pendulum that he began to swing (Figure 3.11). Only one force acts on a free-swinging pendulum, that of *gravity*. Since the force of gravity acts only toward the center of the earth, it would not produce any rotational motion, and yet the pendulum appeared to change the direction of its swing. If he started the pendulum swinging toward one entrance to the Pantheon, he would later find it swinging toward another entrance. The change of direction occurred at a given rate like the hands of a clock. It was then reasoned that the earth itself must be turning under the pendulum in order to produce the observed effect. If this experiment were performed at the north pole, the time required for one apparent rotation of the earth under the pendulum would be approximately 24 hours. As one moves from the pole toward the equator, the apparent time for one rotation of the pendulum increases, and at the latitude of Los Angeles (34°N) the period is 43 hours.

Today astronauts have witnessed the earth's rotation from their vantage point in space. This daily rotation of the earth accounts also for the apparent *diurnal* (daily) motion of the sun, the moon, the planets, and the stars. A photograph of the northern polar region of the sky, taken over a period of several hours, reveals circular star trails. In Figure 3.12, Polaris, the North Star, is seen just off center.

REVOLUTION
OF THE EARTH

Proof of the fact that the earth revolves around the sun did not come as a part of the Copernican heliocentric theory, nor as a part of Galileo's work, although they thought it to be true (see Chapter 1). Rather,

the proof came in the nineteenth century, when techniques were developed whereby the apparent shift of nearby stars could be detected in relation to the background of more distant stars. Were the earth stationary, a given alignment of a nearby star and one more distant would not vary in a period of a few months. However, if the earth does in fact change its position in space, the alignment will also change. This apparent shifting of nearby stars against the background of more distant ones has been observed, and the phenomenon is called *stellar*

Figure 3.11 The Foucault pendulum in the Pantheon, Paris. (Science Museum, London)

Figure 3.12 Star trails in the region of the north celestial pole which result from the rotation of the earth. The trail made by the North Star, Polaris, is seen just off center. (Lick Observatory)

parallax. It is a periodic kind of change, a given star apparently shifting first one way and then the other during the course of one year; hence it must be due to the fact that the earth is revolving around the sun. The change is small—only $1/4800°$ for the nearest star. In Figure 3.13, the parallax angle (α) is greatly exaggerated.

Figure 3.13 Stellar parallax, due to the earth's revolution.

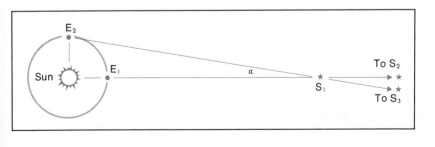

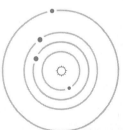

As a consequence of the earth's revolution, the sun appears to move against the background of stars, aligning itself with different stars each day. The particular constellations through which the sun appears to move are called the signs (or "houses") of the zodiac. In Figure 3.14, the sun appears to be aligned with Pisces (the fish), but as the earth revolves about the sun, it will appear next in Aries, and so it will spend about one month moving through each of the twelve signs of the zodiac. The exact number of days which are required for the apparent motion of the sun through all the signs of the zodiac, returning to a given starting point, is not obvious from only one year's observation. However when this period is observed for many years and an average is taken, the period of the earth's revolution is 365.2422. . . days. In order to make a calendar that will be synchronized with this annual cycle over a long period of time, the normal year is assigned 365 days, with 366 days given to each fourth year (leap year). This produces an average year of 365.25 days, slightly too long when compared to 365.2422. To make one further correction, the extra day normally placed in a leap year is deleted three times in a period of 400 years; for instance, it will be deleted in the years 2100, 2200, and 2300 but not in the year 2000, yielding an average year of 365.2425 days—nearly perfect.

Figure 3.14 As the earth revolves about the sun, the sun appears to align itself with each of the signs of the zodiac. The sun is shown aligned with Pisces, but in one month's time it will align with Aries, etc. In one year, the sun will again align with Pisces.

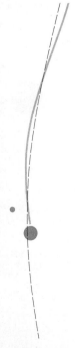

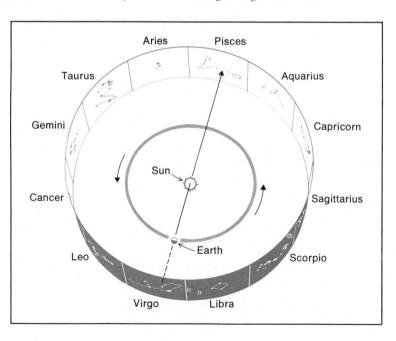

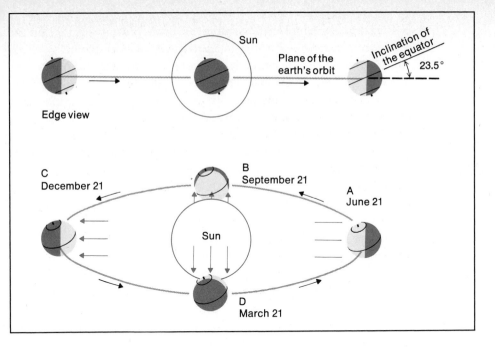

Figure 3.15 The seasons result from the fact that the earth's equator is inclined 23.5° to its plane of orbit (the ecliptic plane).

THE SEASONS

As the earth revolves around the sun, its path defines a plane (flat surface) called the *ecliptic*. The word "ecliptic" derives from eclipse, for it is within this plane that eclipses of the sun and moon occur. If the ecliptic plane is extended until it "cuts" the sky, it will describe a circle through the signs of the zodiac, and that circle becomes the apparent path of the sun from our point of view on earth.

If the earth's axis of rotation were not tilted, that is, if it made an angle of 90° with the ecliptic plane, then the sun's rays would strike the equator of the earth directly at all times and we would not experience seasonal changes. However, the axis of the earth is tilted 23.5° away from a normal (perpendicular) to the ecliptic plane, and it is this tilt, together with the revolution of the earth around the sun, that produces seasonal changes.

In Figure 3.15, position A shows the sun's rays striking directly over a point 23.5° north of the equator. Since direct solar radiation is the most intense, A represents summer in the northern hemisphere. Position B shows the sun's rays directly over the equator and represents autumn in the northern hemisphere. Position C shows the rays striking directly over a point 23.5° south of the equator and so represents winter

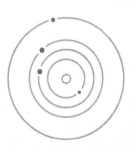

in the northern hemisphere. Position C also represents summer in the southern hemisphere. Position D again shows the sun directly over the equator and represents spring in the northern hemisphere. The extreme northerly position of the sun (A) determines the Tropic of Cancer, 23.5° north of the equator; similarly, the extreme southerly sun (C) determines the Tropic of Capricorn, 23.5° south of the equator. Likewise the Arctic and Antarctic Circles are determined 23.5° from the north and south poles, respectively (Figure 3.15). Note that someone living just inside the Arctic Circle experiences continual daylight in the later part of June, which is why the Arctic has been called "land of the midnight sun." Further, this region is in continual darkness in the later part of December.

TIME—HOW LONG
IS A DAY?

The most fundamental unit of time to which we relate our patterns of behavior and set our routine is that of a day, and yet there are several ways to measure the length of a day. Imagine a line in the sky, running north and south through a point directly over your head. This is called your "local meridian." If you counted time from when a given star crossed your meridian until it crossed once again, you would have measured an earth rotation of exactly 360°, requiring 23 hr 56 min. This is called a *sidereal day*—a day based on a star reference. On the other hand, if you measured a day from the time the sun crossed your meridian until it crossed again, you would find that an average of 24 hr is required for such a rotation. This is called a *mean* (average) *solar day*—a day based on the sun as a reference. Figure 3.16 shows that

Figure 3.16 Observing a sidereal day.

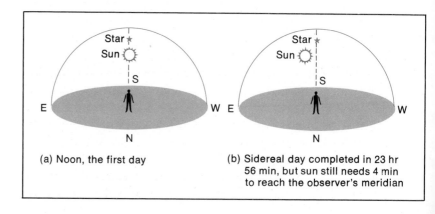

(a) Noon, the first day

(b) Sidereal day completed in 23 hr 56 min, but sun still needs 4 min to reach the observer's meridian

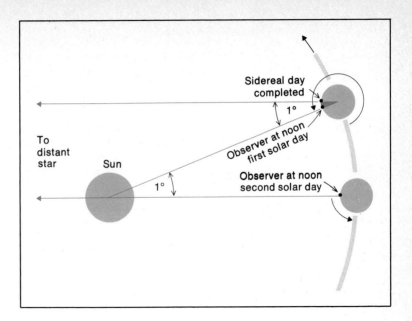

Figure 3.17 The sidereal and the solar day.

To distant star

Sun

Sidereal day completed

1°

Observer at noon first solar day

Observer at noon second solar day

1°

the sun requires approximately 4 min longer to return to the observer's meridian than does the star. Why is this true?

The answer lies in the fact that while the earth is completing one rotation it also moves along its orbit around the sun approximately 1° (360°/365.25 day ≅ 1°/day); therefore, for an observer to see the sun cross his local meridian again requires one extra degree of rotation, a total of 361°. The earth rotates 361° in 24 hr, approximately 15° per hour (361°/24 ≅ 15°/hr), or 1° in 4 min; therefore, a sidereal day is 4 min shorter than a solar day (Figure 3.17). Since most of our daily routine centers about the sun's position in the sky—we eat breakfast soon after sunrise, lunch when the sun is high, and dinner soon after sunset—our clocks are built to agree with solar time (not sidereal time). As a consequence, a given star appears to rise and set about 4 min earlier each night. Thus, if a star is on your meridian at 9:00 P.M. tonight, you may expect the same star to be on your meridian at approximately 8:56 P.M. the following night. At this rate of 4 min/day, a given star rises 1 hr earlier in 15 days and approximately 2 hr earlier each month. After 1 year the star will again be on your meridian at 9:00 P.M. Likewise, night after night each constellation appears to shift a little, and gradually new constellations dominate the early evening sky. This is why we speak of some constellations as being summer constellations and others as autumn, winter, or spring constellations (see Figure 1.3, pages 8 and 9).

In determining a mean solar day, we presume that the earth is moving through the same angle of revolution each day. In reality,

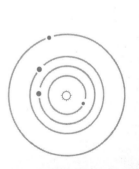

117

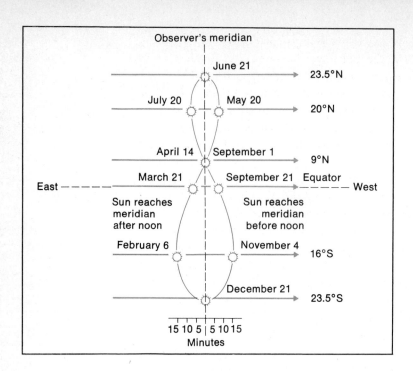

Figure 3.18 The analemma.

this is not the case, for the earth moves fastest when closest to the sun and slowest when farthest from the sun, as expressed by Kepler's second law (see Chapter 1). Thus the earth revolves through an angle of more than 1° per day in the winter and less than 1° per day in the summer, yet its rate of rotation is very nearly constant. For this reason, the sun may actually appear on your local meridian as much as 15 min before or after noon. The difference between true solar time and mean solar time is called the "equation of time."

The *analemma* (see Figure 3.18) found on most globes provides two pieces of information for any day of the year: (1) one can read the declination (the angle which the sun makes with the equator) on that day; (2) one can read the equation of time and correct for the difference between the "true sun" and the "mean sun" for that day. For instance on June 21, the sun is 23.5° north of the equator, and it will cross the observer's meridian at noon (no correction is needed). On February 6, the sun is 16° south of the equator and will cross the observer's meridian 15 min after noon.

LATITUDE AND LONGITUDE

The location of any point on the earth's surface may be indicated by specifying two angles, one called *latitude* and the other *longitude*. How was this system devised? The north and south poles are two very special

118

points on the earth, for they do not move due to rotation (spinning) of the earth. Half way between the poles we imagine a circle called the equator. The angle which a point makes with the equator is called its latitude. In Figure 3.19, angle β (beta) is the latitude of point P. Latitude is specified as north (N) or south (S) of the equator and may be read off a chart showing a system of circles drawn parallel to the equator called *parallels of latitude*. These parallels are usually shown for each 10° of latitude.

In measuring east or west (longitude) there was no natural starting point and so an arbitrary choice was necessary. Based upon the large number of observations of star positions which had been made at the Royal Greenwich Observatory just outside of London, this location was selected as the starting point for measuring longitude. A line running from the north pole, through Greenwich, England, to the south pole is called the *prime meridian*. Additional meridians of longitude may be visualized through any point; however, on a globe map we usually see one meridian for each hour of earth rotation, or 24 meridians in all. Each meridian makes an angle of 15° (360°/24 = 15°) with its neighbor. The smaller angle between the prime meridian and a meridian through point P is called the longitude of P (angle α in Figure 3.19) The longitude of a point is specified as east (E) or west (W) of Greenwich, the prime meridian (Table 3.2).

The meridians may also be thought of as hour lines, for when it is noon at Greenwich, it is 11:00 A.M. at the first meridian (15°W), 10:00 A.M. at the second meridian (30°W), and so on. Thus in Los Angeles which is near the eighth meridian (120°W), it is 4:00 A.M., 8 hr earlier than Greenwich. Usually celestial events are given in Universal Time (Greenwich time). In order to convert to local time, subtract the number of hours equal to the number of meridians your city lies west of Greenwich—that is, for observers near Los Angeles,

Figure 3.19 A system of longitude and latitude.

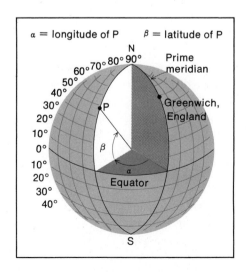

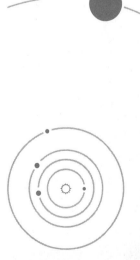

Table 3.2 Longitude and latitude for several well-known cities

CITY	LONGITUDE	LATITUDE
Washington, D.C.	W 77° 04′	N 38° 55′
Los Angeles	W 118° 20′	N 34° 10′
Honolulu	W 157° 45′	N 21° 22′
Rome	E 12° 32′	N 41° 50′
Rio de Janeiro	W 43° 10′	S 22° 40′

subtract eight hours. Likewise cities which lie to the east of Greenwich must add one hour for each meridian. These same meridians serve as the approximate center of each time zone (Figure 3.20).

The latitude of a given point in the northern hemisphere may be approximated by noting the angle that the pole star (Polaris) makes with the observer's horizon. The position of the pole star is determined by extending the axis of the earth until it penetrates the sky. If you lived at the north pole you would expect to see Polaris approximately overhead, near your *zenith*. It would make an angle of 90° with your horizon, an angle equal to the latitude of the north pole. If you lived on the equator, you would expect to see Polaris near your northern horizon, making an angle of 0°, which is equal to the latitude of the equator. Taking an intermediate point, say, 40° north of the equator, we find that Polaris indeed makes an angle of about 40° with the horizon, another proof that the earth is basically a sphere (Figure 3.21).

RIGHT ASCENSION AND DECLINATION

By a system which is very similar to longitude and latitude, astronomers specify the location of stars. Let us imagine that the stars are located on a transparent sphere, called the *celestial sphere,* at a given distance from the earth. When the earth's axis is extended until it intersects the celestial sphere, it determines the *celestial poles,* and the projection of the earth's equator onto the celestial sphere produces the *celestial equator.* In the same way, the projection of the meridians and the parallels of latitude complete the coordinate system in the sky. But again we need a starting point for our east-west measurement. This point cannot be determined by a given point on the earth; rather, it is

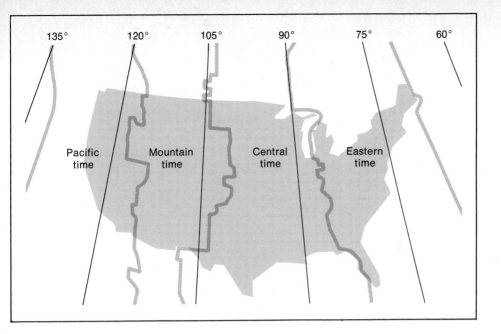

Figure 3.20 Time zones. The solid lines represent standard meridians usually shown on a globe of the earth. The shaded areas
show the approximate boundaries of time zones in the United
States.

Figure 3.21 Polaris marks your
latitude.

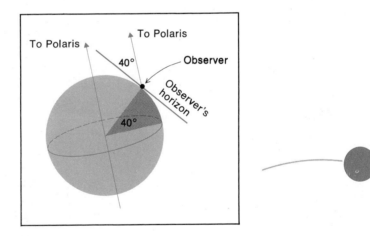

designated as that celestial meridian which lines up with the sun on
the day the sun crosses the equator on its way north. This point is called
the *vernal equinox,* and it marks the position of the sun, in relation
to the stars, on March 21. The projected celestial meridians are called
hour circles, and the hour circle that passes through the vernal equinox
is called the *zero hour circle.* Successive hour circles measured to the

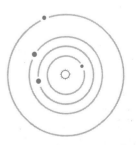

Table 3.3 Similarity between the terrestrial (earth) system and the celestial (sky) system

TERRESTRIAL	CELESTIAL
North and south pole	North and south celestial poles
Equator	Celestial equator
Parallels of latitude —latitude (N or S)	Declination circles —declination (+ or −)
Greenwich, England	Vernal equinox
Prime meridian	Zero hour circle
Meridians of longitude —longitude (E or W)	Hour circles —right ascension (measured eastward only)

east are called first, second, third hour circles, and so on to the twenty-third hour circle. The twenty-fourth hour circle is the same as the zero hour circle (Table 3.3). This angular measure, corresponding to the longitude on earth, is called the *right ascension* of the star and is specified like time. If a star has a right ascension of 5 hr 30 min, we know that it is half way between the fifth and sixth hour circles. Since we have 360° divided into 24 equal hour circles, each hour circle must make an angle of 15° (360°/24 hr = 15°/hr) with its neighbor. If a star has a right ascension of 5 hr 30 min, then it would make an angle of 82.5° (5.5 × 15° = 82.5°) with the zero hour circle.

The north-south measure is similar to that of latitude on the earth and is merely specified by the angle a star makes with the celestial equator. This angle is called the *declination* of the star and is specified as positive (+) if north of the equator and negative (−) if south of it. Therefore the position of any star may be given by two numbers. The star Capella has a right ascension (R.A.) of 5 hr 13 min and a declination (Dec.) of +45°57′ (Figure 3.22).

APPARENT MOTIONS OF THE SKY

While the sky seems to move overhead at the rate of one hour circle for each sidereal clock hour, we should remember that it is the earth's rotation that produces this illusion. Since a given star appears to cross our local meridian about 4 min earlier each night, we should expect the hour circles also to shift by an equivalent amount each night. Table 3.4 presents the hour circle that will be overhead at 9:00 P.M. (local time) for various dates throughout the year.

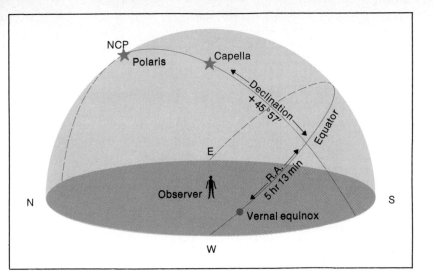

Figure 3.22 Circles in the sky, showing the right ascension and declination of the star Capella. NCP refers to the north celestial pole (Polaris).

Note that on March 21 the zero hour circle is overhead at noon, the first hour circle at 1:00 P.M., the second hour circle at 2:00 P.M., and so on. By 9:00 P.M., the ninth hour circle is overhead. Because the earth does not revolve about the sun with a constant velocity and because the axis of the earth's rotation is tilted to the ecliptic, the values given in Table 3.4 are approximated and the time at which a given hour circle is overhead may vary as much as ±15 min.

Table 3.4 Hour circle overhead at 9:00 P.M. local time

DATE	HOUR CIRCLE	DATE	HOUR CIRCLE	DATE	HOUR CIRCLE
Nov. 6	0	Mar. 21	9	Aug. 6	18
Nov. 21	1	Apr. 6	10	Aug. 21	19
Dec. 6	2	Apr. 21	11	Sept. 6	20
Dec. 21	3	May 6	12	Sept. 21	21
Jan. 6	4	May 21	13	Oct. 6	22
Jan. 21	5	June 6	14	Oct. 21	23
Feb. 6	6	June 21	15	Nov. 6	24[a]
Feb. 21	7	July 6	16		
Mar. 6	8	July 21	17		

[a] Same as zero.

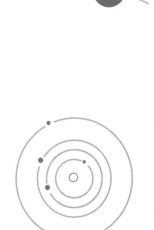

PRECESSION OF THE EARTH

To the more obvious motions of the earth, namely, rotation and revolution, we must add a motion that is detectable only over a long period of time. This motion is called *precession* and requires 26,000 years to complete one cycle. During this period the earth's axis will align itself

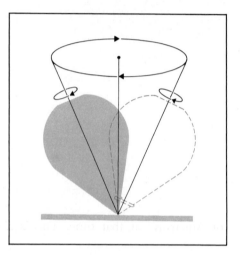

Figure 3.23 Precession of a spinning top.

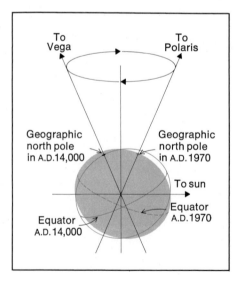

Figure 3.24 Precession of the earth.

with new points in the sky, points other than Polaris. We can compare this motion to that of a toy top which, while it is spinning, slowly describes a circle at the upper end of its axis (Figure 3.23). Like the toy top, the earth is bulged around its equator, and it is rotating on a tilted axis. The gravitational force which the sun and moon exert on the earth tends to straighten that tilt of axis; however, any rotating body possesses a gyroscopic effect—the tendency to maintain a given tilt of axis. Since the earth resists having its axis of rotation straightened, the gravitational energy produces the precessional motion of the earth (Figure 3.24). Because of precession, the axis of the earth, over a 26,000-year period, describes a circle in the sky with a radius of 23.5°. In the year A.D. 14,000, the bright star Vega will be within a few degrees of the north celestial pole. This precessional motion causes the vernal equinox to move westward in the sky approximately 50 seconds of arc per year, and for this reason the full name of this motion is *precession of the equinoxes.*

Since one complete cycle of precessional motion requires approximately 26,000 years, the vernal equinox remains in each of the twelve houses of the zodiac for just over 2000 years (refer to the *fall star map* in Appendix 12). The vernal equinox has been passing through the constellation of Pisces since around the start of the Christian era; but it has been gradually moving westward through the zodiac and will move into the constellation of Aquarius early in the twenty-first century, ushering in the "Age of Aquarius" at that time. This is a happening of special interest to astrologers; astronomers must also be aware of this gradual change, however, because any shift in the position of the vernal equinox is accompanied by a change in the right ascension and declination of all stars. This is true because the vernal equinox defines the zero hour circle in the sky. The right ascension and declination values given in Appendixes 8 and 9 reflect the coordinates for 1950.

OTHER MOTIONS
OF THE EARTH

The earth also shares the motion of the sun, being a part of the solar system. The sun moves among the neighboring stars at a rate of 19.4 km/sec. The entire set of neighboring stars moves in the galaxy of which we are a part at the rate of 242 km/sec, or about 871,000 km/hr; thus the sun and the earth also move through space at this tremendous speed. These motions are discussed in more detail in a later chapter.

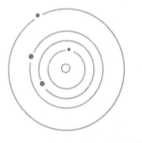

QUESTIONS

1. What is the name given to the lines on the celestial sphere that most closely resemble the meridians on the earth?
2. What are the two most natural points on the earth's surface, as determined by its motion?
3. What motion of the earth is primarily responsible for creating the seasons on the earth?
4. A spherical model of the earth (a globe) usually shows 24 meridians. How many degrees separate each meridian?
5. What is the length of time required for the earth to rotate from one meridian to the next, assuming a total of 24 meridians on the earth?
6. If the earth were tilted more than 23.5°, say, 35°, would the seasons be longer? Would the winter season be more severe? Why?
7. At the present time, the sun is in the constellation of Gemini during the month of July. In ancient times it was in Gemini during the month of May. What phenomenon has caused this change?
8. If you lived on the equator, what percentage of the sky could you see if you stayed up all night?
9. How is the vernal equinox point determined?
10. Through how many hour circles does the sun appear to move each month?
11. What property of an object is measured by each of the following: volume, mass, and density?
12. In going from the crust of the earth to its core, might we expect to find increasing or decreasing density?
13. Eratosthenes observed that the sun's rays struck one city in Egypt at a different angle than they did another city 800 km to the north at noon on a given day. How did this observation prove that the earth is not flat?
14. What is the most abundant element in the earth's atmosphere?
15. Describe the *solar wind* and discuss several effects it may have on the earth.
16. Describe an experiment by which the daily rotation of the earth is proved.
17. Describe an experiment by which the yearly revolution of the earth is proved.
18. What basic motion of the earth causes the sidereal day to differ from the solar day?
19. Twice during the year, the sun appears to move directly over the equator of the earth. List the approximate dates of these occurrences.
20. An observer is located 34° north of the equator. Where will Polaris (the North Star) appear from his point of view?

21. Which basic motion of the earth causes different constellations to be seen on a winter evening than are seen on a spring, summer, or fall evening?

22. What properties of the earth cause it to precess?

23. How do the stars seen by a person in North Africa (say, Casablanca, Morocco, latitude 34°N) compare with the stars seen from Mt. Wilson in California (latitude 34°N) in the evening of the same day?

24. As compared to residents of Florida, New York residents experience which of the following (several answers may be true): (a) longer summer days; (b) longer winter days; (c) same length days all year; (d) shorter summer days; (e) shorter winter days. (Note: here the word "days" refers to the length of daylight hours.)

25. If you placed a stick in the ground at noon on the longest day of the year and then marked the tip of its shadow on the ground at precisely noon each day, what shape would the marks on the ground make in one year?

26. When it is 11:00 A.M. in New York City (approximately 75°W longitude), find the time in a city of 105°W longitude.

SUGGESTED READINGS

Bolt, Bruce A., The fine structure of the earth's interior. *Scientific American* **228** (3), 24–33 (1973).

Dewey, John F., Plate tectonics. *Scientific American* **226** (5), 56–68 (1972).

Hallam, A., Continental drift and the fossil record. *Scientific American* **227** (5), 56–66 (1972).

Kuiper, Gerard P. (ed.), *The earth as a planet.* Chicago: University of Chicago Press, 1954.

Lepp, Henry, *Dynamic earth.* New York: McGraw-Hill, 1973.

Rona, Peter A., Plate tectonics and mineral resources. *Scientific American* **229** (1), 86–95 (1973).

The American ephemeris and nautical almanac. Washington, D.C.: Superintendent of Documents, U.S. Government Printing Office. (Annual publication.)

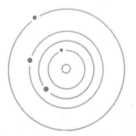

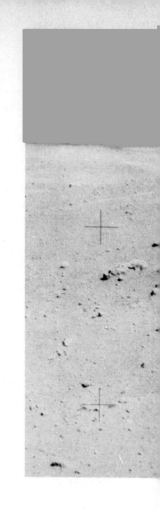

THE MOON

4

We very often think of motion of the earth and moon separately. We picture the earth in its annual motion around the sun and the moon in its monthly motion around the earth, but in reality the earth and moon are better thought of as a binary (dual) system which is orbiting the sun. The term *binary system* may refer to any two objects but usually is taken to mean two objects each having an observable affect upon the other's motion due to their mutual gravitational force. The earth-moon system illustrates this very clearly, as seen in the left-hand flip

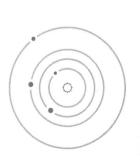

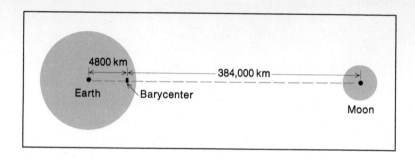

Figure 4.1 If the earth and moon were placed at opposite ends of a rod, the system would balance at the barycenter.

pages beginning on page 162. As you flip these pages, you will see that the earth deviates from a smooth path around the sun by a significant amount, approximately 4800 km on either side of an elliptical path marked by the dashed line. The moon also orbits the sun but deviates approximately 384,000 km on either side of that same dashed path. The only point which moves along the smooth path around the sun is the *barycenter* of the system, equivalent to the point at which the earth and moon would balance if placed at either end of an imaginary rod 388,800 km long.

Since we already know the mass of the earth, this balancing idea will allow us also to determine the mass of the moon. To illustrate this concept, suppose that a father tried to seesaw with his young daughter and they found that they could balance only if the daughter sat three times as far from the pivot (*fulcrum*) as the father. We would then conclude rightly that the daughter weighs only one-third as much as the father. Since the earth and moon balance at their barycenter, 4800 km from the center of the earth and 384,000 km from the center of the moon (Figure 4.1), we conclude that the moon has only $\frac{1}{80}$ the mass of the earth ($4800/384,000 = \frac{1}{80}$), or

$$\frac{1}{80} \times 5.98 \times 10^{27}\,\text{g} = 7.47 \times 10^{25}\,\text{g}$$

BOUNCING RADAR
OFF THE MOON

We may determine the size of the moon by direct observation of its distance and the apparent angle its diameter makes with our eye. Today we merely bounce a radar signal off the moon and record the round-trip time of that signal in order to measure its distance from us. Suppose that on a certain night it requires 2.563 sec for the signal to travel to

and from the moon. We know that radar signals travel at the speed of light, 300,000 km/sec, therefore the round trip distance is equal to

$$2.563 \text{ sec} \times 300,000 \text{ km/sec} = 768,800 \text{ km}$$

The one-way distance then is 384,400 km. Now, if on that same night the diameter of the moon appeared to make an angle of 0.518° with your eye, then we might picture these measurements as in Figure 4.2 and reason as follows: The angle of 0.518° compares to the full circle of 360° in the same way that d (a small part of the circle) compares to the entire distance around the circle (circumference); recall that the circumference C is equal to 2π (pi) multiplied by the radius of the circle ($C = 2\pi r$).

We find that the moon's diameter (3476 km) is about one-quarter that of the earth, yielding a volume of $2.3 \times 10^{25} \text{ cm}^3$, or about $\frac{1}{64}$ that of the earth's volume. This is a useful comparison when we try to visualize just how large the moon really is. When both the mass of the moon and its volume are considered, its average density may be computed:

$$\text{density} = \frac{\text{mass}}{\text{volume}} = \frac{7.5 \times 10^{25} \text{ g}}{2.3 \times 10^{25} \text{ cm}^3} = 3.3 \text{ g/cm}^3$$

Many of the moon rocks have proven to be almost this dense, which suggests that the moon may be more uniform in its density than the earth. This is typical of what we might expect of a relatively small

Figure 4.2 Finding the diameter of the moon.

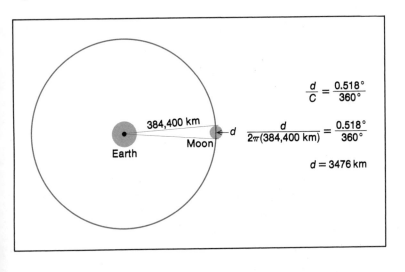

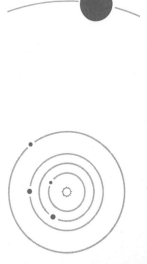

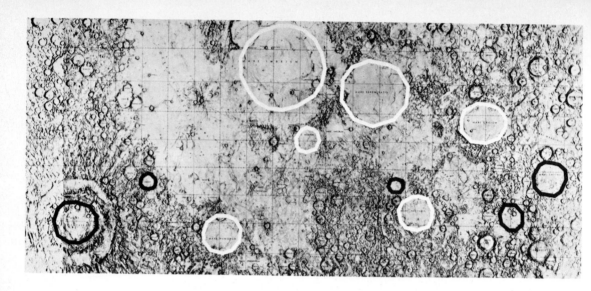

Figure 4.3 Eleven of the twelve known concentrations of mass on the moon. The mascons seem to be associated with a definite type of mare. (JPL–NASA)

object, for pressures in the core would be much less. Four seismic (moonquake) stations have been left on the moon by Apollo crews, and numerous natural and man-made impacts have been recorded, revealing layers of increasing density and the probability of a molten core, 700 km in radius.

Another very interesting method for study beneath the surface of the moon has been developed. The Apollo command module, orbiting around the moon, sends radar signals of various wavelengths toward the moon and times their return (echo). It has been found that signals of 115-cm wavelength penetrate the lunar soil approximately 20 m and signals of 13-cm wavelength penetrate as much as 200 m. Using this method, scientists have concluded that what now appear to be fairly smooth lowland regions of the moon are areas of formerly rugged terrain—valleys and basins that were filled in by molten lava at one stage in the moon's evolution. When a spacecraft flies over certain of these *maria* (lunar "seas") it experiences an increased gravitational attraction, indicating a higher concentration of mass in these areas, which have been called *mascons* (the circled areas in Figure 4.3). Some observers speculate that very dense meteorites may be buried in these regions. In Mare Imbrium the excess gravity is equivalent to that which would be produced by an iron-nickel sphere 70 km in diameter, buried 50 km beneath the surface. Could such objects have been instrumental in forming the maria, melting the lunar surface upon impact? Or could the maria represent a very dense lava flow formed by the eruption of molten material from a more central region? This higher density could account for the greater concentration of mass. Mascons are also known to exist on earth, and they are usually referred to as gravitational anomalies.

SURFACE FEATURES
OF THE MOON

The most obvious distinction that can be made in the surface features of the moon is between the flat lowlands called maria, which usually appear dark in our telescopic view, and the mountainous highlands, which appear bright because of their ability to scatter light. The circular maria range upward to 1130 km in diameter, with irregular regions such as Oceanus Procellarum being significantly larger. Mountain ranges extend for hundreds of kilometers, reaching heights of over 6 km above the level of the "seas." These lunar highlands bear the names of terrestrial ranges, such as the Alps and the Pyrenees.

Superimposed upon both the mountains and to a lesser degree upon the maria are craters that range in size upward to 240 km in diameter. The surface features are best seen near the first- and third-quarter phases (Figures 4.4 to 4.7). At those times the sun's rays strike the moon at an angle to our view, creating shadows. It is these shadows that amplify details on the moon. The length of the shadows may be used as an indicator of the height and depth of various portions of the craters (Figure 4.8). The large crater Theophilus pictured in Figure 4.9 is 104 km in diameter. While its rim is only about 600 m above the surrounding area, it is approximately 4.2 km above the floor of the crater. The central peak rises about 2.25 km above the floor.

The cratered area of the moon occurs in the higher mountainous regions above the maria floor. There is some indication that the maria flows may have covered certain of the original craters, for what appear to be crater peaks still protrude through the maria. This suggests, then, that the maria represent a feature that is more youthful than some of the craters. The craters themselves may vary in age. When smaller craters are seen within larger ones, the smaller must be of more recent origin. Had the larger craters been formed last, they would have obliterated the smaller ones in the process.

The age-old question concerning the origin of the craters remains unanswered. On the one hand, volcanic action is suggested by the lavalike flows, by collapse structures (which resemble certain terrestrial features like Crater Lake in Oregon), and by a limited outflow of gases to this day. Radioactivity would have been a logical source of energy

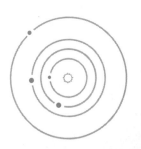

Figure 4.4 First-quarter moon (7 days old). North is at top, as seen by the naked eye. (Lick Observatory)

for such activity. On the other hand, opposed to this theory of volcanic action is the impact theory. Having almost no atmosphere, the moon has long been susceptible to the impact of meteorites. Such crater-producing impacts may have occurred when the moon was in a more

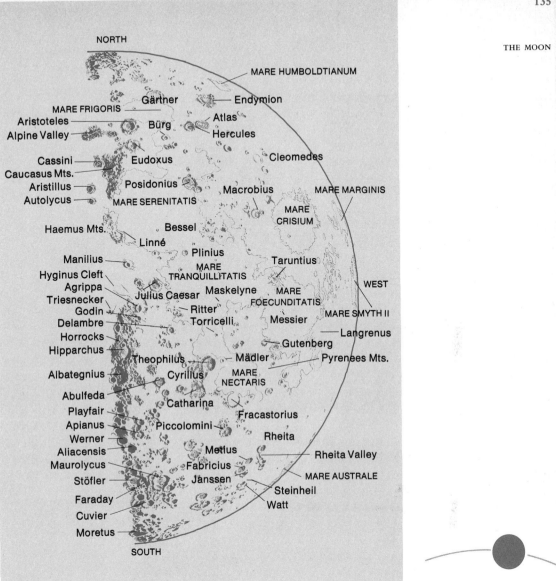

NORTH

MARE HUMBOLDTIANUM

Gärtner — Endymion
MARE FRIGORIS
Aristoteles — Atlas
Alpine Valley — Bürg — Hercules

Cassini — Eudoxus — Cleomedes
Caucasus Mts.
Aristillus — Posidonius
Autolycus — MARE SERENITATIS — Macrobius — MARE MARGINIS

MARE
CRISIUM

Haemus Mts. — Bessel
Linné

Manilius — Plinius — Taruntius
Hyginus Cleft — MARE
Agrippa — TRANQUILLITATIS
Triesnecker — Julius Caesar — Maskelyne — MARE
Godin — Ritter — FOECUNDITATIS — WEST
Delambre — Torricelli — Messier — MARE SMYTH II
Horrocks — Langrenus
Hipparchus — Theophilus — Mädler — Gutenberg
Albategnius — Cyrillus — Pyrenees Mts.
MARE
NECTARIS
Abulfeda — Catharina
Playfair — Fracastorius
Apianus — Piccolomini
Werner — Rheita
Aliacensis — Metius
Maurolycus — Rheita Valley
Stöfler — Fabricius
Faraday — Janssen — MARE AUSTRALE
Cuvier — Steinheil
Moretus — Watt

SOUTH

Figure 4.5 Key to the first-quarter moon.

pliable or molten state, and these features would not have eroded on
the moon, as they did on the earth, because such erosion factors as rivers,
wind, and rain do not exist on the moon. The raylike structure evident
around several craters suggests an impact, with material being thrown

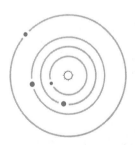

Figure 4.6 Third-quarter moon. North is at top, as seen by the naked eye. (Lick Observatory)

outward. This theory is hard put to explain how enough heat could be generated by impact to produce the maria flows. The surface features of the moon very likely result from both types of activity—some cratered by volcanic action, others by impact (Figure 4.10).

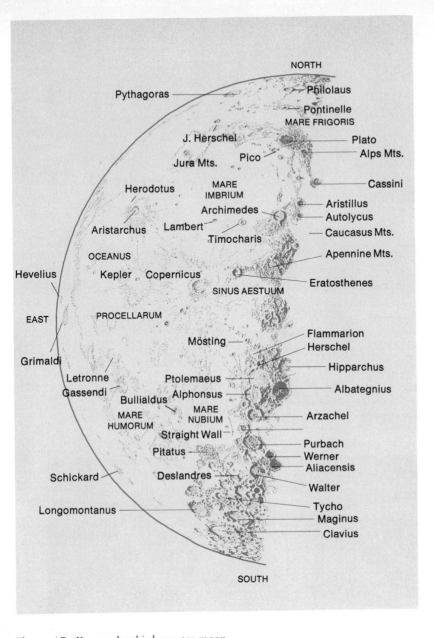

NORTH

Pythagoras —— Philolaus
—— Pontinelle
MARE FRIGORIS
J. Herschel —— Plato
Pico —— Alps Mts.
Jura Mts.
Cassini
Herodotus   MARE
IMBRIUM
Archimedes —— Aristillus
—— Autolycus
Lambert
Aristarchus   Timocharis —— Caucasus Mts.

Apennine Mts.
OCEANUS
Hevelius   Kepler Copernicus
—— Eratosthenes
SINUS AESTUUM
EAST   PROCELLARUM
Mösting —— Flammarion
—— Herschel
Grimaldi
—— Hipparchus
Letronne   Ptolemaeus
Gassendi   Alphonsus —— Albategnius
Bullialdus   MARE
MARE   NUBIUM —— Arzachel
HUMORUM
Straight Wall
Pitatus —— Purbach
—— Werner
—— Aliacensis
Schickard   Deslandres
—— Walter
Longomontanus —— Tycho
—— Maginus
—— Clavius

SOUTH

Figure 4.7 Key to the third-quarter moon.

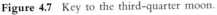

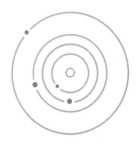

Valleys such as seen in Figure 4.11 are broad features that some-times resemble the bed of a meandering river. Narrower features called *rilles* likewise take on this appearance. No surface water exists on the moon today, however. If water were to appear on the surface, it would

Figure 4.8 The Sea of Tranquillity, including the Crater Cauchy and two rilles. (NASA)

Figure 4.9 The Crater Theophilus. The lengths of the shadows reveal the heights of the rim of this crater to be approximately 4.2 km and the central peak to be 2.25 km. The diameter is approximately 104 km (65 miles). (Yerkes Observatory)

Figure 4.10 Scientist-astronaut Harrison H. Schmitt standing next to a huge lunar boulder during the third Apollo 17 extravehicular activity (EVA-3) at the Taurus-Littrow landing site. (NASA)

Figure 4.11 The meandering Prinz Valleys I and II, running downhill from the Harbinger Mountain area, range in width from 300 to 2400 m. A Lunar Orbiter V photograph. (NASA)

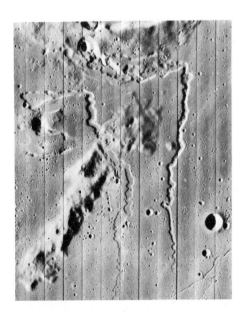

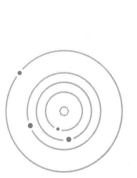

Figure 4.12 A portion of Gassendi Crater on the near side of the moon, as photographed from the Apollo 16 spacecraft in lunar orbit. This view is looking southerly into the Sea of Moisture. (NASA)

Figure 4.13 The far side of the moon as seen by Lunar Orbiter III. This photograph was taken 1400 km above the lunar surface and shows the prominent crater Tsiolkovsky filled with dark material. This crater is about 225 km in diameter. (NASA)

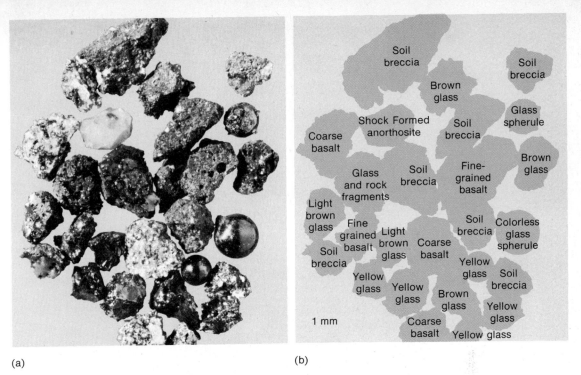

(a)   (b)

Figure 4.14 (a) Moon rock samples. (b) Key to moon rock samples. (Smithsonian Astrophysical Observatory)

immediately boil away because of the lack of atmospheric pressure. Some rilles resemble a fault line along which the lunar soil has slumped downward, traversing even the rim of a crater (see Figure 4.12). Faulting may also exhibit itself by the rising of almost vertical walls in certain regions of the moon, for example, the *straight wall* which rises 200 m above the adjoining plain and extends 130 km.

THE FAR SIDE
OF THE MOON

When we speak of the *face* of the moon, we refer to the "near side," that side which is perpetually turned toward the earth; the "far side" is that side which we never see from earth and, until spacecraft orbited the moon, we had no idea as to its nature (Figure 4.13). Surprisingly, unlike the face, the far side has virtually no maria, but rather it does have several very expansive depressions that are pockmarked with craters. This general cratering of the far side, compared with the sparsely cratered maria of the face, raises numerous questions as to the origin and evolution of the moon's surface. Perhaps a study of its rocks will yield some answers to these questions (Figures 4.14 and 4.15). The

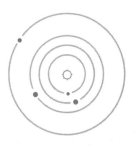

141

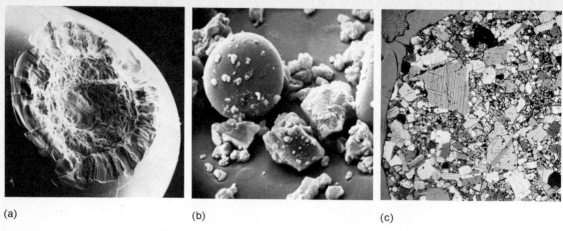

(a) (b) (c)

Figure 4.15 (a) A microscopic view of an iron particle, showing the effect of high-velocity impact by lunar surface material. (b) Lunar dust, magnified 1320 times, showing glasslike sphere and dumbbell shapes and an assortment of the more common irregular shapes. (c) A thin section of anorthosite, enlarged 22 times. (a, NASA; b, official United States Navy photograph; c, Smithsonian Astrophysical Observatory)

elements that compose rocks from the earth and from the moon have a basic similarity yet are found in different proportions. (Table 4.1 presents this comparison.)

When moon rocks are dated by analysis of radioactive elements, a very interesting record unfolds. The material brought from the maria is only 3.5 billion years old; on the other hand, the highland material checks out nearer to 4.5 billion years old. This fact tends to confirm the idea that about 3.5 billion years ago the nature of the moon's surface was drastically changed, perhaps by cataclysmic events. Let us suppose that the moon's crust was heated by radioactivity to a semimolten state and further that it experienced numerous impacts by objects large enough to create the major craters, releasing molten material from beneath the crust. The radioactive time clocks would have been reset within this molten material, resulting in our present 3.5-billion-year estimate of its age. But why would the impacting objects have produced a moon that is so different on one side (the near side) than on the other (far side)? One theory suggests that the moon once orbited the earth within a few thousand miles and moved much faster in its orbit. Such a moon, if on a collision course with debris in space, would experience numerous impacts on its leading side. Assuming that these impacts tended to redistribute the density of the moon in favor of the heavily impacted side, the moon would slowly have turned to point this most dense side toward the earth. It would then have become "locked" into this relative position by the force of the earth's gravity.

142

Table 4.1 Percentages of various elements on the crust of the earth and the moon[a]

	OXYGEN (%)	SILICON (%)	IRON (%)	MAGNESIUM (%)	ALUMINUM (%)	CALCIUM AND POTASSIUM (%)
Highlands of moon	61.0	16.2	3.7	4.0	9.0	6.1
Maria of moon	60.6	16.8	1.8	5.3	6.6	4.7
Earth	61.7	21.0	1.9	1.8	6.4	3.3

[a] Percentages are given in relation to numbers of atoms, not as to weight.

While the crust of the moon appears to have had its last general heating approximately 3 billion years ago, the core of the moon may still be hot, for the moon transfers heat through its crust much more slowly than does the earth. Furthermore, if the interior of the moon has even one-tenth the radioactive material that is contained in its crust, the core must be heated to a molten state. On the other hand, some observers argue in favor of a cold moon because they see little or no sign of volcanic activity. They point out that the moon is able to hold a rather peculiar shape with two significant bulges, one toward the earth and one on the far side, and they reason that the moon would be more spherical if it were hot. These objections have been countered by the suggestion that there may be a rigid cold crust several hundred kilometers thick, with a molten core. Resolution of these conflicting theories is not yet possible, for most of the data gathered by recent lunar missions are subject to a variety of interpretations.

ATMOSPHERE

One of the consequences of the moon's very low mass is its low surface gravity. If an astronaut fully loaded with his space pack weighs 120 kg on the earth, on the moon he weighs only 20 kg. This same fact answers the question, "Why does the moon have no atmosphere?" When molecules of an atmosphere are heated, their average velocity increases; if a molecule attains sufficient velocity, it will overcome the gravitational pull of the moon and be "lost" in space. The heat which the moon receives from the sun is more than sufficient to cause the eventual escape of all lunar atmosphere, for the temperature ranges from 403°K (+130°C) in areas directly under the sun to 103°K (−170°C) on the

night side. This very wide temperature range is due in part to the lack of atmosphere, for an atmosphere normally provides the insulating "blanket" over the parent body and tends to moderate the temperature. On the moon, areas differing in temperature by a hundred degrees or more (Celsius) may exist within a few meters of each other. The lack of an atmosphere means that water can not exist as a liquid on the surface of the moon; if placed there, water would immediately vaporize and soon be lost to space. The phenomena we know as twilight and dawn do not occur on the moon. As the sun goes down darkness is immediate, with the possible exception of reflection from nearby peaks rising above the observer's head. Even the percentage of light reflected is very, very small, in the neighborhood of only 7 percent. The percentage of light which a body reflects is called its *albedo,* and bodies without atmospheres typically have very low albedos. By contrast a planet with a cloudy atmosphere, like Venus, reflects about 76 percent of the light it receives.

REVOLUTION
OF THE MOON

Due to the earth's rotation, the moon appears to move in a westerly direction during one evening's observation. A careful study will show, however, that the moon is moving in an easterly direction against the background of stars. You may verify this by observing the moon when it is just west of a bright star or cluster, such as the Pleiades. If you observe the moon for several hours, it will become apparent that it is actually moving in an easterly direction with respect to the stars.

A more dramatic easterly change takes place when we observe the moon on successive nights, noting its position relative to the stars each night. If we continue this practice for approximately 27 days, we find that the moon will have returned to the same portion of the sky. To be exact, the moon's *sidereal period of revolution* is 27.322 days, which causes it to shift its position in the sky by an amount equal to just slightly more than 13° per day:

$$\frac{360°}{27.322 \text{ days}} \cong 13°/\text{day}$$

We would then expect the moon to move through slightly less than one hour circle in a 24-hr period.

We can also observe that more than 27.322 days are required for the moon to complete its cycle of phases. In fact, the period from one full moon to the next is 29.531 days. This is called the *synodic period* of the moon. Suppose we started counting time when the moon is full,

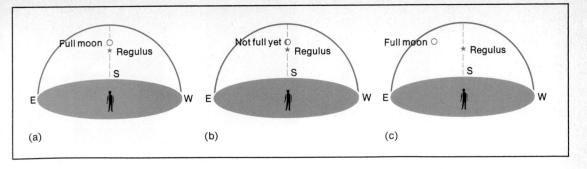

(a)   (b)   (c)

Figure 4.16 The sidereal and the synodic month as seen in the sky. (a) A full moon, in conjunction with Regulus (start counting time here). (b) After 27.33 days—the moon, again in conjunction with Regulus, but not yet a full moon (this is a sidereal month). (c) After 29.5 days—the moon, again full, but now located approximately 30° east of Regulus (this is a synodic month).

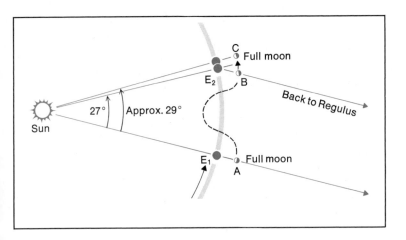

Figure 4.17 The synodic period of the moon.

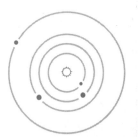

shown in Figures 4.16 and 4.17 as position A. We note that the moon appears near the bright star Regulus. In 27.322 days the moon will return to align itself with Regulus, but in that length of time the earth will have moved through approximately 27° to position E_2, and the moon will then be in position B. Since *full moon* occurs only when the moon is on the opposite side of the earth from the sun, it will not be full until it moves through an additional angle of approximately 29° to position C. This additional revolution requires approximately 2.209 days, hence 27.322 + 2.209 = 29.531 days.

145

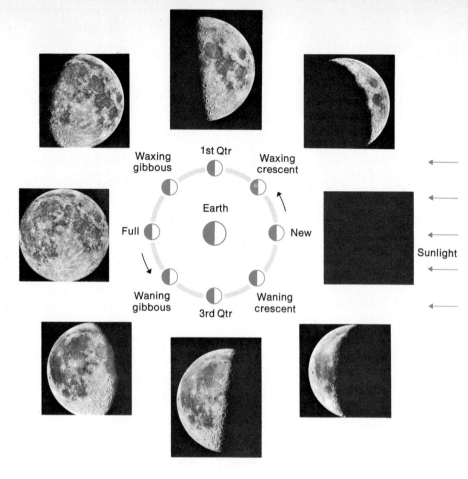

Figure 4.18 The phases of the moon. North is at top, as seen by the naked eye. (Lick Observatory)

Figure 4.19 The synchronous rotation of the moon.

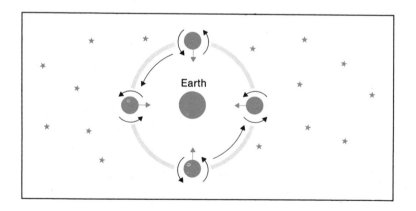

Figure 4.20 Two photographs of the moon showing libration. (Lick Observatory)

In passing from one full moon to the next, the moon appears to go through all its successive phases, as we can see in Figure 4.18. From this illustration, we observe that the *new* (all-dark) *moon* occurs when the moon is between the earth and the sun and that the *first-quarter moon* occurs when the moon makes a 90° angle with the sun as viewed from earth. Midway between these two phases is the *waxing* (growing) *crescent,* the phase which most people incorrectly refer to as the "new" moon, because it is this phase which is the first we see when the moon is starting a new sequence of phases. The next phase is that of *waxing gibbous,* when the face of the moon appears about three-quarters lighted. The *full moon* occurs when the moon is on the opposite side of the earth from the sun. Then follows a series of *waning* phases in which the visible illuminated portion appears to shrink.

Throughout all its phases, the moon presents essentially the same side toward the earth. Does this mean that the moon does not rotate on its own axis? On the contrary: In order always to present one side toward the earth, the moon must rotate once, with respect to the stars, while revolving once around the earth (Figure 4.19). This motion is referred to as *synchronous rotation* and has a period of 27.322 days; however, there are two facts that modify synchronous motion. One of these is that while the moon's rotation is very uniform, its revolution is along an elliptical orbit and hence is not uniform. These motions periodically allow the moon to expose small additional portions along either its western or its eastern edge (*limb*). Secondly, the moon's orbit is inclined 5° to that of the earth, and as it moves in that orbit we periodically view a little beyond the normal polar regions, either north or south. Over a period of several months we are able to view a total of 59 percent of the moon's surface from the earth. The various interactions of these motions are called the *librations* of the moon (Figure 4.20).

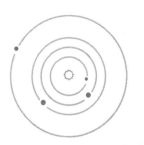

147

A fundamental question must arise from the fact of synchronous rotation. Has the moon always possessed this property, or is it possible that at one time the moon rotated faster (or slower) than it does today?

TIDES PRODUCED BY THE MOON

Let us conduct an imaginary experiment, observing tides of the ocean on several successive evenings when the moon is also visible overhead. On the first night the moon is on your local meridian at 8:00 P.M., and high tide occurs a short time later. On the second night the moon is on your local meridian at 8:50 P.M., and again high tide occurs a short time later. On the third night the moon passes your local meridian at 9:40 P.M.; once more high tide occurs a short time later. Were this experiment conducted for several additional nights, it would be obvious that the timing of the high tide coincides with the passage of the moon and must be due to its presence overhead. What is not so obvious is

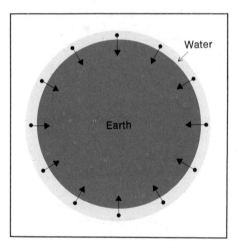

Figure 4.21 Water molecules (dots) distributed evenly over the surface of an imaginary earth, alone in space and without any motion of its own.

Figure 4.22 Tides on the earth.

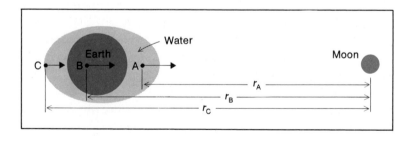

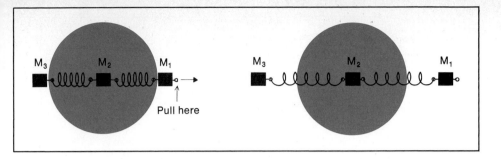

Figure 4.23 A system of springs and masses that illustrates the effect of the moon's gravitational force in producing tides on the earth. The circle attached to the center mass represents the earth.

the reason why there are two high tides in a period of 24 hr and 50 min. That is, why does the earth have a double bulge?

To explain this phenomenon, let us consider an imaginary earth— perfectly smooth, with no mountains or valleys—alone in space, with no motion of its own. If water existed on the surface of this imaginary earth, it would be distributed evenly over the entire surface, for each molecule would experience the same force of gravity toward the center of the earth (Figure 4.21).

If this imaginary earth were then set into rotation, the layer of water would become deeper around the equator and shallower at the poles, due to the rotation. However, this would only produce a constant bulge around the equator and would not account in any way for the fluctuating tide that we experience. If we consider the effect of the moon on all this, we will realize that, owing to gravitation, it must exert a force on the earth and on the waters that cover it. But, as we recall from the law of gravitation, the amount of that force is dependent on the distance between the two objects in question. The greater the separation, the less the force. Suppose that a 1-g mass is situated at each of the three positions shown in Figure 4.22: at A, in the water near the moon; at B, in the center of the earth; and at C, in the water on the side away from the moon. Because point A is closer to the moon than B, it will experience a greater force than B, thus explaining the bulge toward the moon. Likewise, point B is closer to the moon than point C, and it will experience a greater force than on C, pulling the earth away from the water on the far side. The effect of this difference in forces experienced by the three masses is very similar to the effect of stretching the system of springs and masses illustrated in Figure 4.23.

Note that not only did the distance between M_1 and M_2 increase as the spring was stretched, but also the distance between M_2 and M_3. Imagine that the earth, a rigid body, is attached to M_2 and that we

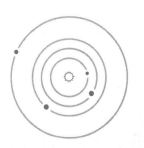

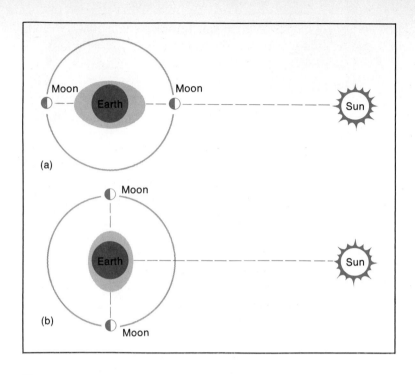

Figure 4.24 (a) Spring tides. (b) Neap tides.

see a bulge in both the direction of the force (pull) and the opposite direction.

Unlike the imaginary earth, our planet is not smooth but has mountains, beaches, and deep trenches under the ocean. As the earth rotates within the bulged surface water, raised portions of the land literally run into the bulge and friction results, slowing the earth's rotation. While this slowing trend only extends the length of a day by approximately 0.002 sec in a period of 100 years, it is the very same phenomenon that once slowed the moon's rotation until it now turns the same side toward the earth at all times. Although the moon is devoid of oceans, the earth once raised moving land tides on a rather flexible primal moon. The friction that resulted slowed the moon's rotation until it coincided with its revolution. Now the cool, semirigid moon has its two earth-produced bulges permanently fixed, one pointing always toward the earth and the other always away from it.

The rate of slowing of the earth's rotation appears rather insignificant, yet in the time periods with which the astronomer deals it is very significant. Along with a lengthening day on earth, the moon is also moving farther from the earth at the rate of 3 cm/year. Could we turn time backward, say, 500 million years, we would find the moon somewhat closer to the earth and the length of a day to be only about 21 hr. This fact is confirmed by the fossil record of daily growth rings of certain corals, for they show 416 daily growth rings in each yearly band. Assuming that the number of hours in a year is approximately the same today as it was 500 million years ago, then a 416-day year would have approximately 21-hr days.

The sun at an average distance of 150 million kilometers (15×10^7 km) also has its tidal effect on the earth's waters, but less than one-half the magnitude of the moon's effect. When the sun and moon tend to make the waters bulge in the same direction, they produce extremely high and low tides, called *spring tides*. As we can see in Figure 4.24(a), these occur during new and full moon. When the forces of the sun and moon act at right angles to each other, the tides are less extreme and are called *neap tides*. Figure 4.24(b) shows that these occur during first- and third-quarter phases of the moon. These same forces act upon the rigid earth to produce land tides and may sometimes trigger the release of stresses in the earth, producing earthquakes.

ECLIPSES

Eclipses occur when one object passes within the shadow of another, and the structure of the shadow itself provides a key to our understanding of the eclipse. If the source of light were that of a star—a point source—then the boundaries of the shadow cast by an object would be simple and well defined, as is indicated by Figure 4.25. In our discussion the sun is the source, however, and because it is nearby it presents an extended source. Under such conditions, the shadow that an object casts is more complex. The dense portion of the shadow is called the *umbra*. If you found yourself within this region, you would see the sun completely covered by the object, in this case the moon (Figure 4.26). The less dense portion of the shadow is called the *penumbra,* and if you viewed the sun from within this region, the moon would appear to cover only part of the sun.

Figure 4.25   The shadow produced by a point source.

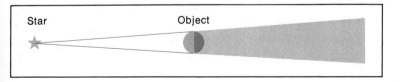

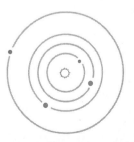

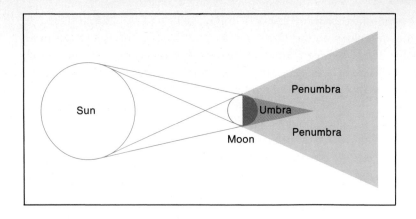

Figure 4.26 The shadow produced by an extended source.

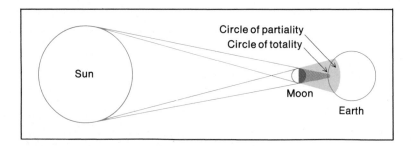

Figure 4.27 A solar eclipse. An observer within the circle of totality will see a total eclipse of the sun, while an observer in the circle of partiality will see only a partial eclipse.

SOLAR ECLIPSE

The length of the umbral portion of the moon's shadow is slightly more than 383,000 km. The distance from the moon to the earth varies between 362,000 and 406,600 km. Thus we may conclude that under certain conditions the shadow of the moon will strike the earth but cover only a very limited region of it at any one time (Figure 4.27).

If you were standing within that region of the earth covered by the path of the dark umbral portion on March 7, 1970, you were able to see a truly spectacular event—total eclipse of the sun. The combined motion of the earth and the moon caused this umbral portion of the shadow to sweep out a narrow path across the face of the earth, traveling at approximately 1600 km/hr. The sun's disk was gradually covered by the disk of the moon.

For just an instant prior to total covering, a portion of the sun was visible shining through a depression in the moon's profile and producing the beautiful diamond-ring effect seen in Figure 4.28. When the sun was completely covered—the time of *totality*—the sky darkened, and the beautiful *corona,* or outer atmosphere of the sun, appeared (Figure 4.29). The corona of the sun is not usually visible, owing to the brilliant glare of the *photosphere,* the body of the sun itself. During the time of totality, many strange things happened: Dogs howled, chickens went to roost, birds ceased their singing, and some flowers closed. Much of the surrounding landscape took on strange hues of

Figure 4.28 The diamond ring effect. (NASA)

Figure 4.29 The corona of the sun, as seen during a total solar eclipse—March 7, 1970. (High Altitude Observatory)

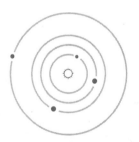

Figure 4.30 The solar eclipse of March 7, 1970. An exposure was made every 6 min. Venus appears above the fifth image from the left. (Maurice E. Snook)

color. The eclipse lasted only a few minutes, and then the moon moved on, again to reveal part of the sun and finally the entire disk (Figure 4.30).

The path of totality for the solar eclipse of March 7, 1970, is shown in Figure 4.31. The eclipse was witnessed by millions of people in the United States and Mexico. Those who lived within this narrow band, or who traveled to reach it, were rewarded by the spectacular sight, and almost every person in Mexico, the United States, and Canada was in a position to see at least a partial eclipse, since all were in the penumbral portion of the moon's shadow, and at least part of the sun would appear covered by the lunar disk. Often partial eclipses go unnoticed because the sun's light is only slightly dimmed by the moon's passage. Television via communications satellite played an unprecedented role in bringing this spectacular event to millions of people all over the world.

In addition to the partial and total eclipse, a third situation may arise. We know that the moon is often farther from the earth than 383,000 km and that its shadow will therefore not reach the earth. If you were standing directly in line with the moon's shadow, you would see the central portion of the sun's disk covered, leaving a ring of sunlight visible around the moon's disk. This is called an *annular* or *ring* eclipse (Figure 4.32).

The paths of solar eclipses between July 1963 and May 1984 are mapped out in Figure 4.33.

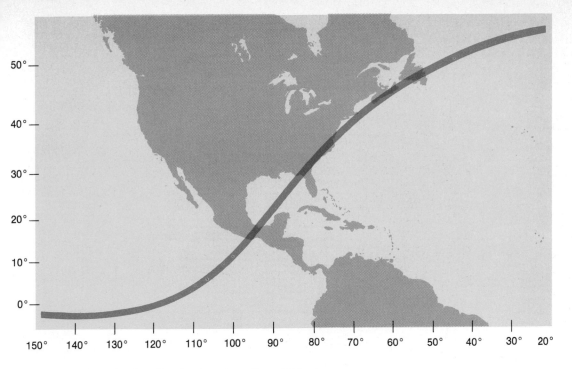

Figure 4.31 The path of totality for the solar eclipse of March 7, 1970. (Nautical Almanac Office, U.S. Naval Observatory, Washington, D.C.)

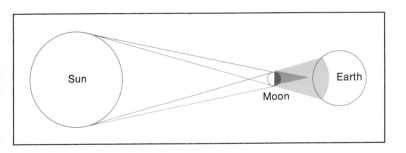

Figure 4.32 An annular eclipse of the sun.

A WARNING

Never look at the sun directly, whether by naked eye or through a telescope or binoculars, for in so doing your eye may be irreparably burned by the sun's radiation. No pain accompanies this experience, so that a person who has observed the sun directly might not immediately be aware that he is being blinded. A solar eclipse may be safely viewed by holding a small piece of cardboard in which a pinhole has

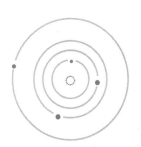

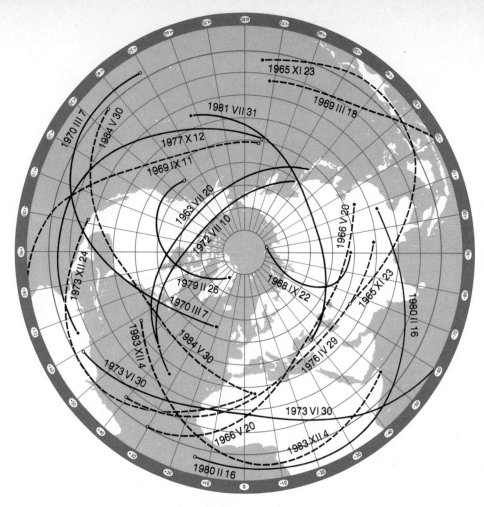

Figure 4.33 The paths of total eclipses between July 1963 and May 1984. A solid line corresponds to a total eclipse; a dashed line, to an annular one. The beginning of the path is indicated by a small white circle; the end, by a black one. (From J. Meeus, K. Grosjean, and W. Vanderleen, *Canon of solar eclipses.* Elmsford, N.Y.: Pergamon Press, 1966)

been made, allowing the sun's rays to pass through the pinhole and fall on a second piece of cardboard (screen). A small telescope may be substituted for the pinhole, as illustrated in Figure 4.34.

LUNAR ECLIPSE

A total lunar eclipse occurs when the moon passes completely within the umbral portion of the earth's shadow, which extends outward approximately 1,380,000 km. At the moon's distance, the umbral

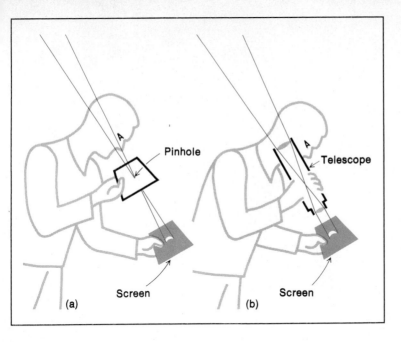

Figure 4.34 Observation of a solar eclipse using (a) a pinhole and (b) a small telescope.

portion is almost 9700 km in diameter. The moon's diameter of 3476 km allows it to fit easily within this shadow (Figure 4.35). The penumbral portion is approximately 16,000 km in diameter at the moon's distance. When a total eclipse occurs, the moon first moves into the penumbral portion of the earth's shadow with only slight dimming. As it moves on into the umbral portion, the curvature of the earth's shadow may be seen on the moon (Figure 4.36). During totality, the

Figure 4.35 Lunar eclipses.

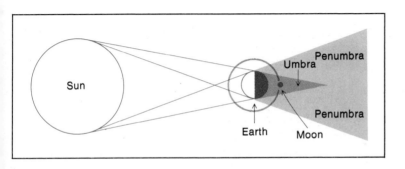

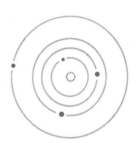

Figure 4.36 The moon is seen moving into the umbra of the earth's shadow. (R. T. Dixon)

moon does not become darkened entirely but rather takes on a copper hue because sunlight, which is refracted by the earth's atmosphere, still illuminates the surface of the moon.

ECLIPSE SEASONS

It would be easy to surmise that we should have a solar eclipse at each occasion of a new moon, when the moon passes between the earth and the sun, or that we should have a lunar eclipse on the occasion of each full moon, when the earth is between the sun and the moon. This turns out not to be true, however, because the moon orbits the earth on an imaginary plane tilted 5° to the plane of the earth's orbit (Figure 4.37).

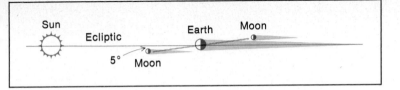

Figure 4.37 The moon's orbital plane is inclined 5° to the ecliptic (the earth's orbital plane).

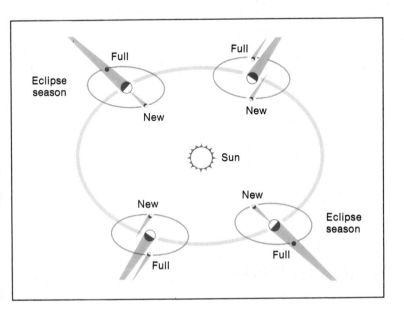

Figure 4.38 Eclipse seasons.

Therefore, the moon's shadow often misses the earth, and the earth's shadow misses the moon. On other occasions the new moon and full moon phases occur when the moon is in the plane of the earth's orbit, producing both solar and lunar eclipses, about 15 days apart (Figure 4.38). This is called an *eclipse season,* such seasons occurring slightly less than 6 months apart. Therefore we should expect two eclipse seasons per year, each lasting for approximately a month. If an eclipse season occurs early in January, another will occur late in June and a third in late December, making three in a year. If a solar eclipse occurred on June 30 one year, we would expect a similar eclipse to occur about June 10, that is, 20 days earlier, the following year. Thus the eclipse cycle advances each year and repeats itself in a period of slightly more than 18 years. This cycle is called the *saros* (a Greek term derived from the ancient Babylonian).

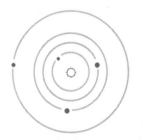

QUESTIONS

1. Which direction does the moon appear to move *against the background of stars?*
2. Why does the sidereal month (27.322 days) differ from the synodic month (29.531 days)?
3. The moon presents almost the same "face" toward the earth at all times. Therefore, which of the following is true: (a) its period of rotation is 27.322 days; (b) its period of rotation is 29.531 days; (c) it does not rotate?
4. At what time of night would you expect to see a full moon overhead on your local meridian?
5. Do coastal ports usually experience one, two, or three high tides per day?
6. The moon appears to shift among the stars: (a) approximately one hour circle (15°) per day; (b) less than one hour circle per day; (c) more than one hour circle per day. Which is true?
7. True or false: The sun and the moon "work" together to produce exceptionally high tides when the moon is new or full.
8. Where is the barycenter of the earth-moon system located?
9. How often does a point on the moon experience a cycle of changing tides?
10. Describe a "mascon."
11. List six types of surface features on the moon.
12. Which major type of surface feature is most conspicuous by its absence on the far side of the moon?
13. Solar eclipses always occur during what phase of the moon?
14. An eclipse season usually lasts for about a month. How many eclipse seasons may occur in one year?
15. What part of the sun is visible during a total solar eclipse?
16. Describe two safe methods for viewing a partial eclipse of the sun.
17. Why do you not see an eclipse of the moon every month?
18. Describe the relative positions of sun, moon, and earth when the moon is full.
19. If high tide occurs at 9 A.M. on a given day, when can you expect the high tide to occur the next morning? Why?
20. Why is the sun a less powerful factor than the moon in producing tides?
21. What is meant by land tides?
22. What does the term *earthshine* mean in relation to the moon?
23. If you lived on Mare Crisium (on the moon), you might expect to see a sunrise once every _____ earth days.
24. What factors of erosion on the earth are *not* found on the moon? Are there any factors of erosion which the earth and moon have in common?

Eglinton, Geoffrey, Maxwell, James R., and Pillinger, Colin T., The carbon chemistry of the moon. *Scientific American* **227** (4), 80–90 (1972).

Goldreich, Peter, Tides and the earth–moon system. *Scientific American* **226** (4), 42–52 (1972).

Levinson, A. A. (ed.), *Proceedings of the Apollo 11 lunar science conference,* 3 vols. New York: Pergamon Press, 1970.

Page, Thornton L., The Third Lunar Science Conference: I and II. *Sky and Telescope* **43** (3), 145–150; (4), 219–222 (1972).

Page, Thornton L., Notes on the Fourth Lunar Science Conference: I, II, and III. *Sky and Telescope* **45** (6), 355–358; **46** (1), 14–17; (2), 88–90 (1973).

THE
PLANETS

5

A binary system (earth-moon)

Moon Earth

While the astronomer is committed to the primary task of describing

objects in space as to their physical properties, appearance, and motion,

he is ever tantalized by the question of their origin and evolution — the

conditions governing their formation and the processes whereby they

change. What are the clues that will unlock these secrets? As we study

the nine planets, 32 moons, and numerous smaller objects that revolve

about the sun, let us test several theories which have been proposed

for their origin. One theory suggests that the planets were formed much

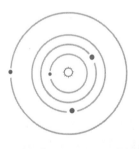

farther from the sun than their present distances indicate and later were captured at random by the sun; this theory may be referred to as the *random-capture theory*. Another theory proposes that the sun may once have passed very near to another star, and due to their mutual gravity a long streamer of material was pulled off as they passed. Then the planets formed from the material in the sun's streamer. This could be termed the *encounter theory*. Still another theory suggests that as the sun condensed out of a huge gas cloud, it rotated faster and faster, spinning off a flattened disk of material from which the planets formed. This theory of the common origin of the sun and its planets has had numerous variations in detail, one which suggested rings of material thrown off to form each planet, another suggesting that smaller condensations (knots) formed in the disk to make each planet. Such planets in the making are called *protoplanets*. Some observers have suggested that the protoplanet might sweep up new material as it moves. This is called *accretion*. Some very general observations concerning planets may assist us in judging certain of these theories as to their fitness for serious consideration.

THE PLANETS
IN GENERAL

All of the planets revolve about the sun in the same direction and along almost the same plane of orbit as the earth—that is to say their motions could quite accurately be shown on a flat piece of paper much like the right-hand flip pages starting on page 95. This one observation alone

Figure 5.1 (a) The orientation of planetary orbits that might be expected if they had been captured at random. (b) The actual disklike nature of planetary orbits.

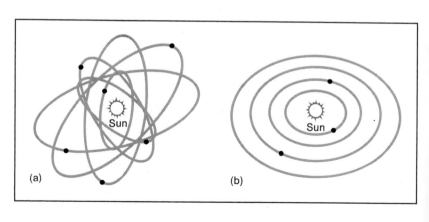

(a)   (b)

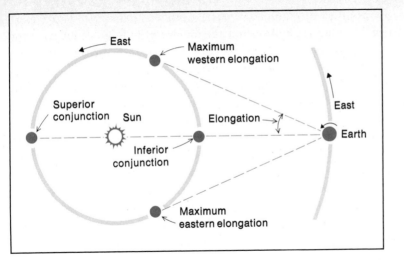

Figure 5.2 Configurations of the inferior planets.

does not seem to suggest a random-capture process, for had the planets been captured at random their motions would likely be oriented in various directions and on various planes (Figure 5.1). We speak of the direction of revolution being counterclockwise as viewed from the "north side" of the solar system, as determined by the side toward which the north pole of the earth points. Because the planets move in virtually the same flattened plane, we see these planets moving, against the background of stars, along almost the same path—that of the ecliptic. Thus the planets appear to move through the twelve constellations known as the signs of the zodiac, and it is natural to describe the position of a planet as being in one of those signs at any given time, for instance, "Saturn is in Gemini." It is also very instructive to describe the position of a planet as it relates to the sun's position. Let's see what configurations (arrangements) are possible by separating the planets into two groups—the *inferior planets* being those which have an orbit inside the orbit of the earth (Mercury and Venus), and the *superior planets* being those which have an orbit outside the orbit of the earth (Mars, Jupiter, Saturn, Uranus, Neptune, and Pluto).

CONFIGURATIONS OF
THE INFERIOR PLANETS

Whenever a planet is aligned with the sun so that both the planet and the sun may be viewed in the same direction from the earth, the planet is said to be in *conjunction* with the sun. In Figure 5.2 we note two

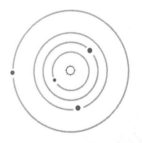

possible positions of alignment, one between the earth and the sun, called inferior conjunction, and one on the far side of the sun, called superior conjunction. During such configurations, the planet is lost to our view due to the glare of the sun. At any time we may describe the position of an inferior planet by the angle it makes with the sun as seen from the earth. This angle is called the *elongation* of the planet, and when this angle increases to its largest value during a given revolution, the planet is said to be at maximum elongation. Since this may occur at either of two different locations, we specify one as a western elongation, if the planet appears to the west of the sun in the sky, and the other as an eastern elongation, if the planet appears to the east of the sun in the sky. The times of maximum elongation are obviously good times to view Mercury and Venus. The right-hand flip pages beginning on page 95 will help you to visualize these various configurations as viewed from the earth.

CONFIGURATIONS OF
THE SUPERIOR PLANETS

When a superior planet is viewed from the earth, there is only one way it may align itself with the sun—a conjunction. A superior planet, however, may make any angle up to 180° with the sun as viewed from the earth, and when it is exactly 180° from the sun, a planet is said to be *at opposition*—on the opposite side of the earth from the sun (Figure 5.3). This is a particularly advantageous time to observe the planet, for it is in this configuration that the planet makes its closest approach to the earth, is fully illuminated by the sun, and so appears at its brightest. It is visible all night because it appears to rise at sunset and set at sunrise. Careful observation will also reveal its apparent retrograde motion against the background of stars, for the earth is actually passing that planet at this time.

These same configurations may be applied to the moon. Note that the moon is full when at opposition.

ROTATION
OF THE PLANETS

Seven of the planets rotate (spin on their axes) in a counterclockwise direction. The two planets which differ in their direction of rotation are Venus and Uranus—their clockwise rotation being referred to as *retrograde rotation,* because it is contrary to the more common direction.

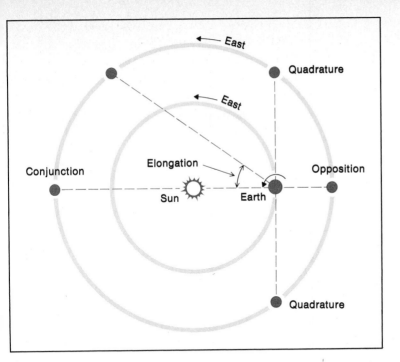

Figure 5.3 Configurations of the superior planets.

SPACING OF THE PLANETS

At first glance, the distances of the planets from the sun may appear
to have no pattern other than that the first four planets are relatively
closely spaced and the remaining planets are widely spaced; however,
in 1766 Johann Daniel Titius of Wittenberg, Germany, pointed out
a very interesting mathematical relationship. This relationship was later
published by Johann Elert Bode (pronounced *Bo'-da*) and is often
erroneously called Bode's law. In the last column of Table 5.1, you
will see the average spacing of the planets measured in astronomical
units (A.U.). These numbers may be closely approximated by the
process depicted in the first three columns. The first column of figures
begins with 0, then the numeral 3, with every number thereafter twice
the value of the one preceding it. A second column is formed by adding
4 to the corresponding entries in the first column. A third column is
then obtained by dividing each entry in the second column by 10; these
numbers (third column) very nearly express the distances to the planets
as measured in astronomical units. Although the discoveries of Uranus,
Neptune, and Pluto were to come later, the Bode-Titius relationship
is here extended to include these planets for our comparison. It is very

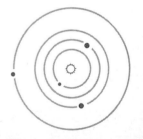

Table 5.1   The Bode-Titius relation

PLANET	FIRST COLUMN	SECOND COLUMN	BODE NUMBERS	ACTUAL DISTANCES (A.U.)
Mercury	0	4	0.4	0.39
Venus	3	7	0.7	0.72
Earth	6	10	1.0	1.0
Mars	12	16	1.6	1.5
	24	28	2.8	
Jupiter	48	52	5.2	5.2
Saturn	96	100	10.0	9.5
Uranus	192	196	19.6	19.2
Neptune	384	388	38.8	30.0
Pluto	768	772	77.2	40.0

evident that this relationship does not fit the observed distances to Neptune nor to Pluto; these are listed in the fourth column in the table.

It is also quite obvious that no single planet corresponds to the 2.8 A.U. figure in the Bode-Titius progression of numbers; as a result, it was thought that an unknown planet might be found at or near this distance. Using Kepler's third law, the period of such a planet was quickly computed and a search was launched for such an object. The search produced not only one object but, within a few years, many small objects had been found having approximately the correct period and orbital distance. These objects are called *asteroids,* and they will be discussed more fully in Chapter 6. Some observers have felt that because the Bode-Titius numbers so closely approximate the observed distances to the planets (except Neptune and Pluto), a force may have been operative to produce this spacing. Others have felt that the spacing is coincidental. It has also been suggested that Pluto originated as a moon of Neptune, their gravitational interaction having disturbed the original spacing of Neptune.

TERRESTRIALS OR JOVIANS

The planets fit very naturally into two categories: (1) those which are earthlike, called the *terrestrial* planets; (2) those which are Jupiterlike, called the *Jovian* planets. The terrestrial planets include, besides the earth,

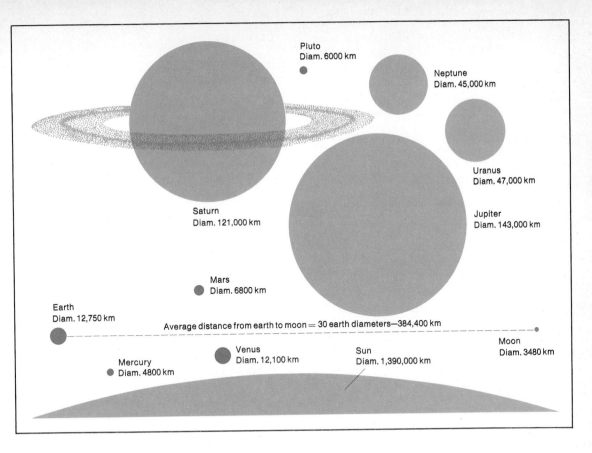

Figure 5.4 Relative size of the planets.

Mercury, Venus, and Mars. The Jovians include Jupiter, Saturn, Uranus, and Neptune. If Pluto were placed in either category it would be in the terrestrial group, but many prefer to consider it separately, more like a moon.

If the physical nature of each planet is visualized as it compares to the earth, the distinctions between the terrestrials and the Jovians will be quite obvious. Table 5.2 reveals that the terrestrials are small (earth size or smaller). They have low mass but high densities when compared to the Jovians. The higher densities of the terrestrials reflect their higher abundance of heavier elements and less significant atmospheres. With the exception of Venus, the atmospheres of the terrestrials are not even taken into consideration when computing their diameters and masses (Figure 5.4).

Why should the planets near the sun tend to have little or no atmosphere? The relatively high temperatures and low masses of these planets essentially tell the story. As energy was received from the sun, molecules of the atmosphere which may once have surrounded Mercury would have absorbed that energy, thereby increasing their velocity until

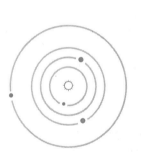

169

Table 5.2 Properties of the terrestrial planets as compared to those of the Jovians[a]

PLANET	DIAMETER	MASS	DENSITY	ROTATION	TEMPERATURE	ATMOSPHERE
Terrestrials						
Mercury	0.38	0.05	5.2	59^d	90° to 700°K (−183° to 427°C)	None
Venus	0.95	0.82	5.3	−243^d	250° to 770°K (−23° to 497°C)	Significant
Earth	1.00	1.00	5.5	23^{h}56^m	199° to 311°K (−74° to 38°C)	Thin
Mars	0.53	0.11	3.8	24^{h}37^m	145° to 293°K (−128° to 20°C)	Very thin
Jovians						
Jupiter	11.23	317.9	1.3	9^{h}50^m	134°K (−139°C)	Very significant
Saturn	9.41	95.2	0.7	10^{h}14^m	97°K (−176°C)	Very significant
Uranus	3.98	14.6	1.3	10^{h}49^m	55°K (−218°C)	Very significant
Neptune	3.88	17.2	1.7	15^{h}40^m	45°K (−228°C)	Very significant
Pluto	0.5	?	5	6^{d}9^h	35°K (−238°C)	?

[a]Diameters and masses are related to those of the earth (as 1). Densities are given in grams per cubic centimeter. Temperatures of the Jovian planets are not meant to be exact but to show a trend.

they literally got going so fast that the gravitational pull of the planet could no longer hold them. They would then have escaped into space. The velocity of escape, for each planet, is shown in Appendix 6 (page 428), and it is clear that some of the molecules which composed the atmospheres of the terrestrials could have been heated by the sun to that escape velocity. The less massive elements such as hydrogen and helium would be most easily accelerated to the escape velocity, so while these elements are very abundant in the universe, today only traces exist in the atmospheres of the terrestrial planets.

The solid (crusty) nature of the terrestrial surfaces contrast with the uncertain nature of the Jovian surface. The Jovians might be characterized as balls of gas with a liquid and/or solid core beneath a very deep atmosphere. The Jovian atmospheres are believed to be mainly composed of hydrogen with lesser amounts of helium. These planets are able to retain the lighter atoms because of their large surface gravity (high mass) and cool temperatures. Let us now consider some of the distinctive characteristics of each planet.*

*You will find the physical properties and motions of the planets and their moons summarized in Appendixes 5, 6, and 7. Not all of these properties will be detailed in the following text. Therefore, these Appendixes should be read as an integral part of this chapter.

MERCURY

Mercury is the most elusive of all the planets that can be seen with the naked eye. It sometimes appears as a morning object, rising just before sunrise, and at other times as an evening object, setting just after sunset. This cycle repeats itself three times during the year. Ancient observers did not realize that they were seeing the same object alternately in the morning and evening. The Greeks named the planet *Mercury* when it appeared in the evening and *Apollo* when it appeared in the morning. Mercury's elusiveness is explained by the fact that it revolves around the sun at an average distance of only 58 million kilometers, or 0.4 A.U., less than half the orbital radius of the earth. As a consequence, it never appears more than 28° from the sun. Since the earth rotates at the rate of 15°/hr, Mercury appears to rise no more than 2 hr before the sun when it is a morning object and appears to set no more than 2 hr after the sun when it is an evening object.

The plane in which Mercury travels is inclined 7° to the ecliptic plane, therefore the planet may appear several degrees above the ecliptic at some times and several degrees below it at others. Mercury's orbit has an eccentricity of 0.206, the second most eccentric orbit in the solar system. This eccentricity is shown in Figure 5.5, which indicates that Mercury's distance from the sun varies between 69 million kilometers at *aphelion* (its most distant point) and 46 million kilometers at *perihelion* (its nearest point). Applying Kepler's law of equal areas in equal time

Figure 5.5 Mercury's orbital speeds and distances.

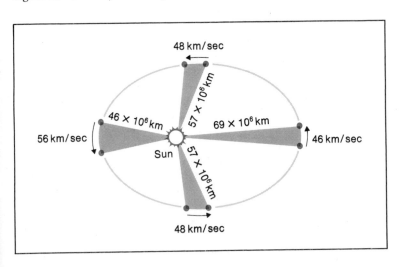

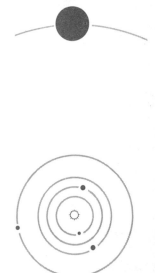

to a planet with such an eccentric orbit, we see a wide range of orbital speeds. At aphelion, Mercury travels at a speed of 46 km/sec; at perihelion, its speed increases to 56 km/sec. Mercury's average speed in orbit is 48 km/sec. A careful study of Figure 5.5 will help you develop a feeling for the motion of this planet and all planets in general. Each successive planet you will study will be farther from the sun and will have successively slower speeds.

The sidereal period of revolution for Mercury is 87.96 days, the time needed for one exact revolution (360°), measured by using the stars as a reference. However, we view the planets from a moving platform, the earth. Observationally speaking, a more meaningful period is known as the *synodic period* of a planet, the time needed for it to move from any given configuration, for example, inferior conjunction, back to the same configuration, as seen from a moving earth. For Mercury, this synodic period is 116 days. Suppose that we begin counting time when Mercury and the earth are in position A in Figure 5.6, an inferior conjunction. Points B, C, and D show the corresponding positions of the planets after 44, 88, and 116 days, respectively. After 116 days, Mercury is again at inferior conjunction as viewed from the earth. The flip pages beginning on page 95 reveal this 116-day synodic period of Mercury.

One of the exciting discoveries of the decade came in early 1965, when R. B. Dyce and G. H. Pettengil, using the 304-m (1000-ft) Arecibo antenna (see Figure 2.51), succeeded in bouncing radar signals off the surface of Mercury. The reflected signals, although very weak, told these researchers that the planet rotates in a period of approximately 59 days. This came as quite a shock, for in 1890 the Italian astronomer Giovanni Schiaparelli had announced an 88-day rotation, and this period had apparently been confirmed by almost every visual observation made from that date until the year 1965. This new discovery was confirmed and refined by subsequent observations, yielding a figure of 58.64 days—almost exactly two-thirds of the revolutionary period

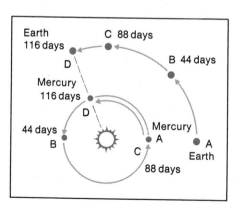

Figure 5.6 The synodic period of Mercury.

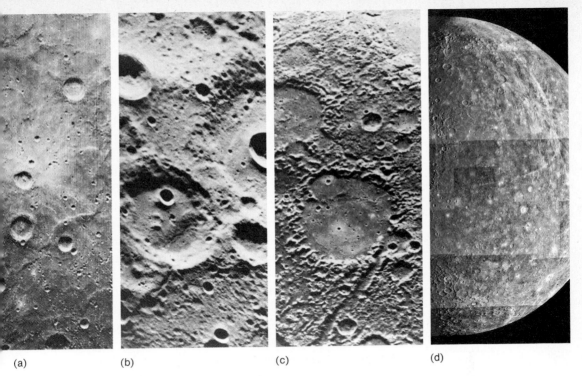

(a)   (b)   (c)   (d)

Figure 5.7 (a) A dark, smooth, relatively uncratered area on Mercury which resembles certain areas on the moon—lava flows being suggested. The largest craters shown are approximately 35 km in diameter. (b) Several fresh (sharp-rimmed) craters are seen in older basins. (c) A heavily cratered area of Mercury, showing many low, hill-like structures. The large valley at the bottom is approximately 100 km long. (d) A photomosaic of Mercury, constructed from 18 photos, taken 6 hr after Mariner 10 flew past the planet on March 29, 1974. Note the distinct bright rayed craters in the upper-right-hand portion of the photograph. (NASA–JPL)

of the planet. This means that for every two revolutions of Mercury ($2 \times 87.96 = 175.92$), the planet makes three rotations ($3 \times 58.64 = 175.92$), and the combined effect of these two motions produces a sunrise every 176 earth days. Recalling how tidal action synchronized the rotation and the revolution of the moon with respect to the earth, we see a similar resonance here in that Mercury points first one face and then the opposite face toward the sun on successive times of *perihelion passage* (times when the planet makes its closest approach to the sun).

On March 29, 1974, Mariner 10 flew within 700 km of Mercury and for the first time revealed its densely cratered surface (see the photograph on page 163 and Figure 5.7). At first glance, Mercury resembles the moon in that it has large, relatively smooth areas somewhat like the maria of the moon, and it has a variety of crater forms

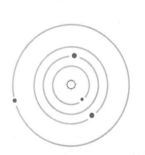

ranging from those which appear to be very old with rounded rims to those which appear very young with sharp rims. We see some deeper craters with central peaks and large shallow ones with evidence of repeated impacting within their basins.

Based upon measurement using the infrared radiometer on board Mariner 10, the surface temperature has a high of from 500°K to 700°K, depending upon the planet's distance from the sun. A drastic drop to 150°K was noted as the spacecraft began to traverse the shadowed portion. Best estimates of the coldest temperature are as low as 90°K, thus giving a variation of 610°K between the hottest and coldest points. These observations are as expected for a planet close to the sun, with virtually no atmosphere to provide an insulating "blanket." Furthermore, due to the combined rotation and revolution rates, a point on Mercury's equator experiences 88 earth days of heating and then 88 earth days of cooling.

The discovery by Mariner 10 which was least expected was the existence of a magnetic field strong enough to deflect the solar wind rather effectively. One does not usually associate a magnetic field with such a slowly turning planet, and while Mercury's magnetic field strength at the equator is only $\frac{1}{150}$ that of the earth, it provides a definite bow shock and prevents particles from the sun from impinging directly on the surface of the planet.

A very tenuous atmosphere was found, with helium positively identified, and the airglow on the dark side suggests elements like argon, neon, and xenon. Consistent with a very thin atmosphere is a low *albedo*—the percentage of reflected light. Like the moon, Mercury reflects only 7 percent of the sunlight which falls on it.

VENUS

Even before Galileo turned his telescope toward Venus to see it go through phases like the moon (Figure 5.8), man had been intrigued by this bright object, which he often saw in the western sky just after sunset and thus called the "evening star." Some men recognized this planet to be the same object that appeared alternately in the eastern (morning) sky, for as Venus swings around the sun in an orbit not much smaller than the earth's it first appears on one side of the sun and then on the other (Figure 5.9). Because the earth is also revolving, this synodic cycle requires approximately 19.5 months (584 days).

Early observations revealed Venus to be very nearly a twin of the earth in terms of its diameter and mass and therefore its density. Yet Venus is really vastly different than the earth. Its cloud cover is so dense that no person has ever seen its surface. In fact, it is the only other

Figure 5.8 The phases of Venus. (Lowell Observatory)

Figure 5.9 The phases of Venus.

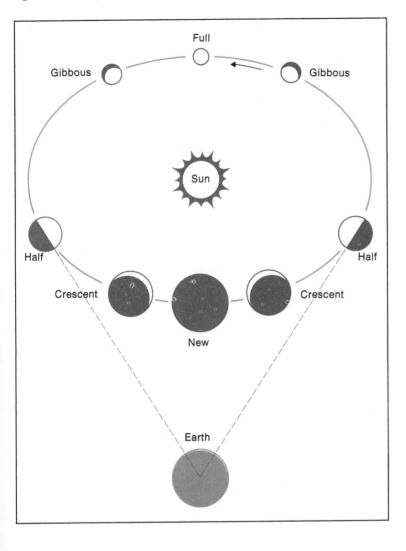

terrestrial planet with any significant atmosphere. Astronomers who have tried to measure the temperature of the planet by analysis of the light it reflects have gotten only a reading for the top of the clouds (approximately 0°C), for it is at that level that the light is reflected. As radio astronomy came into its own in the 1950s, radiation from nearer the surface could be measured in radio wavelengths, and temperatures on the order of 600°K (327°C) were recorded. With this discovery, our concept of Venus changed to one of a desert hot enough to melt lead.

In 1962, using the Goldstone antenna (see Figure 2.50), Roland Carpenter and Richard Goldstein succeeded in bouncing radar signals off this planet and, to everyone's amazement, they discovered that Venus rotates backwards (clockwise) in a period of 243.16 days. Prior to this time, speculation centered around a period of 225 days—synchronized with Venus's revolution. The radar observations were accomplished by noting the Doppler shift due to rotation. A certain wavelength was sent to the planet and a variety of wavelengths returned, for those that were reflected from the approaching limb (edge) were shortened and those which were reflected from the receding limb were lengthened. Using the amounts by which the wavelengths were changed, it was possible to compute the planet's velocity of rotation, hence its period. If you could live on this planet and you were still dividing time into earth days, Venus's retrograde rotation in 243.16 days and its direct revolution in 225 days would produce a sunrise in the west every 117 earth days. An interesting kind of resonance occurs between Venus and the earth. At each occasion of an inferior conjunction, Venus presents the same face toward the earth, even though it has rotated five times with relation to the sun. While the cause of this resonance is not fully understood, a tidal effect somewhat like that which synchronized the rotation and revolution of the moon (with respect to the earth) is suspected.

Radar astronomers are also unfolding for the first time a "picture" of the surface features of Venus. Of course, radio waves do not produce a photograph directly, yet the returning signals may be interpreted to produce a topographic map which is as instructive as a photograph. In Figure 5.10, note the strong suggestion of craterlike structures on Venus as recorded by these radio (radar) signals which penetrated the clouds and were reflected from the solid surface of the planet. The largest craterlike feature is 160 km in diameter and 400 m deep.

Still another very significant phase in the study of Venus was begun in 1962 with the first successful space probe sent to survey the planet at close range. This probe, called Mariner 2, typified the fly-by approach the United States would take in the study of Venus. In contrast, the USSR has set as a goal the landing of probes on the planet's surface.

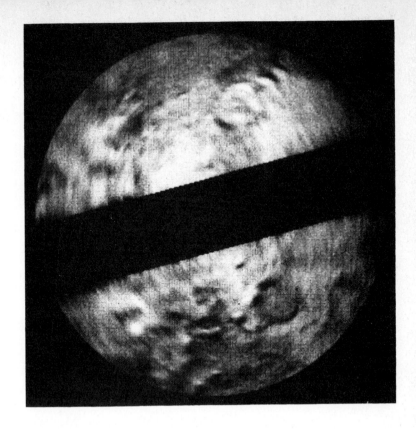

Figure 5.10 Radar signals that penetrated the clouds of Venus and were reflected by its crusty surface reveal the multitude of craters which mark its equatorial region. The largest is 160 km across and approximately 500 m deep. (JPL–NASA)

The first Soviet spacecraft are believed to have been crushed by tremendous atmospheric forces and their communications ceased 24 km before they reached the surface. That problem was overcome, however, and later attempts have produced useful communications for as long as 50 minutes after the craft landed on the surface. Both the fly-by and the landing approaches have been equally effective in supplying data on the characteristics of Venus and have complemented each other in confirming various findings. A synthesis of all recent observations reveals an atmosphere composed of approximately 95 percent carbon dioxide (CO_2), small percentages of water vapor (H_2O), hydrogen (H), helium (He), carbon (C), oxygen (O), hydrochloric acid (HCl), hydrofluoric acid (HF), sulfuric acid (H_2SO_4), and ammonia (NH_3). The atmospheric pressure at the surface is approximately 90 times that on earth, a pressure equivalent to that which would be experienced by a diver 823 m beneath the surface of the ocean.* A very weak magnetic field has been detected, but this field is evidently not of sufficient

*This suggests a very interesting phenomenon that would occur in the atmosphere of Venus if it were optically clear. The atmosphere would refract light to such a degree that it would be possible for a beam of light to travel entirely around the planet. One can imagine the distortion of familiar objects that would result. Under ideal conditions, it might even be possible to see the back of your own head while looking straight forward.

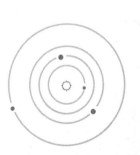

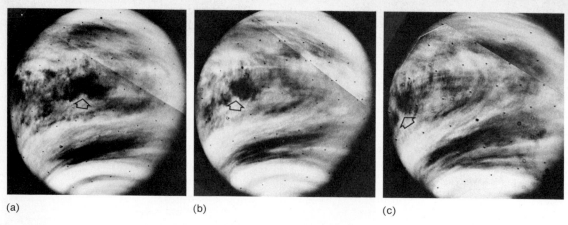

(a)   (b)   (c)

Figure 5.11 A series of ultraviolet photographs of Venus, taken
two days after Mariner 10 flew past the planet on February 5,
1974, during a 14-hr period, showing the rapid rotation rate of
the upper cloud deck. The feature indicated by the arrows is about
100 km across.

strength to support Van Allen belts. There is some indication of a
shallow ionosphere. Winds as high as 160 km/hr have been reported
at an elevation of 45 km, lessening to 16 km/hr at an elevation of
10 km.

A United States probe, Mariner 10, which passed within 6000 km
of Venus in February 1974, confirmed a very distinct pattern of atmospheric currents when it photographed the planet in ultraviolet light.
In fact, these upper clouds move at a very high rate of speed, rotating
in a retrograde motion in a period of 4 earth days. The equatorial
portion of these carbon monoxide clouds seems to lead the way, spiraling
off toward each pole (Figure 5.11).

Mariner 10 measured temperatures throughout the Venusian
atmosphere and found a range of from $250°K$ ($-23°C$) at the cloud
tops to $773°K$ ($500°C$) on the surface. There were at least four inversion
layers—that is, layers in which the warming trend reversed itself over
a distance of several kilometers. Why should the temperature on the
surface of Venus be several hundred degrees hotter than would be
expected based on its distance from the sun, and why should Venus
have such a dense atmosphere when the other terrestrial planets are
almost devoid of any atmosphere at all? The high surface temperature
is attributed to the presence in the planet's atmosphere of CO_2 and H_2O,
which together create a "greenhouse effect."

You have probably experienced the heating effect that occurs inside
an automobile on a sunny day when the windows are closed. The sun's
rays enter the car through the windows, are absorbed by the interior,
and then reemitted at a longer wavelength. This light and heat of longer

178

wavelength is not transmitted out through the windows as readily as the shorter wavelengths are taken in, and a buildup of heat results. This is the same effect that the florist uses to maintain a higher temperature inside his greenhouse.

Even though the earth's atmosphere contains only trace amounts of CO_2 and H_2O, they serve to raise the surface temperature of the earth by at least 45 °C. The very high percentage of CO_2 in the Venusian atmosphere absorbs most of the infrared energy radiated from that planet's surface, and while it is true that any planet must eventually reradiate all of the sun's energy that falls on it, the absorption by CO_2 causes the surface and lower atmosphere to be heated before the outflow of energy balances the inflow.

But why does such a very dense CO_2 atmosphere exist on a planet that is virtually the twin of the earth in size and only slightly closer to the sun? If we assume that in the case of the terrestrial planets any atmosphere that was present at the time of planetary formation would have been driven off by solar radiation, then only as outgassing of other elements occurred (perhaps from volcanoes) did a new atmosphere build up. Carbon dioxide is known to be released by volcanic action. The same processes may have occurred on Venus as on the earth, but Venus retained a much higher concentration of CO_2. Perhaps the earth once released an equivalent supply of CO_2 and most of it was absorbed by its rocky crust. Within surface rocks, the CO_2 might have combined chemically with calcium (Ca) and oxygen to form calcium carbonate ($CaCO_3$), a basic compound of much of the earth's present surface material. If this is true, then why did the CO_2 in Venus's atmosphere not also combine with its surface material? The answer may lie in the fact that since Venus is closer to the sun, the planet probably had a slightly higher original temperature than the earth. This higher temperature might have slowed down the absorption process.

Today, life itself plays a vital role in maintaining a rather constant low CO_2 level in the earth's atmosphere. Plants, through the process of photosynthesis, convert CO_2 to oxygen. Marine organisms remove CO_2 from the ocean waters, allowing these waters to absorb more from the air above. Even a slight change in the rate at which CO_2 is used by living organisms might change the earth's ability to support life. A slight increase in CO_2 content in the atmosphere would increase the greenhouse effect and raise the temperature of the earth accordingly. If such a process got out of hand, conditions on earth might one day resemble those on Venus. On the other hand, we might speculate as to the possibility of changing the Venusian atmosphere to resemble that of our own planet. It is difficult to visualize any familiar form of life existing on that superheated surface at present. However, the Venusian atmosphere does not lack the essential elements for photosynthesis—

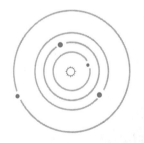

light, water vapor, and CO_2. Carl Sagan, one of the foremost experts on Venus, has suggested a possible habitat for life might be found in the clouds of Venus. Were certain microorganisms introduced there capable of withstanding high temperatures, such organisms could adapt and reproduce, and their very existence might change the entire nature of the planet's atmosphere. Through the process of photosynthesis, they would extract H_2O and CO_2 from the clouds and would produce oxygen and organic (carbon-containing) compounds. The removal of CO_2 and water vapor would tend to lessen the greenhouse effect, causing a gradual cooling of the surface. As the temperature declined, water vapor would tend to liquefy on the surface, resulting in a clearer atmosphere rich in oxygen and perhaps more suitable for higher forms of life. While this may all be a bit of fantasy, there are plausible elements in it.

Surely life survives on the earth as a result of a very delicate balance of factors—the range of temperature, composition of the soil, waters, and air, and by-products of the processes of life itself.

EARTH

In Chapter 3 we studied our own planet primarily from the point of view of an observer on the earth itself. Before proceeding to the planet Mars and to the question of the existence of life on that planet, let us pose the following question: If an intelligent form of life existed on Mars and possessed telescopes like ours, could this intelligence recognize any life form on the earth? What would there be about the earth that could furnish a clue? Even under ideal conditions, it is unlikely that Martian astronomers would be able to recognize any object or form less than 80 km in its smallest dimension. Even when clear skies prevailed on the earth, only large areas such as the oceans, continents, large lakes, polar caps—and perhaps color variations occurring between the plains and the mountainous regions—might be detected. No evidence of freeways, waterways, cities, or farms would be distinguishable. Photos taken of the earth from the proximity of the moon, only about 0.4 million kilometers away, reveal merely the larger continental masses. Mars, at its closest approach to earth, is still 56 million kilometers away.

MARS

More than any other planet, Mars seems to fire man's imagination. Many observers have speculated that some form of life, perhaps as intelligent as our own, might exist on this planet—an idea perhaps due in part to the similarity of Mars to the earth, for Mars does exhibit

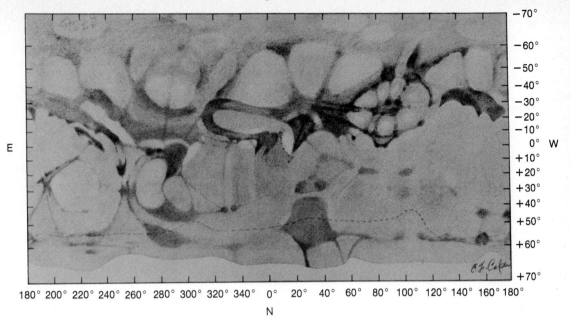

S

—70°
—60°
—50°
—40°
—30°
—20°
—10°
0° W
+10°
+20°
+30°
+40°
+50°
+60°
+70°

E

180° 200° 220° 240° 260° 280° 300° 320° 340° 0° 20° 40° 60° 80° 100° 120° 140° 160° 180°

N

Figure 5.12 A high-resolution photovisual map of Mars showing the seasonal aspects of late Martian summer, 1969. The excellent quality allowed surface details of less than 30 km to be resolved. This map was produced from measurements of 20 photographs, 13 visual drawings, and 15 telescopic micrometer observations. South is at the top as seen in a telescope. (C. Capen, JPL–Table Mountain Observatory)

polar caps and certain seasonal color variations similar to those we find on earth. As early as 1877, Giovanni Schiaparelli, director of the Milan Observatory, asserted that he had seen a network of fine straight lines that seemed to interconnect larger features on the Martian surface. Percival Lowell, an American astronomer, suggested that these lines represented canals, actual waterways built by Martian inhabitants to irrigate their crops and to transport their goods on barges. While this notion of intelligent life on Mars was long accepted by science-fiction writers, we must now look at the evidence based on recent detailed, close-up observations of this planet if we are to give scientific consideration to this matter.

Prior to 1965, man's only observations of Mars were made from earth-based observatories. Because of the obscuring effect of the earth's atmosphere, details as to the Martian surface features, atmospheric composition, magnetic field, and the like, were very sketchy. Figure 5.12 represents the results of hundreds of hours spent by astronomers at the eyepieces of telescopes, sketching areas of momentary clearing.

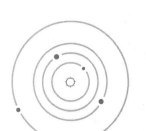

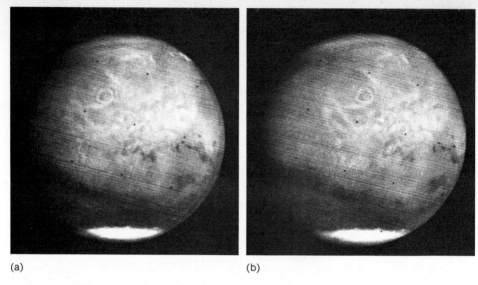

(a)   (b)

Figure 5.13 Mariner 7 photographs of Mars, frames 73 and 74, showing the bright southern cap and the circle of Nix Olympica. The two frames were taken 47 min apart, showing the rotations of the planet. (JPL–NASA)

Anticipating the close approach of Mars in 1965 (at the time of opposition), scientists prepared a probe that would fly within 9600 km of the planet, photograph its surface, and relay these photos, together with other information, to the earth. The photographs which this probe (Mariner 4) returned to earth were far superior to any produced by earth-based telescopes.

Spurred by this success, scientists refined their equipment and prepared for another opposition of Mars in 1969, when the planet passed within 72 million kilometers of the earth (Figure 5.13). In order to conserve rocket fuel, it was thought best to wait for such opportunities of close approach. Because of the combined motion of the earth and Mars, such oppositions occur only at 26-month intervals—the *synodic period*. Owing to the eccentricity of the two orbits, some approaches are much closer than others, as may be seen in Figure 5.14. Although much was learned during the Mariner 6 and 7 flights in 1969, a more extensive period of observation was planned for the 1971 opposition.

In November 1971, Mariner 9 became the first man-made satellite to orbit another planet. For almost one year, this spacecraft radioed back to earth a continual flow of photos and data about Mars, information which significantly changed man's concept of that planet. Mariner 9's cameras first revealed only a huge dust storm obscuring most of the surface features of the planet, but as the storm subsided four large volcanic mountains emerged through the dust. As the Martian atmos-

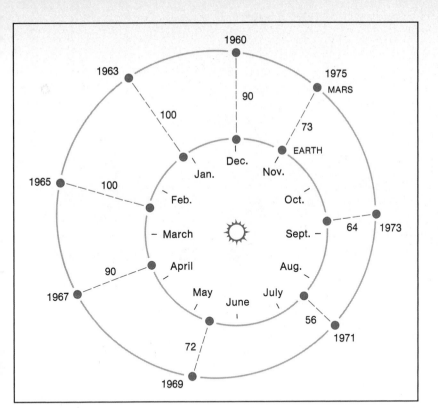

Figure 5.14 Mars–earth oppositions, with distance in millions of kilometers shown by numbers next to the dashed lines.

Figure 5.15 Mariner 9 photo of Nix Olympica, the Martian volcanic mountain: longitude 133, latitude +18°. (JPL–NASA)

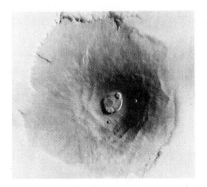

phere cleared, the full extent of the largest volcano, Nix Olympica, was revealed—600 km across at the base and approximately 23 km high, far larger than any mountain on the earth (Figure 5.15). Three additional volcanoes of major proportions are seen in the same vicinity, indicating a region on the planet which has been active more recently

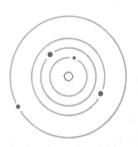

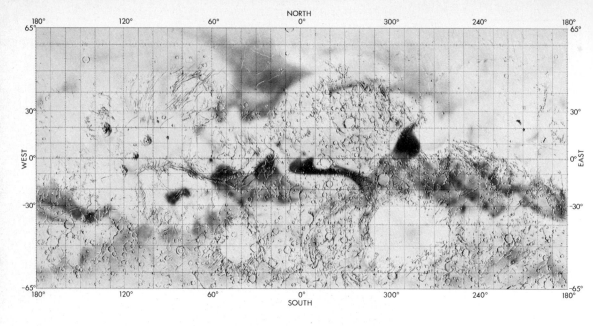

Figure 5.16 A shaded relief map of the entire equatorial region of Mars, based upon the photographic survey by Mariner 10. The principle features include: volcanoes, craters, basins and smooth mantled areas. (JPL–NASA)

Figure 5.17 The Coprates region of the great chasm of Mars, based on Mariner 9 photographs together with large-scale albedo markings as seen from earth. (Prepared by James Roth and Dr. G. de Voucouleurs for JPL–NASA)

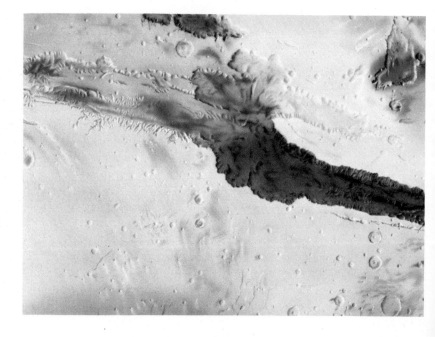

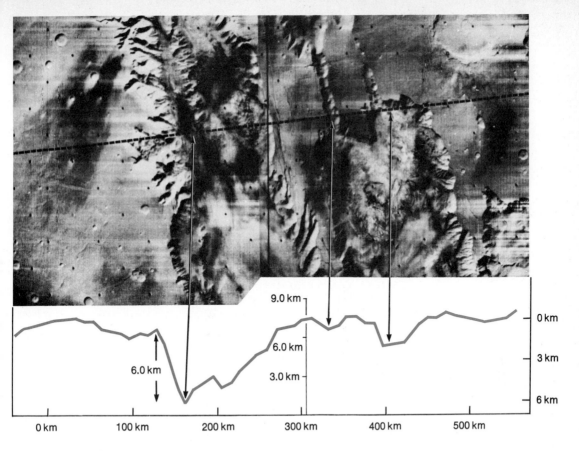

Figure 5.18 A close-up and profile of a portion of the Coprates region centered on longitude 75°, latitude −10°. (JPL–NASA)

than the cratered portions. If the lava-type material which poured forth to produce these volcanoes is similar to that on earth, large amounts of water would have been released into the Martian atmosphere. Thus, these volcanoes may not only reveal something of the molten nature of at least a portion of the planet but may also have a bearing on the question of life on Mars. Volcanic action on earth is often associated with the colliding of crustal plates, one turning under the other (see page 104), thus it is reasonable to ask if this planet also has crustal plates which move.

A second major surface feature is the huge chasm which stretches eastward from the volcanic region for a distance of 4000 km, averaging 100 km wide and having a depth of over 6 km in several places (Figure 5.16). Such a chasm, if superimposed upon the earth, would stretch across the entire United States. The discovery of this huge chasm, together with the details revealed by the close-up views shown in Figures 5.17 and 5.18, have raised many questions as to the process of its formation. The general form of the chasm suggests subsidence

185

of the Martian soil due to faulting. Note the fingerlike pit chains in the right-hand portion of Figure 5.18. These probably represent the beginning stages of a larger chasm that will develop under continued subsidence. The scalloped edges associated with deeper portions of the chasm suggest the enlargement of such pits. On the other hand, the tributarylike complex shown in the upper-left-hand portion of Figure 5.18 seems to suggest erosion due to fluid action, and this immediately raises the question of the existence of water on Mars. It is a well-established fact that liquid water cannot persist on the surface of the planet under its present lack of atmosphere. The atmospheric pressure on the surface of Mars is only $\frac{1}{100}$ of that on earth. Under such low pressure, surface water would vaporize in all but the coldest parts of the planet. For liquid water to have persisted long enough to erode a canyon or produce a river bed, a much denser atmosphere must have once been present.

An alternate to liquid water on the surface of the planet is water in a frozen state beneath the surface. The subsidence of soil may have exposed this frozen water, resulting in evaporation and/or seepage, which in turn loosened material to produce the tributarylike structure. Some geologists believe that the side canyons of the Grand Canyon of Arizona were formed as a result of seepage of ground water.

A more convincing example of water erosion on Mars is shown

Figure 5.19 The Amazonis channel, thought to have been formed by running water. The section shown is approximately 100 km long, and the flow direction is thought to be toward the north (upper right). (JPL–NASA)

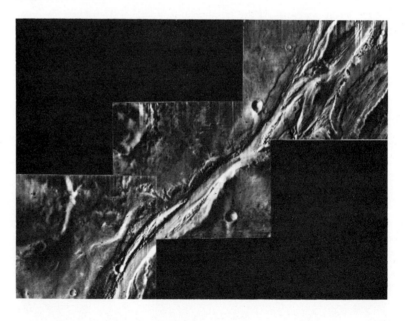

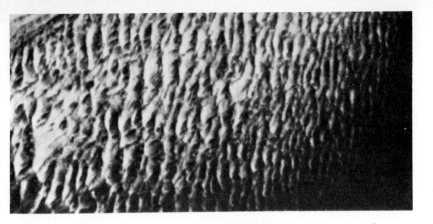

Figure 5.20 A dunelike structure which strongly suggests the influence of winds on Mars. (JPL–NASA)

in Figure 5.19, the Amazonis channel. Whereas the bottom of the great chasm does not fall off in one direction, the Amazonis channel does appear to grade downward to allow a flow from south to north. Furthermore the "bars" and braiding of the channel in its northerly portion are very typical of river beds on earth. The entire Amazonis channel is 350 km long and 100 km wide (at its widest), thus requiring a river the size of the Amazon (after which it was named) to produce such a feature.

Wind is another erosion factor, producing dust storms that often obscure the surface features of Mars; however, this is thought to be a superficial phenomenon involving only a very thin layer of material. Figure 5.20 suggests that the wind does move a significant amount of material. The dunelike structure shown here is found in one of the large craters located at longitude 331° and latitude −47.5°, and it measures approximately 30 km by 60 km. Individual ridges are about 1 to 2 km apart.

There is a marked contrast between the cratered portion of Mars and its smooth basins and plains. The relief map of Mars (see Figure 5.16) shows that cratering is not symmetrical but rather is concentrated in certain areas. In fact, we can say that the portion of the planet near 0° longitude is dominated by craters and two large basins, whereas the portion around 180° longitude is characterized by volcanoes and flat plains, with less distinct cratering. Surely there are clues to the planet's history in its surface?

Two other major surface features are the Martian polar caps. The temperature of the planet is known to range between 293°K (20°C) directly under the sun to 145°K (−128°C) near the poles. However, like the earth, Mars experiences seasonal changes due to the tilt of its

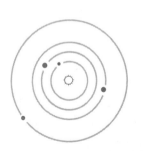

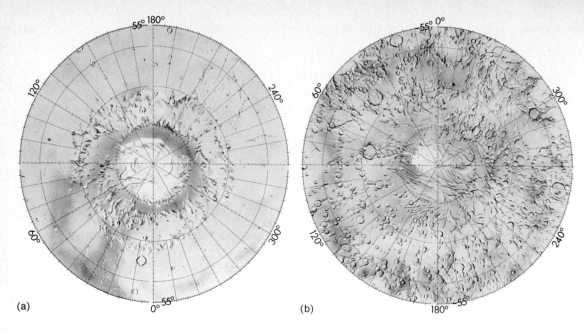

Figure 5.21 The polar regions of Mars: (a) northern region, October 12, 1972; (b) southern region, February 28, 1972. Note the distinctively different pattern of cratering in the two regions. (JPL–NASA)

axis (25°) and its revolution (1.88 year). As each pole experiences its seasonal warming, the cap *sublimates* (turns from a solid directly into a gaseous state). This sublimation takes place with only a slight warming above the 145°K level, an indicator that the polar caps are not ice (frozen water), but rather a compound that sublimates at 150°K, namely, frozen carbon dioxide (known commercially as "Dry Ice"). This fact has been confirmed by analysis of the reflected sunlight spectroscopically. Because the polar caps shrink and grow rather quickly, they are thought to be more like thin layers of carbon dioxide frost. There is the possibility that beneath this layer of CO_2 frost is a layer of H_2O ice, for the caps do not disappear completely. Water ice would remain frozen when the warming occurs because even then the temperature is about −73°C at the poles. The system of parallel ridges which surround the poles (Figure 5.21) may reveal the extent to which water ice has persisted in successive Martian summers. Note also the distinct difference in cratering of north and south polar regions.

The Mariner space probes have supplied the astronomer and geologist with vast quantities of new data concerning Mars, but there is still no conclusive evidence, either pro or con, regarding the existence of life on that planet. We are certain that no canals exist, nor is there any evidence of intelligent life. Certain forms of life would not be

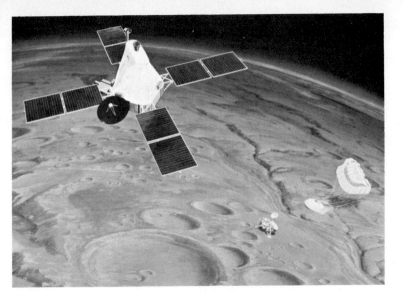

Figure 5.22 The proposed 1976 Mars lander and orbiter.
(JPL–NASA)

Figure 5.23 (a) Phobos and (b) Deimos ("Fear" and "Terror"),
the Martian moons, as seen by Mariner 9. (JPL–NASA)

(a)   (b)

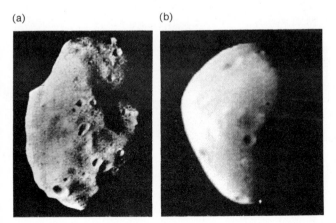

detected on the scale of our observations, however, and so we must
wait for an answer until early 1976, when we hope to land a craft
that will sample the Martian "soil" and analyze its composition (Figure
5.22). If living things ever existed there, a remnant of organic molecules
should remain.

We have known since 1877 that Mars has two natural satellites,
Phobos and Deimos, but not until Mariner 9 turned its video eye their
way did we have any idea of their appearance (Figure 5.23). Somewhat

irregular in shape, they both look like severely pockmarked boulders. Having no atmosphere, they have no protection from impact by other objects. The dimensions of Phobos are approximately 23 km by 15 km; of Deimos, 24 km by 20 km.

JUPITER

Jupiter marks a distinct break with the terrestrial planets in terms of its physical characteristics, and Saturn, Uranus, and Neptune follow suit. These planets are of particular interest to the astronomer since they may resemble much more closely the primordial cloud from which they were formed and thereby may help reveal the origin and early evolution of the solar system. At their greater distances, the energy of the sun has little effect in changing their atmospheres. As the Pioneer 10 spacecraft passed Jupiter at a distance of 130,000 km on December 3, 1973 (Figure 5.24), its spectrometers confirmed for the first time the presence

Figure 5.24 Jupiter, its Great Red Spot at left, and the shadow of its moon Io, as seen by Pioneer 10. North is at top. (NASA)

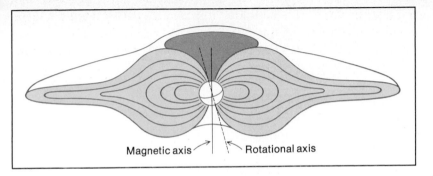

Magnetic axis — Rotational axis

Figure 5.25 The magnetic field of Jupiter as determined by the Pioneer 10 fly-by.

of helium (about 15 percent by volume) in the Jovian atmosphere. The main constituent is hydrogen (almost 85 percent by volume), with only traces of methane (CH_4), ammonia (NH_3), and perhaps other elements and compounds. The relatively high percentage of helium represents a fairly close correlation with the estimates of helium produced in the very early stage of the universe itself and with estimates of the helium content of young stars. In fact, some observers have suggested that Jupiter may be an aborted dwarf star, for it radiates two and one-half times as much thermal energy as it absorbs from the sun. What is the source of this surplus energy? Could there be a starlike process going on in the core of Jupiter? No, for even with its great mass, 318 times that of the earth, Jupiter could not create the high temperature and high pressure necessary to initiate the thermonuclear process characteristic of a star. However, it may generate thermal energy (heat) through continuing contraction. Whenever a body contracts, some of its gravitational energy is converted to thermal energy. This continuing contraction also suggests that Jupiter is in an early stage of evolution—it is evolving very slowly.

While the Pioneer 10 spacecraft was still 12 million kilometers from Jupiter, its sensors detected that the magnetic field of the planet was strong enough to deflect the solar wind (the outflow of charged particles from the sun). As the craft made its pass through the belts of high energy electrons and protons which were entrapped in the magnetic field, the instruments on board were saturated almost to their limit with this radiation—more than 100 times that which would be lethal to man. An integrated picture of Jupiter's magnetic field emerges, showing a total magnetic energy more than 250,000 times that of the earth. The field is tilted 15° with respect to the planet's axis of rotation and is highly flattened and dimpled in toward the poles (Figure 5.25).

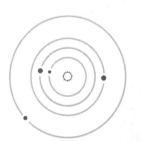

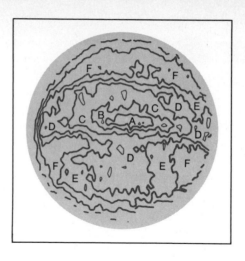

Figure 5.26 A temperature map of Jupiter constructed from infrared readings taken by Pioneer 10. Regions labeled A, B, C, D, E, and F correspond to temperatures of 125°, 124°, 123°, 121°, 119°, and 115°K, respectively.

Jupiter is enveloped by a thick layer of dense clouds that perpetually obscure any hint of a surface. While many models of the planet have been proposed, few have suggested any kind of a solid (crusty) surface directly beneath the clouds; rather, a gaseous nature is thought to prevail for a depth of at least 4000 km. With increasing depth, we also expect increasing pressure and density: thus, a substance, say, hydrogen, would change from the gaseous state to the liquid state with increasing depth; perhaps eventually there would be a solid core, but the dimensions of such layers are not known. Characteristics which have been measured directly are limited to pressure and temperature within the first few hundred kilometers. A map showing regions of equal cloud-top temperature is presented in Figure 5.26. You may note the typical banded appearance within this temperature distribution. (Compare these bands with the visible bands shown in Figure 5.24.) Some observers believe that the coloration of these bands may be due to the manner in which elements such as hydrogen, helium, argon, nitrogen, and sulfur form into various compounds, each one having its own different hue.

The Great Red Spot   The Great Red Spot, seen in Figure 5.24, has always been a mystery, varying in size and brilliance but always visible. Explanations regarding its nature and cause have ranged from a solid body floating in the Jovian atmosphere to a column of stagnant gases extending upward from some surface feature, yet its rate of rotation is not in agreement with any measured rotation rate of the planet itself. The very nature of Jupiter makes it difficult to specify its rate of rotation, for it does not rotate as a solid but has different periods of rotation; at the equator, a cloud top feature requires 9 hr

50 min 30.0 sec to rotate; at $\pm 10°$ latitude, 9 hr 55 min 40.6 sec; and when the rotation of the magnetic field is measured, a period of 9 hr 55 min 29.8 sec is found. The Great Red Spot may represent a mechanism whereby heat is exchanged from lower regions to the top of the atmosphere; its temperature has been measured 1 to 2°K cooler than surrounding areas. This may be interpreted as indicating a higher elevation above the clouds. Pioneer 10 measurements suggest that there is a general increase in atmospheric temperature from the top of the clouds (about 100°K) inward to a depth of several hundred kilometers where temperatures of 250°K are indicated.

The moons of Jupiter The 13 natural satellites of Jupiter fall into three very obvious categories. If you look at the listing of these moons in Appendix 7, you will notice that the first five are all within 2 million kilometers of the planet, and they orbit in direct motion very near the equatorial plane of the planet. The next four orbit in direct motion at a distance of approximately 12 million kilometers and have inclinations of 25 to 30°. The last four moons orbit in a retrograde direction at distances of 21 to 24 million kilometers and have highly inclined orbits. This suggests that the first five moons were formed from the same cloud of gas and dust as was Jupiter, their direction and plane of revolution reflecting the rotation of the original nebula. The remaining moons were probably captured, and their motions reflect the conditions under which this capture occurred. The four larger moons, called the *Galilean satellites* (after Galileo, who first observed them with the aid of his early telescope), can be easily viewed by the amateur with only a very modest telescope. Pioneer 10 sensed an ionosphere around Io and traces of sodium on its surface. In addition to Io, Europa, Ganymede, and Callisto are thought to be at least partially covered by ammonia frost, their temperature being below the freezing point of ammonia, in the range of 148°K ($-125°C$) to 110°K ($-163°C$). The infrared spectrograms of sunlight reflected from these moons reveal absorption bands characteristic of ammonia and sodium.

Pioneer 10 also measured the density of the four Galilean satellites and found a diminishing progression outward from Jupiter as follows: Io, 3.5 g/cm³; Europa, 3.0 g/cm³; Ganymede, 1.73 g/cm³, and Callisto, 1.48 g/cm³. Again this observation suggests the nature of the primordial nebula from which the planet and these four satellites probably formed—decreasing in density outward from center.

As Pioneer 10 passed Jupiter, the gravitational field of this planet produced a slingshot effect on the spacecraft, changing its trajectory by almost 90° and accelerating it on a new route that would bring it near to the planet Saturn.

SATURN

The most beautiful of all the planets, Saturn is second in size and mass and is the only planet with a system of rings (Figures 5.27 and 5.28). In December 1972, the first radar echo was received from Saturn by means of the 64-m Goldstone antenna. Richard Goldstein and George Morris pointed a 400-kilowatt beam toward the planet and after $2\frac{1}{4}$ hr the echo returned, revealing a much more highly reflective surface than had been expected. The signal was not reflected effectively by the planet proper, confirming its gaseous state, but rather the signal was reflected with about 60 percent efficiency from the rings. Whereas the rings were previously thought to be ice crystals, they are now interpreted as being rough solid lumps 1 m or larger in diameter. The solid shapes may be overlaid with frozen gases. When we view the rings of Saturn in a telescope they appear as solid disks, but different parts of the rings have vastly different Doppler shifts, thus confirming that they are composed of many separate bodies. They might be more accurately described as being composed of millions of small moons, each orbiting the planet in the manner predicted by Kepler's laws, the inner particles orbiting the planet in less than 4 hr, the outer ones requiring 14 hr. In fact these particles may be fragments of one or more moons that once orbited Saturn. It is known that the rings lie entirely within a certain distance from the planet called the *Roche limit*. Typically, within

Figure 5.27 Saturn, as photographed with the 2.6-m Mount Wilson telescope. (Hale Observatories)

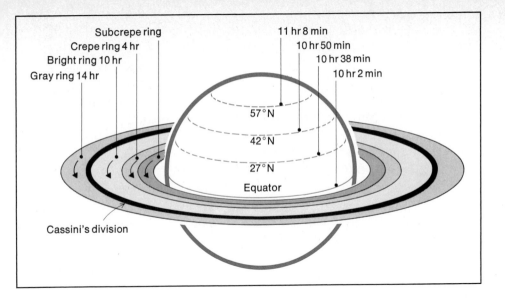

Figure 5.28 The rotation periods of the clouds of Saturn at various latitudes and of selected particles in the rings.

this radius, a moon would experience a tidal gravitational force so much greater than its own gravitational force that it would literally be torn to pieces.

While it is not readily apparent in photographs, four subdivisions of the rings have been identified as the *subcrepe ring* (adjoining the planet), the *crepe ring*, the *bright ring*, and the *gray ring* (Figure 5.28). Between the bright and gray rings, a gap exists, called Cassini's division, within which few particles move. The rings may appear bright or dim depending upon such factors as the density to which the ring is populated with particles, the size, composition, and surface of these particles, and the frostlike covering.

At the time of writing, Pioneer 10 is headed for Saturn, and shortly after this book goes to press, the spacecraft will have sensed and relayed to waiting observers more information about this planet than has been gathered in the more than 350 years since Galileo first recognized its beautiful ringed form. Nevertheless, astronomers have known certain fundamental physical characteristics for some time. These are summarized in Table 5.2 and in Appendixes 5 and 6. These characteristics, together with our present knowledge of Jupiter, permits us to construct a model of Saturn. Its density is only one-half that of Jupiter; this suggests a composition of light elements such as hydrogen and helium (however, helium has not been identified spectroscopically). Like Jupiter, Saturn's atmosphere contains methane and probably ammonia, but the ammonia may be in a frozen state and therefore cannot be identified

spectroscopically. The cloud-top temperature is below the freezing point of ammonia. The fact that the mass of Saturn is less than one-third that of Jupiter suggests a central density consistent with only a liquid core. If a strong magnetic field is found by Pioneer 10, then this may be an additional clue as to the density of the core, for it is thought that a fairly high density is necessary to produce a metallic phase of hydrogen, which in turn is necessary to produce the magnetic field.

Saturn has ten moons in all, the latest having been discovered in 1966 when the rings were seen edge-on. This moon, called Janus, orbits very near the outer edge of the ring structure and is usually lost in its glare. Twice during the 29.5-year revolution period of Saturn, the rings are presented in an edge-on view to earth observers; because the rings are so thin, they seem to disappear—except in the larger telescopes. When this occurred in 1966, astronomers identified Janus. They had previously suspected its existence after noting perturbations (disturbances) that created a small gap in the rings. Each of Saturn's moons creates such a gap, although only Cassini's division is readily visible in a small telescope. (The ability of an observer to identify Cassini's division using a 7.5-cm refractor is a good test of its resolving power and therefore of its quality.)

Figure 5.29   Sir William Herschel's 1.25-m reflecting telescope, which he built himself. (Yerkes Observatory)

Figure 5.30 Uranus, with three moons. (Lick Observatory)

URANUS

Uranus represents the first planet of our study that was not known to the ancients. It is not usually considered to be visible to the naked eye; however, under ideal conditions it may be seen quite easily using only binoculars. Uranus was discovered almost by accident. While it had been seen and its position charted as early as 1690, it was only in 1781 that Sir William Herschel recognized it as a planet; he also discovered two of its larger moons in 1787. Herschel, who was appointed court astronomer to King George III in 1782, had one of the best telescopes of his time, thus making his accomplishment possible (Figure 5.29). Other observers had termed the object a star, but he was able to recognize its disklike appearance (Figure 5.30).

Uranus orbits the sun at an average distance just under 20 A.U. and in a period of 84 earth years. If a man could spend his entire lifetime on Uranus, he would die at the age of only one Uranus year. One of the most distinctive characteristics of this planet is the tilt of its axis, which is 98°. If we imagine a planet whose axis is not tilted at all, we can say that its equator is in the same plane as its orbit. Now imagine that this same planet rotates in a counterclockwise direction, a point on its equator traveling in an eastward direction. Tilt the planet's axis

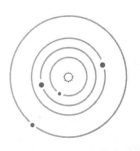

of rotation by 90°; the axis now lies in the plane of its orbit. Continue to tilt the axis of the planet 8° more, making a total of 98°. In what direction will it now be rotating? To answer this question, use your finger to represent the planet rotating in a counterclockwise direction with no tilt at all, then gradually tilt your finger until you have reached the 98° position. You will see that your finger is now rotating in a clockwise direction; likewise the rotation of Uranus is clockwise (retrograde).

Uranus has five moons, all of which orbit in the same plane as the planet's equator and in the same direction as the planet's rotation. Because of the planet's extreme tilt, its moons are sometimes seen circling it in a plane perpendicular to our line of sight; at other times the plane seems to align itself with our line of sight.

NEPTUNE

Following the discovery of Uranus, it became evident that its orbit was being perturbed by still another unknown object. Two astronomer-mathematicians, John Adams of England and Joseph Leverrier of France, working independently, took a mathematical approach to the problem

Figure 5.31 Neptune and its largest moon, Triton. (Lick Observatory)

of finding this unknown object. Each man asked himself where an object must be in order to cause the perturbations that had been observed in the orbit of Uranus. When their calculations had been completed, using Newton's laws of gravitation, a search was made of the area in which they had predicted the presence of another planet, and in a very short time the planet was found (Figure 5.31). Here again it was a matter of recognizing an object, previously called a star, as being truly a planet. The date of this discovery was July 1846, and it represented a real triumph for a theoretical approach which brought together astronomical observations, the known laws of motion and gravitation, and the mathematics necessary to solve the problem.

Using Appendix 6, compare the size, mass, density, rotation, and albedo of Uranus and Neptune. Note their almost twinlike nature. Recent observations of Neptune show a cloud-top temperature of about $45°K$ ($-228°C$).

Neptune has two moons. The larger, named Triton, has a diameter of 4000 km, greater than that of the earth's moon, and orbits the planet in a retrograde direction. Triton is the only moon of significant size that has a retrograde motion in relation to the rotation of its parent planet. All the moons of Uranus orbit in retrograde, but that would be expected because the planet itself rotates in retrograde.

PLUTO

The orbital motions of both Uranus and Neptune were followed with much interest by numerous observers. In the early 1900s Percival Lowell, founder of Lowell Observatory in Flagstaff, Arizona, concluded that Neptune could not account for all the perturbations in the orbit of Uranus. Again, by mathematical calculations he predicted that still another planet might be found in one of two possible locations. In 1930 a planet was found by Clyde Tombaugh, an assistant astronomer at the observatory, who had photographed these regions and later analyzed his plates on a device called the *blink microscope*. Two plates, taken at different times (see Figure 5.32), are placed in the instrument and then alternately illuminated, first the left-hand plate, then the right, and so on back and forth. The illumination is alternated quite rapidly so that any object that has moved against the background of distant stars will appear to jump back and forth in the blink microscope. Pluto was found within 6° of one of the positions predicted by Lowell. Some observers would discredit his calculations, saying that he had too little information with which to work and that therefore the almost perfect coincidence of prediction and discovery was only accidental. This is a question that may never be completely resolved.

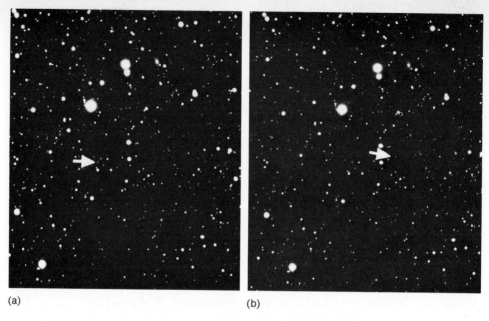

Figure 5.32 Discovery of Pluto. These plates, taken 6 days apart, show the motion of a new planet among the stars (see arrows): (a) January 23, 1930; (b) January 29, 1930. (Lowell Observatory)

Figure 5.33 The orbits of Pluto and Neptune.

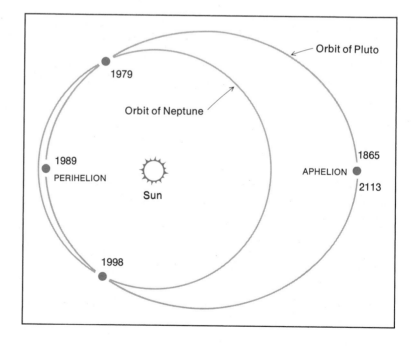

Pluto has the most unusual orbit of all the planets, one that, besides being the most eccentric, is also inclined 17° to the plane of the earth's orbit (ecliptic). Pluto orbits the sun at an average distance of 40 A.U., or 5.5 billion kilometers, but travels within less than 30 A.U. at perihelion and out to almost 50 A.U. at aphelion. The planet appeared at aphelion in 1865 and will again appear at this point in 2113. It will appear at perihelion in 1989. The orbit of Pluto is so eccentric as to bring it within the orbit of Neptune during the interval from 1979 to 1998 (Figure 5.33). During this period, Neptune will be the farthest known planet from the sun. A collision between these two planets is impossible, for while their paths appear to intersect, the planes of orbit do not coincide. Pluto requires almost 248 earth years for one revolution; hence it has not moved very far against the background of stars since its discovery.

Pluto appears only as a tiny speck in even the largest telescopes, and therefore its diameter may only be estimated at about one-half the diameter of the earth; its probable mass is approximately one-seventh that of the earth. Recent observations of its rotation period, based on variations in brightness, produced what are considered to be quite reliable results: 6 days 9 hr 17 min. The temperature of the planet is unknown due to its distance but has been approximated at 35°K (−238°C).

Both the eccentricity and inclination of Pluto's orbit suggest that it may represent an object that was not a member of the original solar system but was captured by the sun at a later time. Adopting this supposition, we will not try to account for the planet's origin in the section that follows. Some have suggested that Pluto may be an errant moon of Neptune, or at least that it may have interacted gravitationally with Triton, Neptune's largest moon. In fact, the physical characteristics of both Triton and Pluto are similar.

PLANET X

In 1971, Joseph L. Brady of the University of California did an extensive computer study on the perturbations of Halley's comet and concluded that a planet more massive than Saturn must orbit the sun beyond the orbit of Pluto. He predicted planet X's period of revolution to be 464 years, and he predicted its location in the constellation Cassiopeia. Extensive photographic searches have revealed no such planet, however. It is now thought to be very likely that the irregularities in the flight of Halley's comet are due to nongravitational effects which will be explained in Chapter 6.

ORIGIN AND EVOLUTION
OF THE PLANETS

We opened this chapter with a question as to how the solar system came into being. Do the generalizations we made earlier or the distinguishing characteristics we have considered point to an answer? We have already suggested that the random-capture theory does not appear to fit the orderly revolution of all nine planets in almost the same plane. We also incline to eliminate the encounter theory, not because it is inconsistent with planetary motion, but rather because of the low probability that the sun passed close enough to another star to have pulled off material from it. Due to the great distances between stars, it is estimated that no more than ten such encounters have occurred in the life of the Milky Way galaxy (10 billion years), and astronomers believe that many solar systems exist in our galaxy.

By 1950 several variations of the *protoplanet* theory had been suggested. This theory may not be the "last word" on the subject, but in many respects it is more plausible than its forerunners. It suggests that the planets were formed about the same time as the sun and out of the same nebular material. The process is thought to have begun when a huge cloud of gas and dust, many times larger than the diameter of the entire solar system, became unstable. Due to gravitational attraction, a condensation (knot) occurred toward one point within the gas cloud. This contraction we would term the *protosun*—the sun in the making. Any such cloud is thought to have some component of rotation and, much like a spinning ice skater pulling in her arms, the cloud rotated faster and faster as it contracted. As a result, it spun some of its gas and dust into a flattened disk surrounding the protosun, and within this disk other condensations formed several protoplanets that continued to move in the same direction and in the same plane as the original disk.

At the same time the planets assumed a rotation and tilt of axis that reflected the combined motion of the molecules and dust particles from which they were formed. The rotation and tilt of the planets show great variation, yet there is a general tendency favoring small angles of tilt and counterclockwise rotation, just what we might expect to happen within a disk revolving in a counterclockwise direction. The same general process of condensation on a smaller scale surrounding each protoplanet may have acted to form the moons. While there is no absolute correlation between the mass of a planet and its number of moons, it is obvious that a tendency exists for the more massive planets to have more moons.

As the material that composed the disk became more concentrated in the protoplanets, the space between the sun and these objects cleared, allowing the sunlight to reach them. This heat was naturally most intense on the inner planets, driving off the lighter elements and perhaps most of the atmosphere they had, leaving only the more dense core of heavier elements. At the distance of Jupiter or beyond, the effect of heating would be greatly reduced, allowing the lighter elements such as hydrogen and helium to remain as part of their atmospheres. This model seems to fit what we have seen concerning the atmospheres. However, we may also surmise that the terrestrial planets went through a period of numerous impacts with objects in space and further that they had active volcanic periods, at which time they developed a secondary atmosphere composed of gases that were expelled from the planet itself.

We are not certain of the answer to one of the most fundamental questions: Why does the sun rotate so slowly? If the sun and the planets were formed from the same rotating cloud of gas and dust, we would expect the sun to rotate faster and faster as it condensed (like the spinning figure skater described earlier; this is called *conservation of angular momentum*). If the sun had done this, it would rotate in a period of only a few hours, not the 24.6 days now required. Indeed it may have rotated much faster when it was first formed, but by some force, such as magnetism, it was slowed to its present rate. Alternately, the solar system may have lost a large portion of its original mass. The sun contains over 99 percent of the mass of the solar system, yet it has less than 3 percent of its angular momentum.

QUESTIONS

1. What basic properties distinguish the terrestrial planets from the Jovian group?
2. The rotation of Mercury was once thought to be 88 days, a period equal to that of its revolution. It is now known to be _____ days, as recently measured by radar.
3. What properties of Mercury cause it to be one of the hottest and at the same time one of the coldest planets?
4. Why is the albedo of Venus so much greater than that of Mercury or of the earth?
5. How many hours after sunset is Venus visible when at maximum eastern elongation?
6. During which phase does Venus appear brightest? Why?
7. The maximum surface temperature of Venus is probably greater than that of Mercury. How is this possible when Venus is farther from the sun?

8. Which configuration of Mars brings it closest to the earth: conjunction, quadrature, or opposition?

9. Where and when is Jupiter seen when at opposition?

10. Which method of observation lends the most detailed information about Mars?

11. Are the straight-line figures (referred to as canals) actually visible at times on Mars?

12. True or false: The volume of Jupiter is greater than the combined volume of all the remaining known planets.

13. List the Jovian planets.

14. How many moons has Jupiter? How many are larger than the earth's moon?

15. What property of Saturn is demonstrated by the fact that it would float in water?

16. What problems would be encountered in maintaining human life on any of the Jovian planets?

17. What is the principal characteristic that distinguishes Uranus from other planets?

18. What kind of observations led to the discovery of Neptune?

19. For a period of 19 years, beginning in 1979, Pluto orbits nearer the sun than does Neptune, yet it is not possible for a collision to take place at any time in the future. Why is this true?

20. What ideas are suggested regarding the origin of the planets by the fact that they orbit the sun in almost the same plane as does the earth?

21. Show by a drawing how Galileo's discovery that Venus goes through all possible phases from new to full and back to new again disproves the Ptolemaic model of the planetary system.

22. Suppose you could stand on the visible surface of Saturn at a point near its equator. Describe the apparent motions of particles in each ring from your point of view.

23. Find the semimajor axis of a planet which has an aphelion distance of 160 million kilometers and a perihelion distance of 100 million kilometers.

24. Find the period of a hypothetical planet that orbits the sun at an average distance of 8 A.U. (You may wish to refer to Chapter 1.)

25. Speculate as to how life on the earth might have been affected if Jupiter had been a dim star which together with the sun formed a binary system of stars.

26. What are several fundamental differences between stars and planets?

27. Why do observers believe that Venus lost its original atmosphere and then developed a secondary atmosphere? How was it possible to develop a secondary atmosphere?

28. What characteristics of Venus were revealed or confirmed by probes which either landed or flew by the planet?

29. What are the possible dangers of releasing ever-increasing amounts of carbon compounds into the earth's atmosphere by the burning of fossil fuels?

30. Group the planets into categories according to the predominant elements in their atmospheres: (a) hydrogen; (b) nitrogen; (c) carbon dioxide; (d) other elements.

SUGGESTED READINGS

Beer, Arthur (ed.), *Vistas in astronomy,* Vol. 10, pp. 175–206. London: Pergamon Press, 1968.

Kuiper, Gerard P., and Middlehurst, Barbara M. (eds.), *Planets and satellites.* Chicago: University of Chicago Press, 1961.

Lewis, John S., The chemistry of the solar system. *Scientific American* **230** (3), 50–65 (1974).

Mariner Mars 1971 Project: Final Report, Vol. VI (Science results). Pasadena, Calif.: Jet Propulsion Laboratory—NASA, July 15, 1973.

Mariner 10 Venus encounter. *Science* **183,** 1289–1321 (1974). (Many authors; a variety of reports.)

Murray, Bruce C., Mars from Mariner 9. *Scientific American* **228** (1), 48–69 (1973).

Newburn, R. L., Jr., and Gulkis, S., A survey of the outer planets— Jupiter, Saturn, Uranus, Neptune, Pluto, and their satellites. *Space Science Reviews* **3,** 179–271 (1973).

Pioneer 10 mission to Jupiter. *Science* **183** (4122), 292–324 (1974). (Many authors; a variety of reports.)

Shklovskii, I. S., and Sagan, Carl, *Intelligent life in the universe.* San Francisco: Holden-Day, 1966.

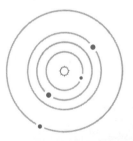

ASTEROIDS, COMETS, AND METEORS

6

The asteroids, comets, and meteors constitute the lesser members of the solar system. The orbits of these objects reveal their kinship to the planets, for they all show the effects of the sun's gravitational field on their motions.

When the Bode–Titius relationship was first published in 1772, no object was known to orbit the sun at 2.8 A.U.; however, the very fact that the other numbers in this relationship so nearly agreed with the actual distances to the known planets suggested the existence of an

object at that distance. Searches were initiated but remained fruitless until 1801, when quite by accident Giuseppe Piazzi, director of the observatory at Palermo, noticed a small starlike object that was not recorded on his charts. Watching it for several nights, he noticed a slight shift among the stars. At first he thought that the object was a comet; however, after continued observation and computation, it was identified as a small planet orbiting the sun at an average distance of 2.76 A.U. Thinking he had found the lost planet, Piazzi called this small object Ceres. Within a year, Heinrich Olber, a German astronomer, found another object in a very similar orbit and named it Pallas. This second discovery gave the clue that there might be many more such orbiting objects and in fact marked the beginning of a long series of discoveries of asteroids (see Table 6.1).

ASTEROIDS

By the late nineteenth century, important new photographic techniques had been developed. In order to take a time exposure of a given star field, the camera must be turned slowly to compensate for the rotation of the earth and thus produce sharp star images. Any object that is moving in relation to those stars will produce a streak on the film. By means of this photographic technique several thousand asteroids have been definitely identified. As new discoveries are made, they are numbered in order: (1) Ceres; (2) Pallas; . . . (1566) Icarus; and so on. While most asteroids orbit the sun between Mars and Jupiter, a number have rather eccentric orbits. Of particular interest are Hermes, Apollo, Adonis, Icarus, Geographos, and Eros, because their orbits cross that of the earth, thus bringing them relatively close to the earth at

Table 6.1 Discovery of asteroids

YEAR	NAME	DIAMETER
1801	Ceres	785 km
1802	Pallas	490 km
1804	Juno	190 km
1807	Vesta	400 km
1845	6 known	
1890	300 known	

Figure 6.1   The asteroid Icarus, showing motion among a field of stars. (Hale Observatories)

times. In 1932 Apollo passed within 3.2 million kilometers of the earth; in 1936 Adonis passed at a distance of less than 1.6 million kilometers; in 1937 Hermes came within 0.8 million kilometers. Icarus and Geographos passed within 6.4 million kilometers in 1968 and 1969, respectively.

Asteroid Icarus is of special interest because it passes closer to the sun than any other known asteroid—within 27 million kilometers—and then moves out beyond the orbit of Mars (Figure 6.1). Of all the known asteroids, it has the shortest period (409 days) and the highest eccentricity of orbit (0.83), and it orbits in a plane that is inclined 23° to that of the earth (Figure 6.2).

Icarus was discovered by Walter Baade when he photographed a star field using the 1.22-m Schmidt telescope at Mt. Palomar. Because of its sun-grazing orbit, it was called Icarus after the mythological young man who flew too near the sun. With his father, Daedalus, he attempted to escape an island prison by flying away on artificial wings. Daedalus, a master craftsman, had fashioned two sets of wings and attached them to their bodies with wax. He warned his son not to fly too high, for the wax would be melted by the sun's heat. The boy was so thrilled at being free and able to fly, however, that he soared higher and higher. The wax melted, and Icarus fell to his death in the sea.

When the motion both of asteroid Icarus and of the earth is considered, it is only every 19 years that they approach each other within a few million kilometers. Icarus is among the smallest of the

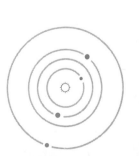

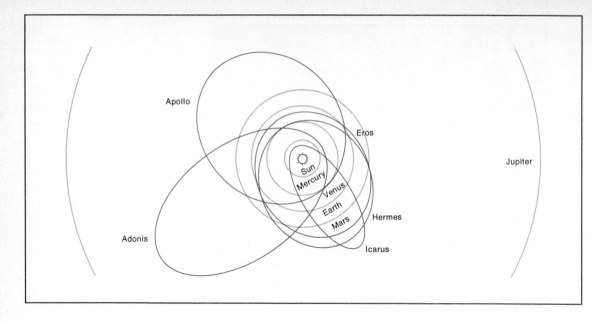

Figure 6.2 The orbits of selected asteroids.

asteroids (approximately 1.5 km in diameter), while Ceres, the first to be discovered, is also the largest, with a diameter of almost 800 km. There are well over 25,000 such objects orbiting the sun, yet the total mass of the entire group is estimated to be less than the mass of our moon. Most are irregular in shape, as is indicated by the fact that they reflect varying amounts of light as they tumble through space (Figure 6.3). Their shape suggests that they may be the product of a collision or an explosion.

COMETS

A comet presents one of the most spectacular apparitions in the sky. Often unheralded, it appears first as a small source of light, somewhat fuzzy and often resembling a nebula or distant galaxy. As the comet moves closer to the sun, however, a vaporous tail is driven from the head of the comet by the sun's radiation. The length of the tail continues to increase as the comet nears the sun, but it always extends away from the sun. Such comets presented a fearsome sight to ancient man. The tail was thought to contain poisonous gases and to be within the earth's atmosphere.

    If a comet moved within the earth's atmosphere, then it would streak across the sky like a meteor, but because it is millions of miles from the earth even at its closest approach it has only the slightest

210

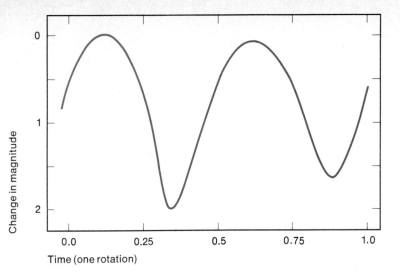

Figure 6.3 The asteroid Geographos shows this periodic variation of two magnitudes, which is interpreted as resulting from one rotation of the object.

apparent motion in a period of a few hours. Thus, whenever a bright comet appears it will likely be seen for several weeks. Most comets are not bright enough to be seen with the naked eye and so they go unnoticed by the casual observer.

Comets, like the planets and asteroids, are orbiting the sun and so are members of the solar system. Their very eccentric orbits distinguish them from the other members, as does the fact that the planes of their orbits are often inclined to the ecliptic. This is to say that a comet may appear at any point in the sky and move in direct or retrograde motion. Comets seem to be randomly oriented in the system. Since they move in an orbit primarily dictated by the gravitational influence of the sun, their paths represent a conic section, usually that of an ellipse. The comparison between the earth's orbital shape and that of the comet Kohoutek may be seen in Figure 6.4. Some comets have very long periods, in the order of 10,000 to 50,000 years (or longer), and they have very eccentric orbits that take them to distances of several thousand astronomical units from the sun. Other comets have short periods, ranging from 3 to 200 years, and their orbits are less eccentric and are generally confined to distances less than that of Pluto. If a long-period comet approaching the sun is perturbed by the gravitational field of a planet that it happens to encounter, the shape of its orbit may be altered so that it becomes a short-period comet (Figure 6.5). Jupiter has perturbed the orbits of a number of comets (45 to 50; the *Jovian group*), which now orbit the sun in a period of from 5 to 10 years.

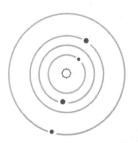

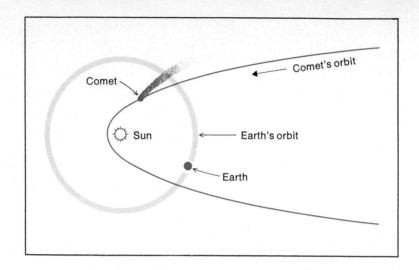

Figure 6.4 The highly eccentric orbit of the comet Kohoutek (1973f) compared to the almost circular orbit of the earth. The shape of the comet's orbit is almost like that of a parabola, typical of long-period comets.

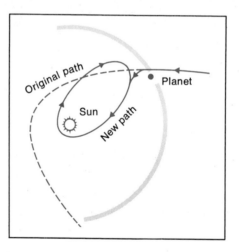

Figure 6.5 A comet may be perturbed by a planet so that the shape of its orbit is changed.

It was not at first realized that the same comet was being observed over and over again; however, in 1705 the British astronomer Edmond Halley published the orbits of 24 comets and noted the similar periods for the comets of 1531, 1607, and 1682, each date separated by 75 or 76 years. He predicted the return of this comet in 1758. The comet did in fact reappear on Christmas night of that year and has since been called Halley's comet (Figure 6.6). The period of the comet is known

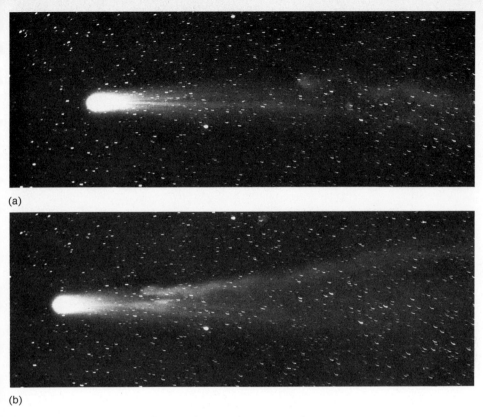

(a)

(b)

Figure 6.6 Halley's Comet of 1910. The two photos were taken a day apart; by examining the position of the comet relative to the background of stars, you can detect the motion of the comet. (Lick Observatory)

to vary between 74 to 79 years due to perturbations by the Jovian planets. It is interesting to note that Halley's comet appeared in the year of Mark Twain's birth (1835) and reappeared in the year of his death (1910), just as he had prophesied. The comet's next passage near the sun is expected in 1986. (The flip pages beginning on page 215 depict the flight of Halley's comet.)

ORIGIN OF THE COMETS

The comets that become visible are not likely to have been interstellar wanderers that only by chance entered the gravitational influence of the sun; rather, they are members of a "comet cloud" surrounding the solar system at some distance beyond 50,000 A.U., perhaps extending half way to the nearest star, α (Alpha) Centauri, which is located at a distance of 260,000 A.U. Examples of periodic comets that orbit to

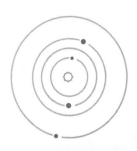

Figure 6.7 The comet Kohoutek (1973f), as observed on January 12, 1974. (Hale Observatories)

these great distances include the Pons-Brooks comet, the Giggs-Mellish comet, and others with aphelion distances of 30,000 to 60,000 A.U. Members of the great comet cloud are thought to be perturbed by major planets, causing them to assume an elliptical orbit which brings them close to the sun. Further perturbations may then entrap them in a smaller orbit which makes their return more predictable. This theory of a comet cloud was set forth by J. H. Oort of Leiden University Observatory in 1950. In 1973 we viewed a comet which tends to confirm Oort's theory, for calculations based upon the almost parabolic shape of the orbit of comet Kohoutek show that it came near the sun from a great distance (several thousand A.U.). On December 28, 1973, it passed within 21 million kilometers of the sun (Figure 6.7).

Astronomers believe that comets were formed as some of the earliest members of the solar system, prior to the formation of the sun and planets, while the solar nebula was still a very large cloud of gases and dust. Our study of comets therefore takes on added significance in that they may give us clues as to the origin of the solar system. What are comets like, and of what are they made?

PHYSICAL NATURE
OF COMETS

When a comet is far from the sun, it consists of only a nucleus that we might characterize as a "dirty snowball," or a swarm of dirty snowballs. Such a description implies a mixture of rocky and metallic particles bound together by frozen carbon dioxide, methane, ammonia, and water molecules. As the nucleus approaches the sun, the solar radiation causes the frozen material to vaporize (*sublimate*), thus producing a large gaseous region surrounding the nucleus called the *coma*. The thin nature of the coma is revealed by the fact that stars are seen shining through it. Although the nucleus is very small—often only a few kilometers in diameter—the coma may grow to a size larger than that of the earth. When a comet passes quite near the sun, its temperature may rise to several thousand degrees. At this time, not only can the absorption spectrum of reflected sunlight be seen, but also a bright-line spectrum is produced by the comet itself. A comet's emission spectrum results primarily from the ultraviolet radiation of the sun, exciting the gases to fluorescence, revealing the presence of iron, nickel, calcium, sodium, argon, cyanogen, carbon, potassium, copper, chromium, and traces of other metals. The Skylab crews had a particularly good opportunity to photograph comet Kohoutek and to analyze its composition spectroscopically because of their freedom from atmospheric interference.

Most comets produce a tail only after approaching the sun within about 2 A.U. The gas and dust which is liberated by the heat of the sun experiences a force away from the nucleus in this sublimation process; however, these same molecules and particles also experience two other fundamental forces that ultimately determine their direction of motion. One force is due to the radiation of the sun. The other is due to the solar wind, an outflow of particles from the sun. Which is the most effective force—that due to solar radiation, or that due to the solar wind? The answer depends upon the size of the particles. Gas molecules are very small and experience the greatest force from the solar wind, whereas the dust particles are considerably larger and experience the greatest force from solar radiation. Thus we might expect comets to develop two tails: a gas tail that tends to point more directly away from the sun, and a dust tail that tends to curve and lag behind the gas tail. The separation of these two tails will become more apparent as the comet recedes from the sun, for it is at that time that the gas tail precedes the head of the comet and the dust tail tends to follow

A comet in motion (Halley's)

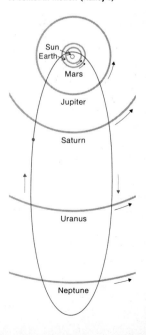

the head at least to a limited degree (see the lower portion of Figure 6.8). A dust tail was quite obvious in the case of comet Arend–Roland of 1957. The motion of the comet is upward (Figure 6.9), with the gas tail preceding the head and the dust tail tending to follow.

The tails of some comets have reached the tremendous length of more than 160 million kilometers, a distance greater than that from the sun to the earth. The nebulosity of the tail is revealed by the fact that stars may easily be seen through it (Figure 6.10). Only when we see the tail of a comet at right angles to its length do we see it full length. If we view the comet from a direction in line with its tail, then no tail is apparent at all.

HOW ARE COMETS DISCOVERED AND RECORDED?

It is evident from the limited list given in Table 6.2 that the names of many persons have been immortalized by their discovery of a comet. Comets are listed as they are discovered in any given year by assigning the letters a, b, c, d, . . . in the order of their discovery: a comet listed as *1967d* is therefore the fourth to be discovered in 1967. In addition, the designation p/Tempel II, for example, indicates that this comet is a periodic (p) comet, merely returning to the sun, and that it was originally discovered by Tempel as his second comet (II). Those comets

Figure 6.8 The tail of a comet, showing the separation of the gas and dust tails.

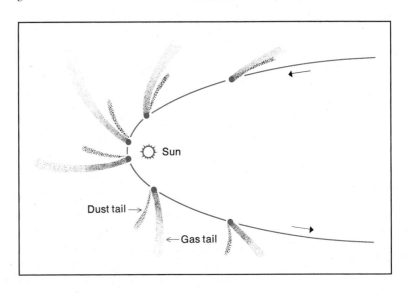

| April 26 | April 27 | April 29 | April 30 | May 1 |

Figure 6.9 Comet Arend–Roland of 1957, showing an antitail, which certain comets develop. (Hale Observatories)

lacking the "p/" designation represent comets newly discovered in 1967. Are the discoverers' names those of professional astronomers alone? No! There is no such criterion for the naming of comets. The only requirement is that the name be that of the person who saw the comet first. Lubos Kohoutek, a professional astronomer, found comet 1973f while searching photographic plates for asteroids; most amateurs do not have access to such plates, however. Still, comets are sometimes found by visual observation, especially in dark regions of the sky where no photographs are being taken. Remember that comets may appear at any point in the sky and do not always follow the ecliptic as did comet Kohoutek.

The tools with which a comet search may be conducted include a telescope of short focal length, say, one with a focal ratio of $f/4$ and a low-power eyepiece. This combination will provide a large, bright field of view, allowing the observer to recognize the rather faint, diffuse image that a comet presents at early stages of visibility. Since the image of a comet often resembles that of a nebula or distant galaxy, an adequate sky map is essential. Known diffuse objects, such as nebulae, clusters, and galaxies will be shown on such a map and, by the same token, a newly apparent comet will not. It was this need to be able to recognize the different types of objects that led Charles Messier, a French observer whose primary concern was comet searching, to compile a catalogue of known nebulae, clusters, and galaxies. These kinds of objects kept

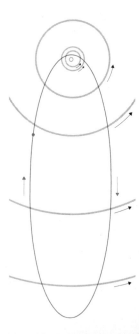

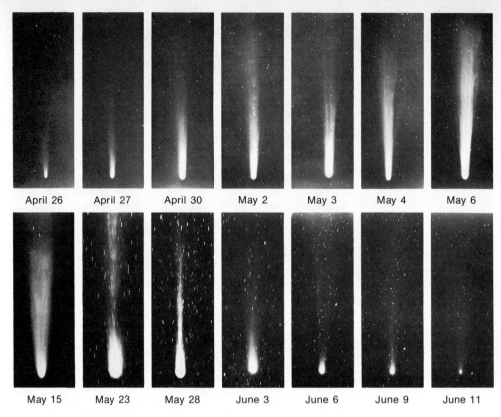

| April 26 | April 27 | April 30 | May 2 | May 3 | May 4 | May 6 |

| May 15 | May 23 | May 28 | June 3 | June 6 | June 9 | June 11 |

Figure 6.10 Halley's Comet of 1910, showing the growth of the tail as the comet approached the sun in April and May and then the decline of the tail as the comet receded from the sun in June. (Hale Observatories)

getting in his way as he sought comets. The Great Galaxy in Andromeda, as an example, still bears his catalogue number M31; in fact, Messier is better known for his catalogue of nebulae than for his comet discoveries. Together with the more recent *New General Catalogue* (NGC) and *Index Catalogue* (IC), this list provides an essential tool for cometary searches today. (The *Messier Catalogue* is given in Appendix 9.)

If a certain diffuse (fuzzy) object is seen that does not appear on the sky map, check the object for any apparent motion against the background of stars. A comet will show such motion, but this motion may not be evident unless the observer stays with the object for hours or even days. Make drawings and notations of its position among nearby stars. Note its right ascension and declination from a sky chart. If in fact the object does display movement and is diffuse in appearance (asteroids also display movement but are not diffuse), you have probably discovered a comet. What does one do next? To record your discovery, send a telegram to the Central Telegram Bureau, Smithsonian Observatory, Cambridge, Massachusetts 02138, stating your name, the date

Table 6.2 Comets sighted in 1967

DATE		NAME
Jan. 3	1967a	p/Tuttle
Feb. 4	1967b	Seki
Feb. 11	1967c	Wild
Feb. 12	1967d	p/Tempel II
June 5	1967e	p/Reinmuth II
June 29	1967f	Mitchell-Jones-Gerber
Aug. 7	1967g	p/Finlay
Aug. 3	1967h	p/Encke
Aug. 8	1967i	p/Schwassmann-Wachmann II
Oct. 5	1967j	p/Wolf
Oct. 5	1967k	p/Wirtanen
Oct. 5	1967l	p/Arend
Oct. 5	1967m	p/Borrelly
Dec. 28	1967n	Ikeya-Seki

and time of observation (Universal Time), the nature of the object (diffuse), it right ascension and declination, the direction of motion, and the estimated magnitude. This will set into motion a series of events by which your observation will be verified and the orbit calculated. If this is a periodic comet that you have merely rediscovered, it will of course not bear your name; but if this is indeed a new comet and your telegram stating the facts of your observation arrives first, your name will be given to that comet. While comets are often seen after they have moved close to the sun, thus developing a tail, it is not easy to spot the dim image of a comet that is just becoming visible at a distance of more than 500 million km from the sun. For your observations, find a location as far away from city lights as possible and direct your attention to the darker portions of the sky. Good hunting!

METEORS

In contrast to the comet, which seems almost fixed among the stars throughout an evening's viewing session, the *meteor* is a phenomenon that only lasts for a few seconds. The word *phenomenon* is used here

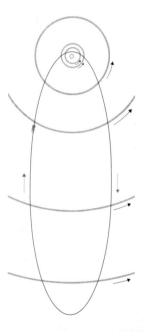

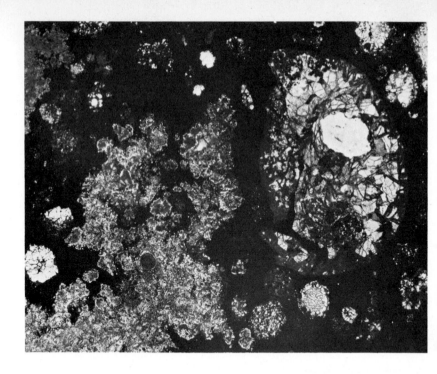

Figure 6.11 A photomicrograph of a section of the Allende meteorite showing inclusions (white) of pure oxygen 16 (^{16}O). (Courtesy of Richard J. Kjarval, Graphic Arts Facility, Physical Science Division, University of Chicago)

to stress the fact that what you see shooting across the sky is not the object itself but rather a streak of light caused by the passage of a small solid body into the earth's atmosphere. The object itself, called a *meteoroid* while still in flight, experiences the heating effect of friction between itself and atoms that make up the atmosphere. As a result of this heat the air is ionized, the atoms losing electrons. As the ionized atoms "find" free electrons with which to recombine, downward transitions of these electrons occur, and light is produced.

Occasionally, the object that produced the meteor survives its flight and falls to earth. Such an object is called a *meteorite.* Since most meteoroids are only the size of a grain of sand or pebble at the most, they are destroyed in flight. The rare meteoroid of larger size often produces a spectacular display called a *fireball,* or *Bolide meteor.* The streak of light persists, often with explosions and loud noises accompanying the event. Objects that exhibit this rapid motion and that sometimes deposit material on the earth are obviously very close phenomena; in fact, they are usually within 160 km of the observer during their visible flight.

The meteorite itself is of great interest to the astronomer, for until recently it had represented the only sample of extraterrestrial material man has had to work with. These objects may carry clues to the origin of the solar system and to life elsewhere in it. Careful analysis of certain meteorites has shown that they contain as many as 18 different amino acids and also hydrocarbons. Six of the 18 amino acids are of the type normally found in living cells—specifically in proteins. Figure 6.11 shows a photomicrograph of a section of meteorite in which investigators at the University of Chicago have found inclusions (white spots) containing a form of oxygen (isotope ^{16}O) so pure as to suggest its origin in interstellar material before the birth of the solar system. On earth, other isotopes of oxygen (^{17}O and ^{18}O) are usually found together with ^{16}O.

OBSERVING METEORS

Are meteors predictable? Where should one look to see a meteor or meteor shower? It is usually possible to see a few meteors on almost any night by simply assuming a reclining position and staring at the sky. Your eye will pick out streaks of light quite easily (Figure 6.12). However, there are some guidelines for viewing meteors. In general,

Figure 6.12 Meteor trail near the Pleiades. (Yerkes Observatory)

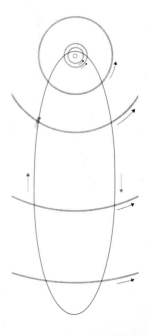

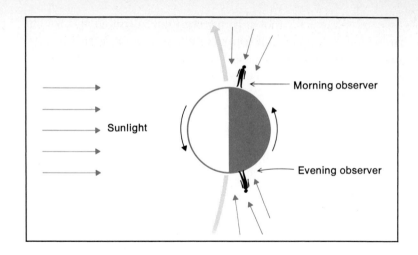

Figure 6.13 Viewing meteors.

Figure 6.14 The radiant point of the Leonids.

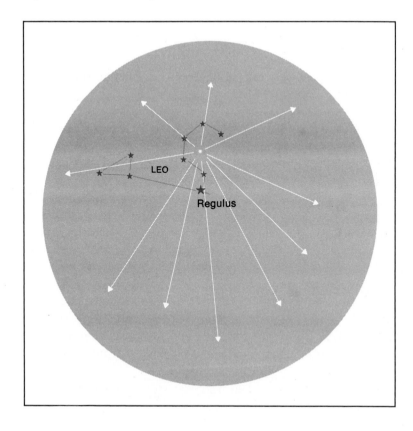

the best time is during the early morning hours before dawn. The brilliance of a meteor depends largely on the speed with which it enters the earth's atmosphere. In the evening hours, the meteors you see would be overtaking the earth and hence would be entering the atmosphere quite slowly (15 km/sec). In the early morning hours, the meteors that you see would result from the earth's running into the objects, in effect adding the earth's speed to their speed, resulting in relative speeds as high as 70 km/sec (Figure 6.13).

METEOR SHOWERS

On certain nights it will become very apparent that more than the usual number of meteors are in evidence. The streaks of light may appear in many parts of the sky, yet if we extend imaginary lines backward from the direction in which the meteors move, these lines will appear to intersect in a definite point called the *radiant*. We are seeing a *meteor shower*, many particles entering the earth's atmosphere within a short period of time.

The meteors appear to radiate from a given point (Figure 6.14); however, this is merely an optical illusion. The individual particles that produce the shower are actually traveling in parallel paths, but even as parallel railroad tracks appear to converge at a single point in the distance, so these parallel streaks of light seem to emerge from a single point. An analysis of the orbits of these particles reveals that they are associated not only with each other but also with a comet that passed along the same orbital path at an earlier time. The particles are very likely debris left from the comet itself. Since the earth crosses the orbit of a given comet at about the same time each year, these meteor showers are predictable, and the list provided in Table 6.3 can be used for any year. A given shower is named for the constellation in which its radiant is located.

A given shower may be better one year than the next because the particles that produce it tend to travel in swarms rather than be evenly distributed along the orbit of the comet (Figure 6.15). When the earth passes through a swarm, a spectacular display results. On November 13, 1833, the earth passed through a swarm associated with the comet of 1866 I (not yet discovered), and it is estimated that more than 30,000 meteors per hour were visible. An outstanding display of this shower, the *Leonids*, occurs in a cycle of 33 years, the same as that of the comet that is the ultimate cause of the shower. Further verification of the 33-year cycle came when spectacular showers were observed in 1932 and 1965.

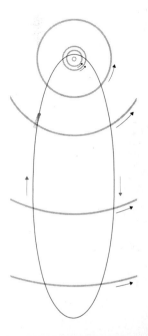

Table 6.3 Meteor showers

| APPROXIMATE DATE | NAME OF SHOWER | ASSOCIATED COMET | RADIANT | | DEC. |
| | | | R.A. | | |
			HR	MIN	DEG
Jan. 1–4	Quadrantids	—	15	20	+52
Apr. 19–23	Lyrids	1861 I	18	4	+33
May 1–6	May Aquarids	Halley	22	16	−2
July 26–31	Delta Aquarids	—	22	36	−11
Aug. 10–14	Perseids	1862 II	3	8	+58
Oct. 9–11	Draconids	Giacobini-Zinner	17	40	+55
Oct. 18–23	Orionids	Halley	6	8	+15
Nov. 1–15	Taurids	Encke	3	40	+17
Nov. 14–18	Leonids	1866 I	10	00	+22
Dec. 10–16	Geminids	—	7	32	+32
Dec. 21–23	Ursids	Tuttle	14	28	+75

Figure 6.15 Orbit of the swarm of particles which produces the Leonids.

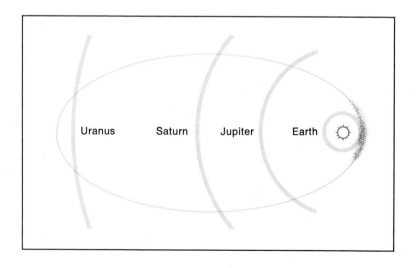

Figure 6.16 A polished slice of a stony-iron meteorite from Brenham County, Kansas. The dark material is olivine. (Ronald Oriti, Griffith Observatory)

Actually more prevalent than the shower meteors are the sporadic meteors that enter the earth's atmosphere almost continuously. They seem to bear no specific relationship to the comets and may appear in any part of the sky at any time.

PHYSICAL PROPERTIES OF METEORITES

A typical meteoroid is a small, porous, easily fragmented body that disintegrates in flight. The average meteoroid recorded by the camera has a computed density of about 0.26 g/cm^3, a density somewhat like that of pumice stone. The exceptional meteoroid that reaches the earth is usually much more dense—approximately 2 to 5 g/cm^3. Such meteorites fall into one of three main categories; however, the specialist subdivides these into several additional types.

The *irons* (siderites) represent 5 to 6 percent of all meteorites, *stony irons* (siderolites) represent 1 to 2 percent, and the *stones* (aerolites or chondrites) about 92 percent (Figures 6.16 and 6.17). This immediately poses the question why museums and planetariums usually display a predominance of irons and stony irons. The simple answer lies in the fact that these two types are much easier to recognize when one is looking for meteorites in the countryside. The "stones" are so similar to ordinary rocks that they often go unnoticed. The irons are quite easily "suspect" because of their high density; however, this is not a proof by itself. The irons, upon cutting, polishing, and etching with a mild acid, reveal a very interesting pattern of lines and geometric

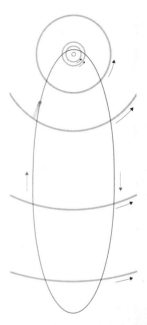

Figure 6.17 Stony meteorites with dark fusion crusts. (Ronald Oriti, Griffith Observatory)

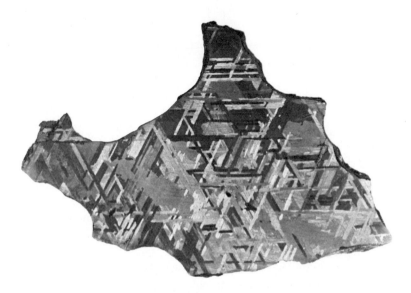

Figure 6.18 The polished section of an iron meteorite, showing Widmannstätten lines. (Ronald Oriti, Griffith Observatory)

designs (Figure 6.18). These are called *Widmannstätten lines,* and no natural rocklike material found on earth possesses such a pattern. The irons contain from 1 to 20 percent nickel as well. Nickel does not appear in this proportion along with iron in terrestrial materials.

ORBIT AND ORIGIN OF METEORITES

The facts mentioned immediately above point to an origin of meteorites outside the earth. The temperatures that the irons have experienced to produce the evident separation of materials of different density must have been much higher than anything experienced on the crust of the earth or during their flight to earth. We have seen from the discussion of meteor showers the close relationship between meteors and comets. It has been reported that of the more than 400 meteors for which the Harvard Observatory has computed the original orbit, the large majority possessed a cometlike orbit, and a cometary origin is quite likely. Several had orbits that suggested asteroidal origin, and radioactive dating of meteorites indicates an age of 4 to 5 billion years. Some observers have suggested that prior to, or coincident with, the creation of the planets, other objects of lesser size formed. The centers of these objects experienced very high temperature, perhaps from short-lived radioactivity, creating a molten core. Materials of higher density gravitated to the center and, upon gradual cooling, remained in that separated state. The object later experienced a collision and broke into many smaller chunks, the core producing the iron meteorites, the outer portions producing the stones, and the intermediate layers the stony irons.

METEORITE CRATERS

If one stands on the rim of the Barringer Crater, near Winslow, Arizona, one cannot help but wonder what cataclysmic event could have caused this great natural depression in the earth's surface. What evidence do we have of its origin? Will an answer to this question shed any light on the origin of similar features on the moon? If we assume that the Barringer Crater is the result of the high-speed impact of a massive object from outside the earth, then we should expect that upon impact the object itself suffered some damage. It might have partly fragmented, leaving a portion buried deep within the ground; it might have fragmented entirely, distributing its mass over the area surrounding the crater; or it might have vaporized completely, leaving no visible trace. The fact that more than 30 metric tons of meteoric material have been found around the Barringer Crater strongly suggests its impact origin; however, no central object has yet been found (Figure 6.19).

We should also expect to see evidence of the high temperature and high pressure that would naturally have accompanied such an impact. Surrounding a number of craters there exists a very dense form of silica called *coesite*. Silica of this density is not generally found, and it is believed to result from the tremendous shock wave that accompanies the impact of a large object on the earth. Under this sudden increase of pressure, rocks do not always shatter along their normal fracture lines, and the shatter structure of the crustal materials that surround the impact area very often shows a special form. High temperature may exhibit itself in the formation of glasslike objects from constituents of

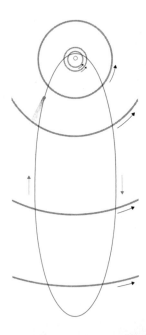

the soil. Tektites, to be discussed in the next section, may be a by-product of such an impact.

With these tools the scientist sets out to test specific features of the earth's surface. Where does he look? Unlike the moon, the earth has only a very limited number of sites that resemble a crater structure. The most obvious sites have been tested, and many reveal their impact origin by meeting at least two of the criteria mentioned above. Less obvious sites are sometimes revealed by satellite photography or by a very careful study of topographic maps that show the contours of a given region. While a certain site may look almost flat today, at an earlier time its crater form may have been very obvious. The change would have taken place gradually as a result of erosion. Atmospheric factors such as wind, rain, and temperature variations have effectively obliterated the once obvious surface features. Lacking an atmosphere, the moon craters are subject to almost no erosion and therefore remain almost unchanged for thousands of years.

The age of a crater can be roughly inferred from its appearance. The Barringer Crater, the result of a relatively recent event, is probably no more than 30,000 years old. On the other hand, the Vredefort Crater of South Africa, almost undiscernable now, is probably 250 million years old. The impact force that produced the Vredefort is estimated to be 500,000 times that which produced the Barringer. The Vredefort Crater has a diameter of almost 10 km, whereas the diameter of the Barringer is about 1.3 km.

Figure 6.19 The Barringer Crater, near Winslow, Arizona. (Meteor Crater Museum)

Figure 6.20 Some tektites from Thailand. (Ronald Oriti, Griffith Observatory)

In this century there have been two large falls, both in Siberia—one in 1908, and the other in 1947. Even at the rate of one large fall for every 1000 years, the earth should have experienced 1000 such events in the past 1 million years, yet no such frequency is indicated by the number of known craters. Perhaps many eroded craters lie undiscovered.

Large-impact craters are primarily caused by iron or stony-iron meteorites or asteroids, for only these falling objects have sufficient mass and density to survive their fiery flight to earth. The meteorite that is believed to have produced the Barringer Crater is estimated to have had a weight of over 100,000 metric tons.

TEKTITES

We will discuss the subject of *tektites* separately because there is a great deal of controversy about their origin. Are they objects that have been thrown from the moon as a result of meteorite impact there, or were they created right here on earth by a similar event? These represent the two basic schools of thought. Tektites are small glassy black objects that when held to the light may be translucent and take on a brownish or greenish color. They appear in several characteristic shapes, as shown in Figure 6.20.

Tektite falls have been discovered in several restricted parts of the world, the largest occurring in the Southwest Pacific area, including

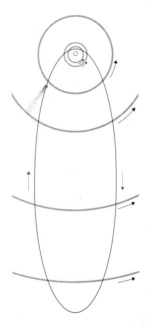

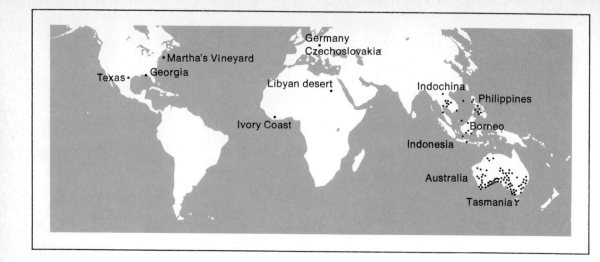

Figure 6.21 Tektites are found only in a limited number of locations on the earth's surface. Each dot represents a field over which tektites were strewn.

Figure 6.22 Australites—tektites from Australia. (NASA)

Australia, Indochina, the Philippines, and Indonesia (Figure 6.21). Other lesser falls have been discovered along the Ivory Coast of Africa, in Czechoslovakia, and in the United States (Texas and Georgia). The very fact that these falls seem to occur only in certain areas suggests an earthly origin; but if such is the case, a crater—or some other evidence of the event that produced these objects—should be visible. This is especially true in the case of the *australites* (Australian tektites; Figure 6.22),

230

because their age is estimated at only 5000 years. Natural erosion would not have covered such a crater in that length of time, and no such evidence has been found. In the case of the *indochinites,* with an estimated age of at least 100,000 years, or those that are still older, a crater associated with these objects might have been obliterated by erosion processes.

An analysis of the composition of tektites reveals a close similarity to certain igneous (once molten) rocks that are high in silica, and also some resemblance to sedimentary types. Those who favor a lunar origin argue that the composition of the moon is quite similar. The crust of the moon is now known to be basaltic in composition and igneous in origin—at least in the areas surveyed thus far. The shape of certain tektites resembles that of a droplet, indicating that they were once molten, then solidified; furthermore, their peculiar surface texture indicates that they passed through the atmosphere, during which time some of their material was lost. The australites in particular may indicate two periods of melting, the first upon impact and the second upon passage through the atmosphere, at which time more material was lost from one side than from the other (Figure 6.22). Those who favor a terrestrial origin would say that the australites were thrown higher than other types. The controversy concerning the origin of these objects will be settled only as a result of further research in the area.

MICROMETEORITES

In addition to meteorite and tektite falls, approximately 1000 metric tons of material fall on the earth each day from extraterrestrial sources. Most of this material may be termed *micrometeorites:* individual particles so small that they are not heated as they pass through the earth's atmosphere and therefore produce no visible streaks of light. This form of deposit may actually serve to enrich the soil in certain lean areas of the earth's surface.

QUESTIONS

1. The first asteroids discovered had orbits that lie between the orbits of which two planets?
2. What is the general range of size of the asteroids?
3. Why are astronomers particularly interested in the asteroids having very eccentric orbits that carry them close to the sun and across the orbits of several planets?

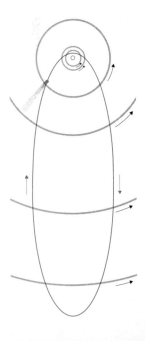

4. New asteroids are discovered most easily on a photographic plate that has been exposed for an hour or more. During the exposure, the telescope is moved to follow the stars. How is an asteroid recognized on such a plate?

5. If all the material of the known asteroids could be combined into one "planet," how would that planet compare in size and mass to that of the earth?

6. Does a comet have a tail during its entire orbit around the sun? Explain.

7. The planets all orbit the sun in the same direction and along almost the same plane. Is this also true of comets? Explain.

8. Explain what is meant by the "Jovian group" of comets.

9. What is thought to be the primary nature of the head of a comet?

10. Why does the tail of a comet always extend away from the sun?

11. May only professional astronomers have their names associated with a new comet? Explain.

12. Describe the usual appearance of a comet when it is first discovered.

13. When is the best time to observe meteors? Why?

14. What is the range of size of most meteoroids as they begin their fiery flight into the earth's atmosphere?

15. Meteor showers are thought to be associated with what other astronomical object?

16. Why is the occurrence of a meteor shower predictable?

17. List the different types of meteorites.

18. Most meteorites that have been dated by radioactive elements have been found to be which of the following: (a) much younger than the earth; (b) about the same age as the earth; (c) much older than the earth?

19. Why have we not found a meteor crater for each large meteorite that has hit the earth in the last 1 billion years?

20. True or false: The composition of tektites prove their origin on the moon. Explain.

21. What evidence does the astronomer have for thinking of asteroids as objects of irregular shape?

22. Why is it true that comets often develop two tails? How would you recognize the composition of each tail?

23. In addition to the theory that proposes a comet cloud surrounding the solar system, can you think of any other theory which might explain the origin of comets?

24. In what ways do Kepler's laws apply to comets? How is the period of a comet related to its average distance from the sun?

25. Why is it impossible to predict the approximate number of meteors that will be seen during a given meteor shower, even if that same shower has been observed many times before?

SUGGESTED READINGS

Cameron, I. R., Meteorites and cosmic radiation. *Scientific American* **229** (1), 64–73 (1973).

Jacchia, Luigi, The brightness of comets. *Sky and Telescope* **47** (4), 216–220 (1974).

Jacchia, Luigi, A scientist's comet. *Sky and Telescope* **47** (3), 153–158 (1974).

Lawless, J. G., Folsome, C. E., and Kvenvolden, K. A., Organic matter in meteorites. *Scientific American* **226** (6), 38–46 (1972).

Middlehurst, Barbara M., and Kuiper, Gerard P. (eds.), *The moon, meteorites and comets*. Chicago: University of Chicago Press, 1963.

Whipple, Fred L., The nature of comets. *Scientific American* **230** (2), 48–57 (1974).

Wood, John A., *Meteorites and the origin of the planets*. New York; McGraw-Hill, 1968.

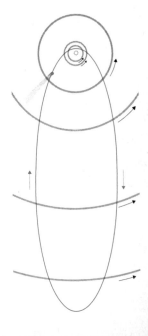

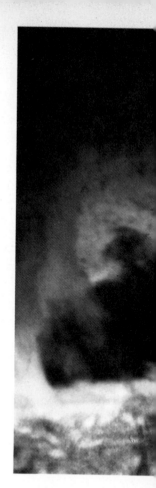

THE SUN

7

To speak of the sun as a star is to designate its true nature, which is drastically different from that of the planets, the moon, the meteors, and the comets. The sun is a tremendous seething inferno, generating its own energy from within. Most of the sources of energy on the earth may be traced back to the sun. Fossil fuels, such as coal and oil, are derived from once-living organisms that were dependent on the sun for their existence. Life as we know it today depends upon energy from the sun for its continuance. In this respect we must

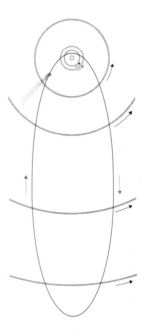

235

realize that the earth is situated at a very strategic distance from the sun. As was defined earlier, the average distance of the earth from the sun is called the *astronomical unit,* a fundamental unit of measure upon which rests the determination of the distances to the other planets. Modern methods, using radar, have greatly simplified the task of finding this distance; however, if a radar signal were directed toward the sun, its echo would be very difficult to detect against the background of other radio signals that the sun itself emits. Therefore an indirect approach is employed to find the astronomical unit. A radar signal is directed toward a given planet or asteroid, and the time required for the echo of that signal to be heard is noted. Since the observer knows the speed with which the radar signal travels, he may then compute the distance to the object from the time required for the two-way trip. Knowing both the distance and period of an object that orbits the sun, he can then calculate the astronomical unit using Kepler's third law, which says that the square of a planet's period is proportional to the cube of its average distance from the sun. For instance, suppose that the average distance between the earth and Mars is found by radar observation to be 78,389,294 km, the computation of the astronomical unit would take on this form (Figure 7.1):

$$\frac{P_1{}^2}{P_2{}^2} = \frac{r_1{}^3}{r_2{}^3}$$

$$\frac{(1.88)^2}{(1)^2} = \frac{(x + 78,389,294)^3}{x^3}$$

$$x = 149,597,890 \text{ km} \quad \text{(details of solution not shown)}$$

Here P_1 is the period of Mars, and P_2 is that of the earth; r_1 is the average distance of Mars from the sun, and r_2 (equals x) is the average distance of the earth from the sun. Thus, 145,597,890 km is the internationally adopted value of the astronomical unit (A.U.).

PHYSICAL CHARACTERISTICS
OF THE SUN

The determination of the diameter of the sun follows directly from our knowledge of its distance from the earth as well as the apparent angle that its diameter makes with our eye. Let us suppose that the sun makes an angle of 0.532° on a day when its distance is 149,598,000 km. The calculations that follow exemplify a very useful technique which requires only a simple proportion and arithmetic to solve for the diameter of a distant object.

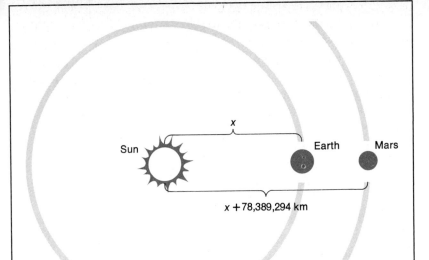

Figure 7.1 Average distance between the sun and earth, and between the sun and Mars. The period of Mars (P_1) is 1.88 years; the period of the earth (P_2) is 1 year.

It is evident in Figure 7.2 that the angle of 0.532° compares to the entire angle at the center of the circle (360°) in the same way that the diameter of the sun (d) compares to the entire circumference of the circle ($2\pi r$):

$$\frac{0.532°}{360°} = \frac{d}{2\pi(149,598,000 \text{ km})}$$

Solving for d:

$$d = \frac{0.532(2\pi)(149,598,000)}{360} = 1,390,000 \text{ km}$$

This gives a diameter of approximately 1,390,000 km, almost 110 times that of the earth.

The great volume of the sun is hard for us to visualize: more than 1 million earths might be dropped into the space occupied by the sun. The mass of the sun is determined by the gravitational effect that it has on the earth, causing the earth to "fall" toward the sun at all times,

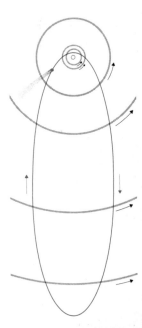

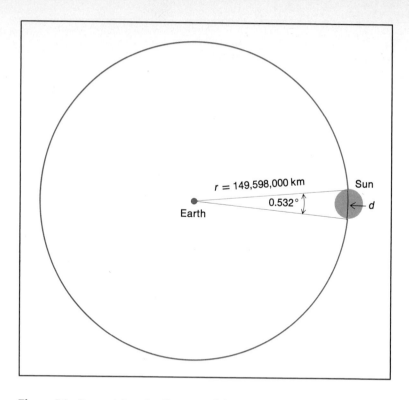

Figure 7.2 Determining the diameter of the sun.

thus maintaining the earth in its orbit. Using Newton's laws of motion, the mass of the sun is found to be approximately 2×10^{33} g, more than 300,000 times the mass of the earth. When mass and volume are compared, we see that the average density of the sun is only one-fourth that of the earth, or 1.4 g/cm³. This density is similar to that of certain rocks on the crust of the earth. Does this suggest that the sun is of a crusty nature, rigid in shape and form? No. The sun must be characterized as a ball of gas that under certain conditions of temperature and pressure can have a higher density without being of a solid nature.

ROTATION OF THE SUN

With the development of an early telescope, Galileo recognized sunspots as being associated with the visual surface of the sun and noted the rotation of the sun by watching their movement. Modern methods have refined his observations principally by use of the Doppler shift. Any object that is rotating on an axis perpendicular to the observer's line of sight presents one edge that is moving away from the observer (the *receding limb*) and another that is moving toward him (the *approaching*

Table 7.1   Period of solar rotation at various latitudes

LATITUDE	DAYS
0°	24.6
15°	25.4
30°	26.4
60°	31.0
75°	33.0

limb). Light from the receding limb will exhibit a shift of its spectral lines toward the red end of the spectrum; similarly, light from the approaching limb will exhibit a shift of its spectral lines toward the blue end. The amount by which the spectral lines are shifted indicates the speed of recession or approach. When measured at different latitudes on the sun, the period of rotation varies as shown in Table 7.1.

These observations indicate that the sun does not rotate as a solid at a uniform rate but rather as a gas with points near the equator completing one rotation in the least time. Sunspot observations that were made by early astronomers or that you could make today would confirm these rates very closely (Figure 7.3).

THE SUN, A HYDROGEN FUSION REACTOR

We often use the expression, "The sun is burning." Were the sun merely burning, however, it could not begin to produce the vast amount of energy that radiates from its surface. The astronomer now realizes that the true source of the sun's energy is a nuclear reaction similar to that of the hydrogen bomb but under controlled conditions which produce a quiescent release of energy. At the temperature (15 million degrees Kelvin and up) and pressure (1 billion atmospheres) found at the core of the sun, changes take place within the nucleus of the atoms. The hydrogen atom supplies the "fuel" for this reaction. Hydrogen is the simplest atom in the universe, consisting of one *proton* (positively charged particle) in the nucleus and one *electron* (negatively charged particle), which is thought to orbit the *nucleus*. For the purpose of this

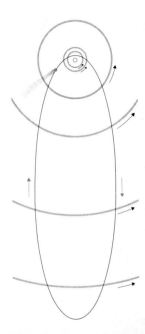

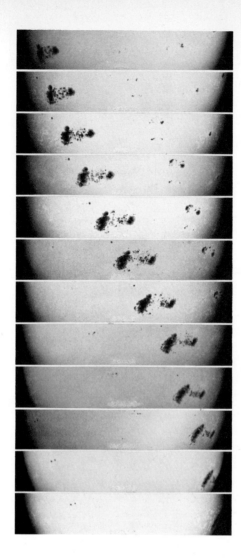

Figure 7.3 The sunspots show the rotation of the sun, photographed daily from April 2 to 13, 1947. North is at right. (Hale Observatories)

discussion, the electron may be ignored, for we are primarily concerned with nuclear changes only. The first step in this chain reaction occurs when two hydrogen nuclei combine to form a special type of hydrogen called *deuterium* ($^2_1$H). This may be pictured as follows, where $\oplus$ represents a proton and $\text{\textcircled{N}}$ represents a neutron:

$$\oplus + \oplus \rightarrow \oplus\text{\textcircled{N}} + \text{positron}$$

or

$$^1_1\text{H} + {}^1_1\text{H} \rightarrow {}^2_1\text{H} + {}^0_1\text{e}$$

A positron ($^0_1$e) is viewed as a particle similar in mass to an electron but with a positive charge. The second step occurs when the deuterium atom combines with still another hydrogen atom to form helium 3 ($^3_2$He) plus a gamma ray:

⊕Ⓝ + ⊕ → ⊕⊕Ⓝ + gamma ray

or

$^2_1$H + $^1_1$H → $^3_2$He + gamma ray

The third step occurs when two such helium 3 ($^3_2$He) atoms combine to form an atom of helium 4 ($^4_2$He) and two hydrogen atoms:

⊕⊕Ⓝ + ⊕⊕Ⓝ → ⊕⊕ⓃⓃ + ⊕ + ⊕

or

$^3_2$He + $^3_2$He → $^4_2$He + $^1_1$H + $^1_1$H

Since two hydrogen atoms are given back in the final reaction, only four hydrogen atoms were used in forming the one helium 4 atom; however, the mass of the helium 4 atom is less than the total mass of the four hydrogen atoms. It is this difference in mass, which has been converted into energy, that constitutes the source of energy for the sun and for stars in general.

Each hydrogen nucleus has a mass of 1.008 amu (atomic mass units), making a total of 4.032 amu for four such nuclei. The helium 4 nucleus has a mass of 4.003 amu, hence 0.029 units have been converted into energy. How much energy? The relationship between mass and energy was expressed by Albert Einstein in the equation $E = mc^2$, where E is the amount of energy (in ergs), m is the mass that is converted (in grams), and c is the velocity of light (in centimeters per second). The velocity of light has been found to be approximately 3×10^{10} cm/sec. This number squared would equal 9×10^{20}. Therefore Einstein's equation, stated in words, says that the total amount of energy produced is equivalent to 9×10^{20} (that is, 900,000,000,000,000,000,000) times the mass that is converted, using the units mentioned above. The sun converts almost 4.5 million metric tons of mass per second, producing energy at a rate of almost 4×10^{33} erg/sec. Even at this fantastic rate, the sun could continue this reaction for 150 billion years without depleting its supply of hydrogen appreciably; however, other factors will likely influence the reactions, and the sun is not expected to remain as it is now for that length of time. This nuclear reaction is called the *proton-proton cycle* and is initiated and sustained by a central core temperature of about 15 million degrees Kelvin. At higher temperatures, a reaction called the *carbon cycle* may become more important, but the net result is almost the same. Four

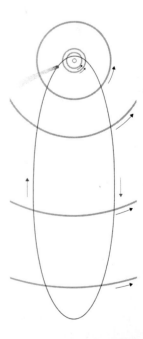

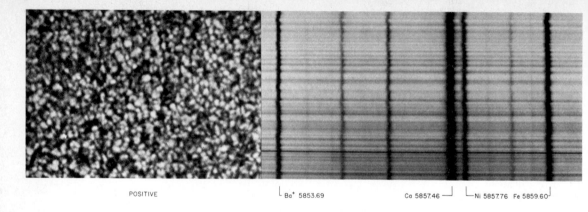

POSITIVE   Ba⁺ 5853.69   Ca 5857.46   Ni 5857.76 Fe 5859.60

Figure 7.4 The granulation of the photosphere. The rising columns of gas cause a Doppler shift in the spectrum in one direction, whereas the falling gases cause a shift in the opposite direction, producing the waviness of the spectral lines. (Aerospace Corporation; Sacramento Peak Observatory)

hydrogen nuclei react to form one helium 4 nucleus, the difference in mass having been converted into energy. Carbon merely serves as a catalyst for the reaction. (The carbon cycle is considered in detail in Chapter 12.)

LAYERS OF THE SUN

The fusion of hydrogen into helium is continually building a helium core within the sun, with the immediate layer surrounding that core being the layer of thermonuclear reactions (hydrogen "burning"). Tremendous quantities of energy are being produced and must be transported to other layers and ultimately to space. Astronomers believe that the major transport mechanism within the body of the sun is radiation. Energy generated in the core of the sun travels through the *radiation zone* by means of a multiple absorption and reemission process until it contacts a layer that is opaque to this means of transport. This layer is called the *convective envelope* and, as its name implies, it transports energy only by means of the motion of the material within it, hot gases rising to deliver energy to the visible surface of the sun and then the cooled gases falling to be reheated. We can imagine the violent motion which must take place in order to transport the vast quantities of energy being emitted from the core through the radiation zone, but what evidence do we have of this turbulent motion? When the sun is photographed in white light, its "surface" takes on a spotty appearance called the *granulation of the photosphere* (Figure 7.4). The bright spots are interpreted as rising columns of hot gases; the darker regions, as

242

cooled gases that are returning to lower levels to be heated once again. This interpretation is borne out when we inspect the spectrogram accompanying Figure 7.4. The waviness of the spectral lines is due to the Doppler shifts caused by the motion of the gases; blue shifts are associated with the rising spots that are approaching the observer; red shifts are associated with the cooler gases receding from the observer.

The layer immediately above the convective envelope is called the *photosphere*. You will see that this layer presents a sharp outline in the white light photograph (Figure 7.5); it also shows some depth, however, by the darkening which is seen near the limb (edge) of the sun. When we look at the central portion of the solar image, we can see through the photosphere to its lower levels, where temperatures are in the order of 6000°K. When we look near the limb of the sun we are seeing the higher levels of the photosphere, where temperatures are reduced, and the limb therefore appears darker to us. This temperature decrease not only explains limb darkening but is an essential factor in the formation of the solar spectrum. The spectrum of the sun is an absorp-

Figure 7.5 A white light photograph of the sun showing limb darking due to the cooling trend in the upper levels of the photosphere. (Hale Observatories)

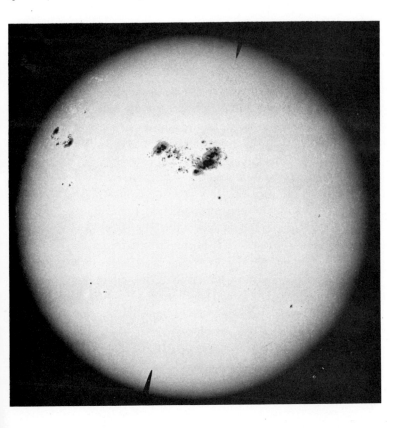

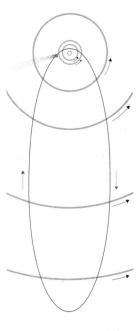

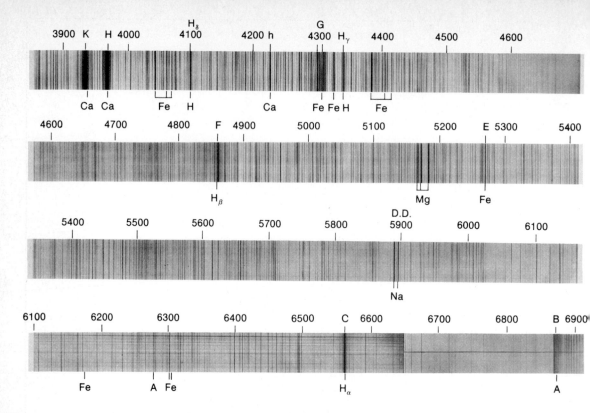

Figure 7.6 The solar spectrum, with certain lines identified with known elements. (Hale Observatories)

tion spectrum (Figure 7.6), and it is within this photospheric layer that absorption takes place, according to the elements that are present. In other words, if we could look at the sun's spectrum at the lower boundary of the photosphere, it would likely be of a continuous nature, but as we view it from the upper boundary, it is an absorption spectrum. As a result it reveals the composition of the photosphere and lower chromosphere, not the core or other interior layers (Figure 7.7).

The next layer of the solar atmosphere is called the *chromosphere* (colored sphere), and it extends approximately 10,000 km above the photosphere. The chromosphere is normally invisible due to the brilliance of the photosphere; however, when the central disk of the sun is covered by the moon during an eclipse, the reddish light of the chromosphere may be seen. When the light from this layer is allowed to enter the spectrograph, the bright-line spectrum of the chromosphere is revealed (Figure 7.8). The chromosphere is composed largely of hydrogen gas that produces a bright red line in its spectrum; hence it takes on its characteristic reddish hue. No longer must the astronomer wait for the occurrence of a solar eclipse to study the chromosphere,

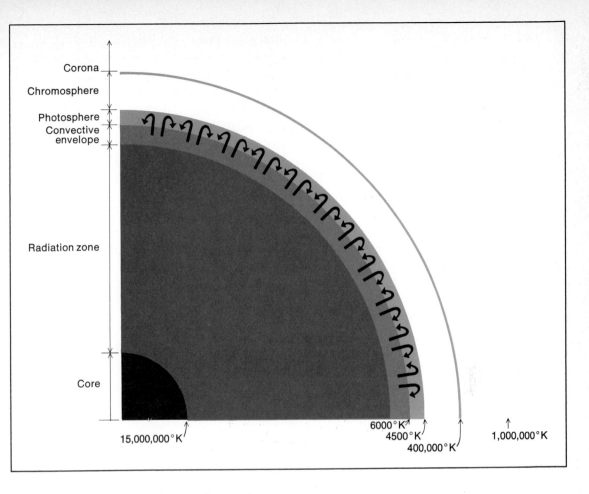

Figure 7.7 Layers of the sun, shown with approximate temperature distribution.

for he may artificially cover the solar disk near the focal plane of his telescope and thereby photograph only the chromosphere itself. Such a device is called a *coronagraph*. The spectrum of the chromosphere reveals a temperature gradation from 4500°K near the photosphere to 400,000°K in its upper levels.

The third principal layer of the solar atmosphere is the *corona* (Figure 7.9). Like the chromosphere, the corona is normally invisible, owing to the brilliance of the photosphere; however, if it is viewed during a total solar eclipse or photographed using the coronagraph, its extended luminous region becomes visible, largely as a result of the scattering of light by particles in the corona. The visible portion is only a very small part of the corona, for the latter is now known to extend beyond the earth itself. In fact, most of the sun's family of planets is continually bathed in its outflow of material. It is true that the sun

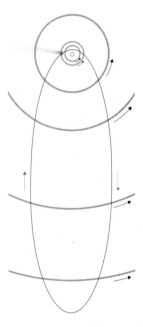

245

sends out in every direction many forms of electromagnetic disturbances, such as light, radio, and X rays; however, this is not the full extent of its radiation. There also appears to be a continual outflow of particles from the sun. These include negatively charged electrons and positively charged protons, the component parts of the hydrogen gas that is the basic constituent of the solar atmosphere. While the corona is more static near the sun, farther out in the vicinity of the planets it constitutes an expanding envelope and therefore produces a rapidly moving stream of charged particles called the *solar wind*. We have seen its effect on the tail of a comet, always driving it away from the sun. At the earth's distance from the sun, the solar wind has a velocity of about 1,450,000 km/hr. The amount of material that is removed from the sun, in the form of this solar wind, is approximately 1×10^9 kg/sec; however, in terms of the total mass of the sun, this represents a very negligible amount of material. As these charged particles approach the earth's magnetic field, they are deflected into a spiral path around the earth and eventually spiral toward the north or south polar regions, where they react with the atoms of the earth's atmosphere to produce the northern or southern lights.

The temperature of the corona can be determined by the degree to which elements in this layer are ionized. Iron, for instance, has 26 electrons in each atom under normal conditions of pressure and tem-

Figure 7.8 The bright line spectrum of the chromosphere, photographed during a total solar eclipse. (Hale Observatories)

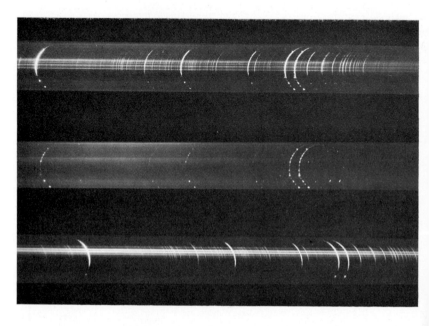

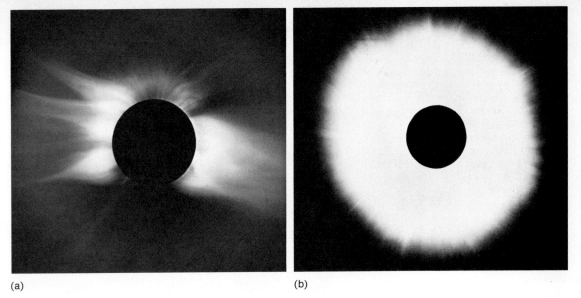

(a)   (b)

Figure 7.9 The corona: (a) during a sunspot minimum; (b) during a sunspot maximum. (High Altitude Observatory; Yerkes Observatory)

perature. In the corona of the sun, the spectrum reveals that as many as 13 of these electrons have been lost, indicating a temperature of about 1 million degrees Kelvin. The mechanism whereby the corona is heated to such a high temperature is presently unknown. One theory suggests that shock waves produced in the convective envelope may be instrumental in producing this high temperature.

THE SOLAR SPECTRUM

The electromagnetic radiation of the sun exhibits itself in many forms; the light that we see, the infrared and ultraviolet light on either side of the visible spectrum, radio, X rays, and so on. Figure 7.10 shows a plot of the average output of the sun in these various wavelengths. The total area under the curve denotes the amount of solar energy received by the earth at the outer edge of its atmosphere. This amount is the so-called *solar constant* and is equivalent to approximately 2 cal/cm^2/min. One calorie (cal) of energy is sufficient to raise the temperature of 1 cm^3 of water 1°C. While the amount of energy the earth receives from the sun is tremendous, we must remember that the earth intercepts less than one-billionth of the total energy that is radiated from the sun. The remainder is received by other planets or dissipated in space.

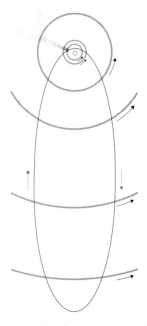

247

Figure 7.10 The solar spectrum. The total solar energy received at the top of the earth's atmosphere is represented by the total area under the curve. This is called the solar constant and amounts to approximately 2 calories per square centimeter per minute. (Compiled by H. H. Malitson, NASA—Goddard Space Flight Center)

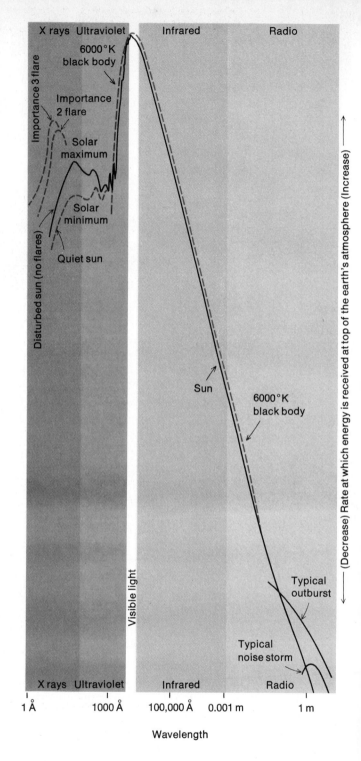

Figure 7.11 A small portion of the solar spectrum. The central bands with dark lines represent the spectrum of the sun. The bright lines above and below the solar spectrum represent the spectrum of iron (photographed for comparison). (Hale Observatories)

Because of its high intensity, the visible spectrum of the sun is the easiest natural spectrum with which we may work; it may be spread out over a distance of 13 m or more, thus revealing more than 30,000 absorption lines. It is presumed that most of these lines were formed in the photosphere of the sun. It should be pointed out, however, that the earth's atmosphere may also create some of the lines, in which case they are called *telluric lines* and are usually associated with such elements as nitrogen, oxygen, and water vapor, which are found in the earth's atmosphere. Telluric lines may be distinguished from the spectral lines of the sun in that they show no Doppler shift, whereas the spectral lines of the receding and approaching limbs of the sun show a Doppler shift due to rotation. How may the astronomer determine which elements are indicated by the some 30,000 lines in the solar spectrum? The spectrum of a known element must be placed alongside the solar spectrum to see if all the lines of the given element match their corresponding lines in the solar spectrum. In Figure 7.11 you will see that the lines of iron do in fact match a given set of spectral lines in the solar spectrum, from which we conclude that iron is present—in a vaporized form—in the photosphere of the sun. Following this procedure, approximately 70 of the 92 natural elements that occur on the earth have been found to exist within the solar atmosphere.

The spectrum of the sun also gives an indication of temperature. The photosphere radiates maximum energy at a wavelength of approximately 4700 Å (angstroms), indicating a surface temperature of 6000°K. This follows directly from a consideration of the energy radiated by a black body at various temperatures. A *black body* is any object that absorbs all the energy that falls on it and then radiates all the energy that it has received. As the temperature of the black body increases, not only does the total energy radiated increase, but the

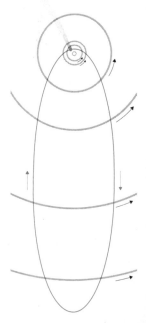

249

wavelength at which maximum energy occurs also changes (Figure 7.12). The sun's energy distribution best fits the black body curve corresponding to a temperature of 6000°K.

SPECTROHELIOGRAPH

Solar activities can not be easily seen in photographs taken in the ordinary light of the sun. A *spectroheliogram* is a photograph of the sun taken in the light of only one narrow portion of the spectrum. The word itself reveals this meaning, for if we take it apart in reverse order, "gram" means picture, "helio" means sun, and "spectro" means that we use the spectrum to obtain the picture. The *spectroheliograph* is the instrument by which such a picture is taken. This may be accomplished either by use of a filter that allows only the desired wavelength to pass or by use of a more complicated arrangement of spectrograph and a moving slit. If we choose to use the light in the first red line of the hydrogen spectrum—the *hydrogen-alpha* (H_α) line—we shall obtain a picture of the sun that represents the upper photosphere. If we want to view the lower chromosphere, we may use the light of the K line of ionized calcium (Ca II). The temperature within the bright regions, as viewed in the light of calcium, may reach 20,000°K—despite the fact that these same regions are usually directly over a sunspot, a relatively cool region of the photosphere [see Figure 7.13(c)].

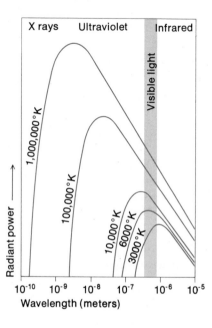

Figure 7.12 The energy distribution for a number of different temperatures.

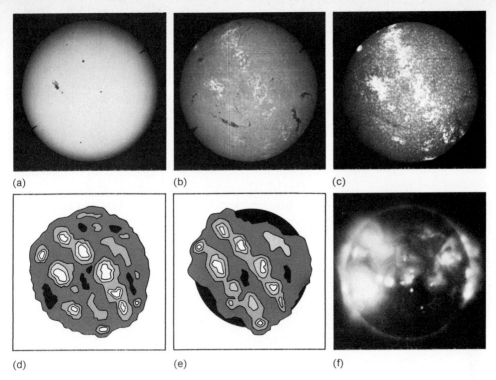

(a) (b) (c)

(d) (e) (f)

Figure 7.13 The sun: (a) in ordinary light; (b) in the light of H$_\alpha$; (c) in the light of Ca II; (d) in ultraviolet radiation of O VI; (e) in ultraviolet radiation of Si XII; (f) X-ray photo. [a–c, Hale Observatories; f, from L. P. VanSpeybroeck, A. S. Krieger, and G. S. Vaiana, *Nature* **227,** 818–822 (1970)]

With the increasing use of the Orbiting Astronomical Observatories, astronomers can now study the sun in ultraviolet wavelengths. In order to interpret these results, as seen in Figure 7.13(d,e), we must first recognize how they were obtained. We have just referred to Ca II, which stands for calcium atoms that have been ionized once (that is, which have lost one of their electrons); Ca I stands for neutral calcium, atoms that have the same number of electrons as protons. The representation of the sun shown in Figure 7.13(d) was derived from information received from an ionized form of oxygen, namely, O VI. This is oxygen which has been ionized five times. In such an atom, certain electron transitions are possible that are not possible in neutral oxygen. One such transition produces an ultraviolet wavelength of 1032 Å, and it was at this wavelength that the information was received. Furthermore, a temperature in the range of 350,000°K is necessary to ionize oxygen to this degree, and such a temperature exists in the upper chromosphere; hence we have a "picture" of the sun at that level. It is not a photograph in the usual sense, but rather a plot showing the hot spots (lighter areas) and cooler regions (dark areas).

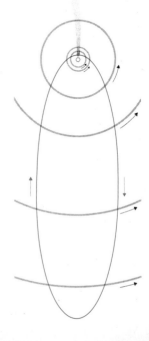

Suppose we want to look at a higher level of the sun. We choose a wavelength produced by an ionized atom at still higher temperature, say, 2,000,000°K. Silicon XII (Si XII) is such an atom, emitting an ultraviolet line at 499 Å. We can now "see" the sun at a level well into the corona [Figure 7.13(e)].

Rockets fired above the earth's atmosphere have given us still another view of the sun. Revealed in X-ray wavelengths [Figure 7.13(f)] are perhaps the most energetic regions of the sun, areas of the corona where very high temperatures prevail and certain photospheric activities, like flares, occur. The nature of flares will be discussed shortly.

Thus, by expanding his use of the entire spectrum, the astronomer has gained a multilevel view of the sun.

SUNSPOTS

The *sunspot* is a region on the visible surface of the sun that consists of gases which are approximately 1000°K cooler than those surrounding the area. A typical sunspot consists of a very dark central portion called the *umbra,* surrounded by a less dense *penumbral* region (Figure 7.14).

Figure 7.14 Details of a sunspot group photographed in white light. The darkest portion is called the umbra and the gray portion is called the penumbra. Sunspots represent cooler regions on the visible surface of the sun. This same sunspot group, photographed in the red light of H$_\alpha$ is seen in Figure 7.16. (Hale Observatories)

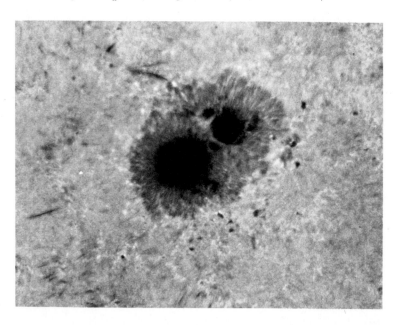

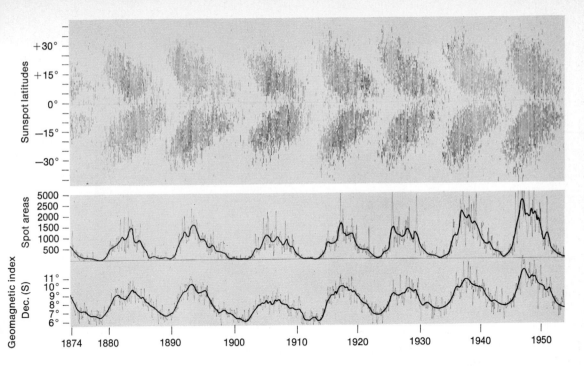

Figure 7.15 The butterfly pattern of sunspots from 1874 to 1953. The top view shows the plotting of the sunspots according to their latitude on the sun. The middle graph shows the number of sunspots. The lower graph shows the variations in the magnetic fields on the sun's surface. Note here the very close correlation between the sunspot cycle and the magnetic cycle. All three graphs reveal the 11-year cycle of these phenomena. (Royal Greenwich Observatory)

Let us trace the appearance of sunspots over a period of eleven years. First, consider the sun when it is devoid of spots—a "quiet" sun—as it appeared in 1944–1945. Next we see a few sunspots appearing in the northern and southern hemispheres at about 30° latitude. As the number of spots continues to increase, we observe that they also appear closer to the solar equator. Completing the 11-year period, the spots diminish in number as they move near the equator. A plot of the spots that occurred between 1874 and 1953, as shown in Figure 7.15, resembles a butterfly pattern; this pattern repeats every 11 years.

Further study indicates that strong magnetic disturbances on the sun are associated with sunspots; in fact, some astronomers believe that the spots are a direct result of these magnetic disturbances. Just how does the astronomer determine the existence of a strong magnetic field in the vicinity of a sunspot? A photograph of a sunspot region, if taken in the light of hydrogen (Figure 7.16), suggests a magnetic field around the spot, but it is not in itself a conclusive proof.

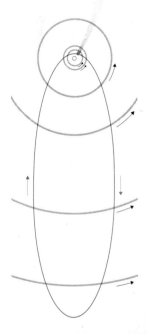

253

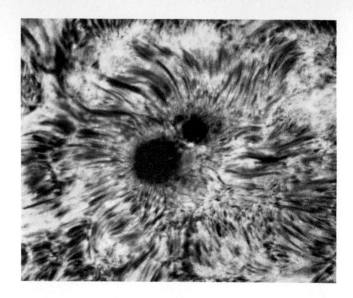

Figure 7.16 A spectroheliogram showing dark filaments in the vicinity of a sunspot group. Strong magnetic fields are suggested in this Big Bear Solar Observatory photo. (Hale Observatories)

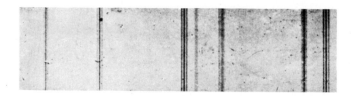

Figure 7.17 The Zeeman effect. The splitting of spectral lines results from the presence of a magnetic field on the region of radiation. (Yerkes Observatory)

ZEEMAN EFFECT

It has been observed that when light is created in the presence of a magnetic field, the lines of its spectrum are broadened or even split, depending upon the strength of the field. This is called the *Zeeman effect*. The degree to which the lines are split indicates the strength of the magnetic field, and the direction of optical polarization of the lines indicates the polarity of the field at any point (Figure 7.17).

If the sun is scanned on any given day, a plot of its magnetic properties may appear as it does in Figure 7.18. The brighter areas represent the stronger fields. Note the strong suggestion of magnetic fields about the regions of the sunspots. It is also evident that sunspots usually occur in pairs and that the two members of the pair have opposite magnetic polarity. This polarity is not always the same; however, in successive 11-year cycles the polarity is reversed. Figure 7.19 reveals the pattern of polarity in successive 11-year periods. Note that

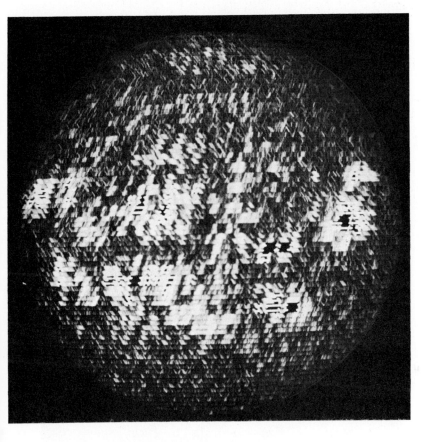

Figure 7.18 The magnetic fields of the sun. The brighter areas represent the stronger fields, and the slant of a region indicates the polarity of that region. (Hale Observatories)

Figure 7.19 Successive 11-year cycles of magnetic polarity of sunspots.

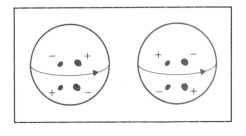

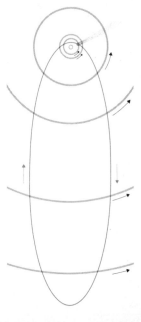

the polarity of sunspot pairs in the northern hemisphere is opposite to that of pairs in the southern hemisphere. When this reversal of polarity is considered, the sunspot cycle actually requires 22 years.

PLAGE AND FACULAE

The bright areas that appear in the region of sunspots, as revealed in the light of calcium or hydrogen, represent very active areas in the chromosphere, known as *plages*. Their presence where no sunspots are apparent may foretell the appearance of new spots or may be lingering indications of spots that have disappeared. They usually represent regions of high magnetic disturbances. Bright spots that appear in ordinary (white) light are called *faculae*.

SPICULES

Near the *limb* (edge) of the sun, in the upper chromosphere, the spectroheliogram reveals spikelike columns of gas jetting out much like the rising columns of gas in the photosphere. These *spicules* may show speeds of up to 32 km/sec and may sometimes reach to heights of 16,000 km (Figure 7.20).

Figure 7.20 Spicules in the sun's chromosphere photographed in red light of H_α at Big Bear Solar Observatory, April 30, 1972. (Hale Observatories)

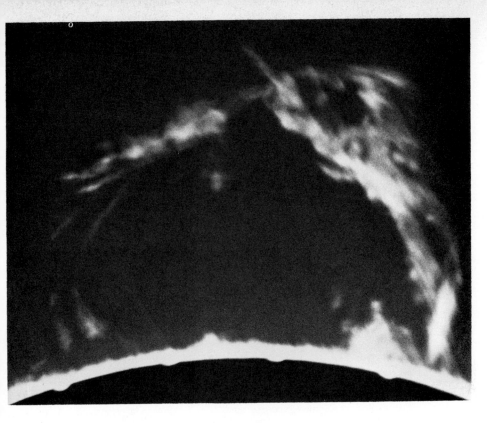

Figure 7.21 A solar prominence that reached a height of 330,000 km, photographed in the light of calcium (K line). (Hale Observatories)

PROMINENCES

For many years, activities of the solar atmosphere were observed only during a total solar eclipse, when the entire photosphere of the sun was covered by the moon. Gigantic protrusions were observed at that time. Now, by use of the spectroheliograph, these *prominences* may be studied at will. One kind of prominence may extend more than 320,000 km into the solar atmosphere and remain relatively fixed. This is known as the *quiescent* type. A second type called a *loop prominence*, takes on the shape of an arch or loop and exhibits motion within the loop, suggesting the presence of a magnetic field (Figure 7.21).

A third type of prominence is the *eruptive* type, which may send material out thousands of kilometers into the corona of the sun at speeds up to 640 km/sec (Figure 7.22).

The dark filaments, as seen in H$_\alpha$ light, represent prominences viewed from above. They tend to form along the boundary between the regions of opposite magnetic polarity associated with sunspots.

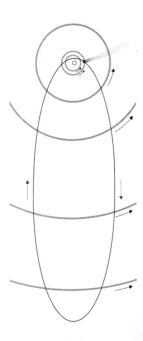

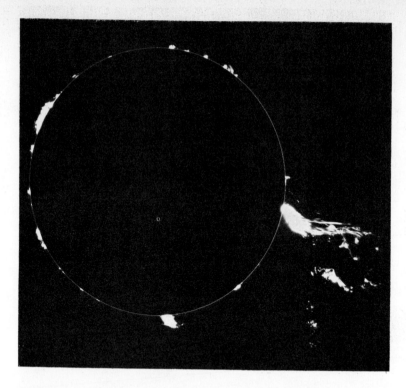

Figure 7.22 Prominences visible on March 1, 1969. The very large eruptive prominence extends approximately 645,000 km above the surface of the sun. (Haleakala Observatory, Institute for Astronomy, University of Hawaii)

THE SOLAR FLARE

The *solar flare* represents the most dynamic activity associated with the surface or atmosphere of the sun; it represents a tremendous release of energy in a very short time (Figure 7.23). The sudden brightening, usually in the vicinity of a sunspot, accompanies a violent outthrusting of material. A flare may occur over an area 160,000 km in diameter, and the temperature associated with such an event may exceed 100 million degrees Kelvin. Flares often occur along the boundary between positively and negatively polarized regions of sunspot groups. It appears as though the magnetic fields had focused vast amounts of energy into a relatively small area, thus producing the flare.

Solar flares have a direct influence on the earth and on man. Radiation from a major flare could kill an astronaut if he were not protected by an atmosphere or by some artificial means. A flare may radiate more X rays than the entire sun for a limited period of time. The ionospheric layers of the earth's atmosphere are altered by such

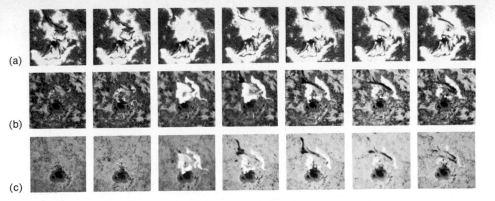

(a)

(b)

(c)

Figure 7.23 Solar flare. This sequence of spectroheliograms was taken over a period of 1 hr in the light of (a) H$_\alpha$ (hydrogen-alpha); (b) H$_\alpha$ plus 0.6 Å; (c) H$_\alpha$ plus 0.9 Å. Each sequence shows the development of the flare at a different level and also its association with a sunspot. (Aerospace Corporation; San Fernando Observatory)

Figure 7.24 The active sun.

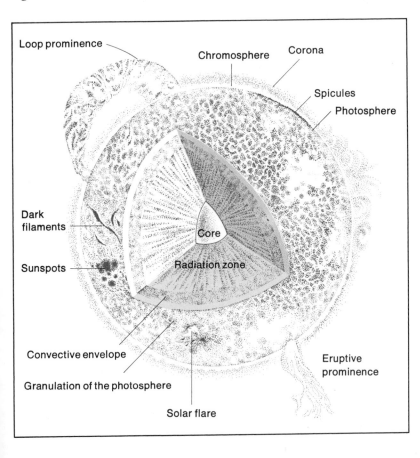

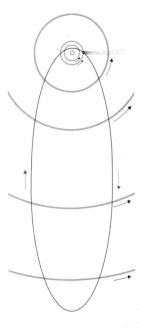

an outburst and may fail to reflect radio waves, thereby causing a communications blackout on the shortwave radio bands; the blackout may last for a few hours or up to a few days. About a day after the occurrence of a flare, the magnetic properties of the earth are usually disturbed, causing the needle of a compass to react in very strange ways.

OUR NEAREST STAR

The sun is our nearest star, and we have been able to examine it quite closely (Figure 7.24). As we move out into space, to the other stars of our Galaxy, we ask the same questions about them: How far? How big? How massive? Do they rotate? What kind of atmospheres? Do they have spots like the sun? Do they have a magnetic field? What is their temperature? What kinds of energy do they radiate?

QUESTIONS

1. What basic characteristics identify the sun as a star rather than a planet?
2. What is the apparent diameter of the sun, as measured in degrees? How does this compare to the apparent diameter of the full moon?
3. List several means by which the rotation of the sun is measured.
4. Does the sun rotate as if it were solid? Explain.
5. What does the granulation of the photosphere seem to suggest?
6. State the minimum temperature necessary to sustain the process whereby hydrogen is converted to helium in the core of the sun.
7. If hydrogen is considered to be the "fuel" of the thermonuclear process mentioned in the previous question, then what occurrence within the process explains the tremendous release of energy that results?
8. How much material (mass) of the sun is converted into energy every second?
9. The dark line spectrum of the sun is produced at what level (or layer) of the sun?
10. List the things that an astronomer might deduce from the solar spectrum.
11. Of what does the solar wind consist?
12. The temperature of the corona of the sun has been measured by its ionization level and found to be approximately _____ °K.
13. Define the solar constant.
14. List the kinds of electromagnetic radiation that the sun produces.
15. The number and location of sunspots seem to be repeated in a cycle of how many years?
16. When the spectral lines of the sun appear split, what condition is indicated?

17. When the sun is photographed in the light of hydrogen or of calcium, levels of the sun may be seen other than the photosphere. Explain what is seen in each of these lights.

18. The prominences of the sun are not seen in ordinary light. How may they be viewed?

19. What is the most dynamic activity associated with the sun?

20. How do solar activities affect the earth?

21. The normal spectrum of the sun is an absorption spectrum (dark lines). Why does the sun show an emission spectrum (bright lines) during a total solar eclipse?

22. Why is the chromosphere red?

23. The sun is now being photographed in the light of oxygen VI (ultraviolet) and in X rays. What do these photographs reveal by contrast with those taken in white light or in H_α (hydrogen–alpha) light?

24. What condition within a star or its atmosphere is necessary to ionize oxygen five times?

25. Supposing that the sun converted 5 million metric tons of mass into energy every second, find how much mass it has converted in 5 billion years.

SUGGESTED READINGS

Gingerich, O. (ed.), *Frontiers in astronomy* (Introductions to Chapters 8, 9, and 10). San Francisco: Freeman, 1970.

Goldberg, Leo, Ultraviolet astronomy. *Scientific American* **220** (6), 92–102 (1969).

Kuiper, Gerard P. (ed.), *The sun*. Chicago: University of Chicago Press, 1953.

Livingston, W. C., Measuring solar photospheric magnetic fields. *Sky and Telescope* **43** (6), 344–349 (1972).

Noyes, Robert W., Ultraviolet studies of the solar atmosphere. *Annual Review of Astronomy and Astrophysics* **9**, 209–236 (1971).

Pasachoff, Jay M., The fiery sun. *Natural History* **81** (5), 49–53 (1972).

Pasachoff, Jay M., The solar corona. *Scientific American* **229** (4), 68–79 (1973).

Zirin, Harold, *The solar atmosphere*. Waltham, Mass.: Blaisdell, 1966.

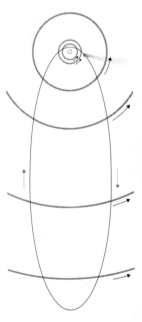

STARS
IN GENERAL

8

In order to determine factors such as the direction, distance, velocity, size, temperature, and luminosity of the stars, the astronomer must rely entirely upon his ability to interpret the radiation that he receives from them. Let us first consider the method for determining the distance to nearby stars.

When it is necessary to measure an inaccessible distance on the earth, the surveyor uses a method of triangulation. For instance, suppose that we wish to know the distance from a dock (A) on the

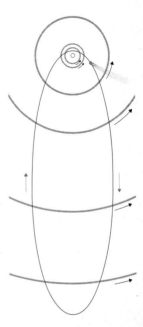

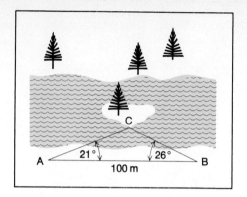

Figure 8.1 Triangulation.

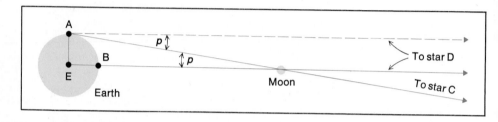

Figure 8.2 Geocentric parallax.

The proper motion of stars

bank of a river to a dock (C) on an island in the middle of the river (Figure 8.1). By laying off a base line AB along the bank of the river, say, 100 m long, and then measuring the angles formed at A and B, one can solve for side AC and get the desired distance.

For an object such as the moon, let us suppose that two observers are stationed at positions A and B on the earth (see Figure 8.2) and that they are in radio communication with each other. Observer B radios that he sees the moon in alignment with star D. At the same time, Observer A sees the moon in alignment with star C. Observer A can measure the angle between stars C and D, and since the rays of light from star D are almost parallel for both observers, we see that the angle between the stars is equal to the angle formed at the moon. This fact is expressed by the geometric theorem: *Alternate interior angles of parallel lines are equal.* Since the base line AE—the radius of the earth—is a known distance, it is possible to calculate the distance from A or B to the moon. This method, called *geocentric parallax,* is of only limited usefulness, owing to its relatively short base line. However, the usefulness of the idea may be extended by using a much longer base line, namely, the radius of the earth's orbit (see Figure 8.3). Suppose that when the earth is in position A the nearby star S aligns with the

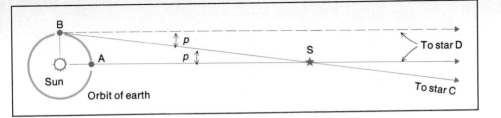

Figure 8.3 Heliocentric parallax.

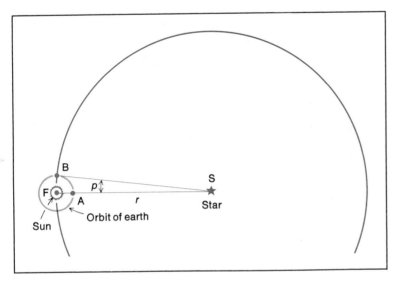

Figure 8.4 Properties of small angles.

more distant star D, but that three months later, when the earth is at position B, star S aligns with star C. By measuring the angle between stars C and D, the astronomer then knows the angle formed at the star S. This angle is called the *heliocentric parallax* of the star and is always less than 1 second ($\frac{1}{3600}$ degree) in size. Triangles that have such a small angle can be solved by a special method. Consider a very large circle with center at star S and with radius equal to the distance r (see Figure 8.4). The base line (BF) is a small part of the large circle and compares to the entire circumference of the circle as the angle of parallax (p) compares to the entire circle of 360°, giving

$$\frac{BF}{2\pi r} = \frac{p°}{360°}$$

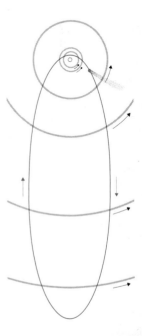

Solving for *r*, we get

$$r = \frac{360° \text{ (BF)}}{2\pi p°}$$

Changing units so as to use *p* in seconds and clearing the factor 2π yields:

$$r = \frac{206{,}265 \text{ (BF)}}{p''}$$

Since BF is equal to 1 A.U., we can now find *r* in astronomical units:

$$r = \frac{206{,}265 \text{ A.U.}}{p''}$$

If we let 206,265 A.U. equal 1 parsec, we get a much simpler expression:

$$r = \frac{1}{p''} \text{ parsec}$$

A *parsec* is simply the distance at which a star must be situated in order to exhibit 1 second of parallax, using 1 A.U. as a base line. The term "parsec" is a contraction of the two words *parallax* and *second*. Further calculations show that 1 parsec is equal to 3.26 light-years. Notice that the greater the distance (*r*) to the star, the smaller will be its parallax angle (*p*). Our nearest star, *Proxima Centauri,* has a parallax of 0.75 seconds, hence a distance of $1/0.75 = 1.33$ parsecs, or 4.3 light-years. This method of heliocentric parallax is limited to stars within 100 parsecs. Additional methods for distance determination will be presented later in this chapter.

MOTIONS OF STARS

Stars show very little evidence of motion and yet most are traveling at phenomenal rates of speed. These motions are not readily apparent, owing to their great distances from us. However, if we could watch the stars in the Big Dipper over a period of 100,000 years, we would realize that these stars are really moving in various different directions. Figure 8.5 shows the approximate location of the stars 100,000 years in the future. The small arrows indicate the direction of motion. (The left-hand flip pages beginning on page 264 reveal this proper motion of the stars in the Big Dipper.)

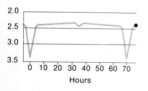

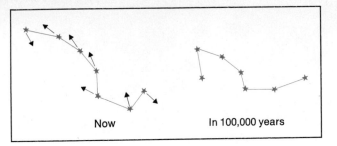

Now   In 100,000 years

Figure 8.5 Motions of stars in the Big Dipper.

PROPER MOTION

The proper motion of a star is the rate at which its position in the sky changes and is measured in terms of seconds of arc per year. Many stars exhibit such small changes that they must be photographed over many years in order to measure that change. A star that shows a shift of 2 seconds of arc in a period of 10 years has a proper motion of 2 seconds divided by 10 years, or 0.2 seconds of arc/year. Barnard's Star has the largest observed proper motion, equal to 10.25 seconds of arc/year (Figure 8.6). This star shows relatively large proper motion because it is the second closest star to the sun. While slightly more than 300 stars have proper motions of at least 1.0 seconds of arc/year, the average star seen with the naked eye has a proper motion of less than 0.1 seconds of arc/year. If the distance to a star is known, its proper motion can be translated into a *velocity* (speed) that is at right angles to the line of sight. This is called the tangential velocity of the star. Suppose that a star A is traveling in a direction AB, as is shown in Figure 8.7. Its tangential velocity is shown by AC and its radial velocity by AD.

RADIAL VELOCITY

Radial velocity is that component (part) of the velocity AB that is along the observer's line of sight, and it is represented by line AD in Figure 8.7. Radial velocity can be measured directly by the Doppler shift of a star's spectral lines. Since we can determine AD and AC, it is possible to calculate AB using the relationship

$$(AB)^2 = (AC)^2 + (AD)^2$$

a relationship that is true for any right triangle. In our discussion thus far the motion of the sun and of our solar system has been ignored,

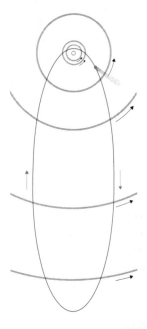

(a)

(b)

Figure 8.6 Barnard's Star, showing its change in position (proper motion) over a period of 22 years: (a) Aug. 24, 1894; (b) May 30, 1916. (Yerkes Observatory)

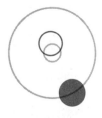

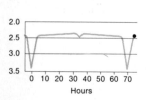

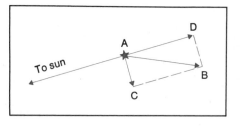

Figure 8.7 The motion of a star relative to the sun.

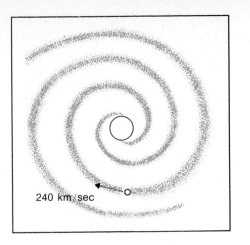

Figure 8.8 The sun's motion within the Milky Way galaxy.

240 km/sec

therefore AB represents the motion of the star with respect to the sun and not with respect to any absolute standard. This is called the star's *space velocity*. Is it difficult to find an absolute standard when we realize that our own sun is moving at the rate of approximately 240 km/sec around the center of the Galaxy and that our Galaxy is moving with respect to all other galaxies? (See Figure 8.8.) There seems to be no single standard; rather, we must be content to express the motion of any object as it relates to some stated frame of reference. If we select a group of stars, say, those within 100 parsecs of the sun, we could average out their velocities and arrive at one that described the motion of this entire group of stars in general. To illustrate this idea, consider yourself driving on a freeway. Some cars would pass you from time to time and likewise you would pass some cars. Some might also be changing lanes at times. Nevertheless it would be possible to describe the general motion of the entire group of cars within one mile of yourself. Now suppose that a helicopter is flying overhead and that the pilot adjusts his speed and direction in order to fly along with your group of cars. His speed and direction might then be used to describe the speed and direction of the entire group. In this same manner, the local group of stars (within 100 parsecs of the sun) has a general speed and direction that may be called the *local standard of rest*. Thus when we take into account the sun's own motion and specify a star's velocity with respect to the local standard of rest, we refer to its velocity as its *peculiar velocity*. Then any star that is moving with the same speed and direction as the local group has a peculiar velocity of zero.

The proper motion of stars provides an approximate means for measuring distance, for it is evident that a nearby star seems to move through a larger angle in a given time when compared to the angle

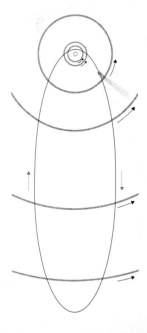

through which a more distant star moves in the same time. Picture someone running the 100-m dash. If you stood near the track, the runner's position would seem to change through an angle of perhaps 160°, and yet if you stood off at a great distance and observed the same race, the angle of change might be only 30° (Figure 8.9). The runner who is close to you surely has the larger "proper motion," and, in general, the stars that are close to you have the largest proper motions.

Methods for determining distances for the more remote stars and galaxies will be discussed later.

BRIGHTNESS OF STARS

In the second century B.C., Hipparchus classified the brightest stars as first magnitude and the faintest naked-eye stars as sixth magnitude, with other stars ranked second, third, fourth, or fifth magnitude. He produced the first real catalogue of stars showing both position and brightness. Of course, he was forced to rely upon his own ability to

Figure 8.9 The proper motion of objects near and far.

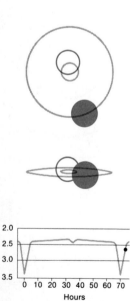

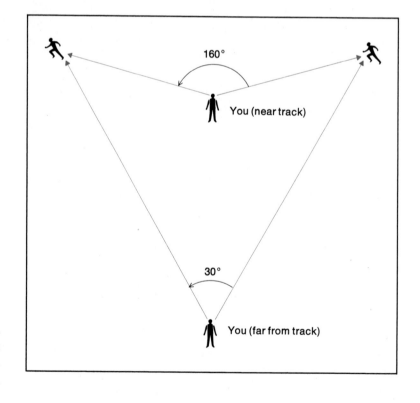

Figure 8.10 The apparent magnitude of a star may be judged from the size of the image it makes on a photographic plate. (Hale Observatories)

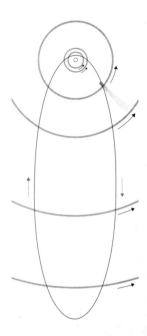

judge brightness without the aid of any instrument. Modern methods for measuring stellar brightness—the techniques of *photometry*—are much more precise, of course.

Photography has played a very important role in this aspect of astronomy. The apparent magnitude of a star may be judged by the size of the image it makes on a photographic plate (Figure 8.10). The brighter the star, the larger the image on the film. A photographic film has a distinct advantage over the eye, for an image will continue to build up over time, causing a darker image to be formed as the exposure time is increased (Figure 8.11). The "image" formed on our eye fades and must be continually reinforced, so there is no buildup.

A more precise method, however, is that of photoelectric photometry. You are probably familiar with an exposure meter used in

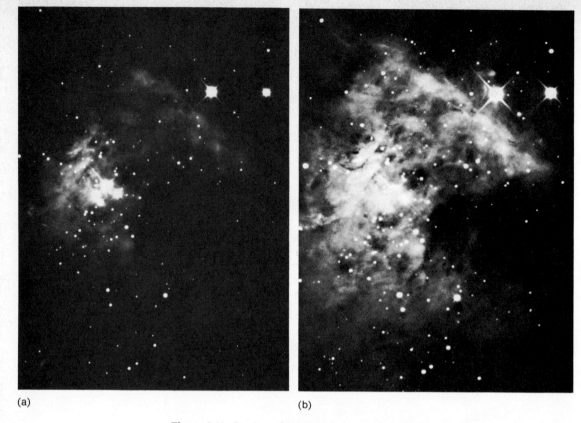

(a)   (b)

Figure 8.11 Region of Orion Nebula, showing effect of aperture
and time exposure on formation of star images. (a) Small aperture
and/or short time exposure. (b) Large aperture and/or long time
exposure. (Lick Observatory)

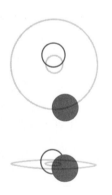

photography. When light falls on a sensitive surface at the front of the
meter, a small electrical current is produced. This current then causes
a needle to move, indicating the intensity of the light falling on the
sensitive surface. With a similar but much more sensitive device, the
astronomer may bring the light of a star through the telescope and cause
it to fall on the sensitive surface of a *photomultiplier.* The small current
that the light produces in the photomultiplier is amplified to the point
where it may be recorded. This method provides an extremely accurate
means for ranking stars by brightness (Figure 8.12).

THE SCALE OF BRIGHTNESS

In an effort to preserve the familiar scale of Hipparchus, the modern
astronomer has set forth the following scheme. Allowing each brightness
magnitude (each smaller magnitude number) to represent a star ap-

272

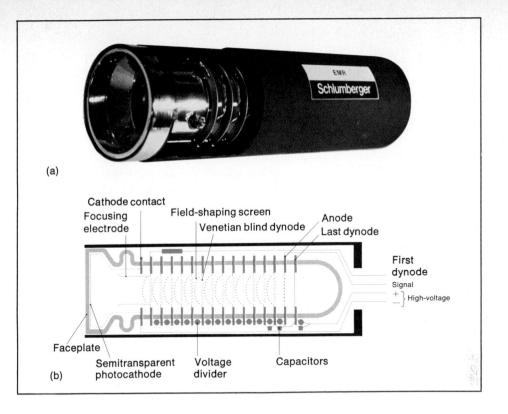

(a)

Cathode contact
Focusing
electrode
Field-shaping screen
Venetian blind dynode
Anode
Last dynode
First
dynode
Signal
High-voltage
Faceplate
Semitransparent
photocathode
Voltage
divider
Capacitors
(b)

Figure 8.12 A photo multiplier tube showing (a) a cut–away view and (b) a functional diagram. The complex physical and electronic nature of this tube makes it sensitive to very small fluctuations in light intensity. (EMR Division of Weston Instruments, Inc.)

proximately 2.5 times as bright as the preceding magnitude, 5 magnitude steps will then correspond to a star 100 times as bright, because

$$(2.5)(2.5)(2.5)(2.5)(2.5) \cong 100$$

This scale closely approximates that of Hipparchus with several notable exceptions, such as Sirius, which must be rated at a magnitude of -1.4 on this scale, whereas Hipparchus called Sirius a first magnitude ($+1$ mag) star. Table 8.1 shows light ratios for given changes in magnitude: A star 3 mag brighter than another is 15.9 times as bright.

A magnitude change such as 17, not found in the table, may be calculated as follows. Since a change of 5 mag corresponds to a factor of 100 in light ratio, and of 2 mag corresponds to a factor of 6.3, then a total of 17 mag steps corresponds to a light ratio of 6,300,000:1:

Magnitude change: $17 = 5 + 5 + 5 + 2$
Light ratio: $(100) \times (100) \times (100) \times (6.3) = 6.3 \times 10^6$

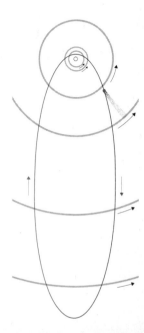

Some familiar objects have been listed in Table 8.2, showing their apparent magnitude. Study this table carefully, for it will aid your understanding of the magnitude scale. Note that the scale has been extended in a negative direction in order to accommodate the very bright objects, such as the sun and the moon, and in a positive direction to accommodate the very dim objects, such as distant galaxies.

We observe that the use of binoculars alone will allow us to see much dimmer stars and so will bring many hundreds of objects to our view that are not visible to the naked eye; therefore it can be a valuable tool to the beginning amateur astronomer. The 15-cm telescope will add still more, allowing us to see objects down to +13 mag under ideal seeing conditions.

If astronomers merely looked through the 5-m Palomar telescope, they might see objects as faint as +20 mag; however, by use of sensitive photographic film exposed for several hours, it is possible to photograph objects down to +23.5 mag. This is called the photographic limit of the 5-m telescope. Here again we see the tremendous advantage of using sensitive film over reliance on the eye for observation.

ABSOLUTE MAGNITUDE

Because of the fact that stars are situated at widely different distances from us, it would be a serious error to assume that apparent magnitudes indicate actual luminosity. We have all experienced the fact that as we

Table 8.1 Light ratios for various magnitude changes

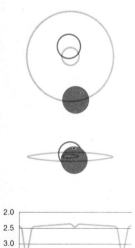

MAGNITUDE CHANGE	LIGHT RATIO
0.5	1.6
1.0	2.5
2.0	6.3
3.0	15.9
4.0	39.8
5.0	100.0
6.0	251.2
10.0	10,000.0
20.0	100,000,000.0
25.0	10,000,000,000.0

Table 8.2 Apparent magnitudes of familiar objects

OBJECT	MAG
Sun	−26.5
Moon (full)	−12.5
Venus (when brightest)	−4.4
Jupiter (when brightest)	−2.5
Sirius	−1.4
Vega	+0.4
Aldebaran	+1.0
Polaris	+2.0
Naked-eye limit	+6.0
Binocular limit (average)	+9.0
15-cm telescope limit	+13.0
5-m telescope limit	
—visual	+20.0
—photographic	+23.5

move away from a source of light, its *intensity* (brightness) seems to diminish. If we could accurately measure its intensity as we moved away, we would find that when we were twice as far from the lamp, its intensity would be only one-fourth what it was from our starting position (Figure 8.13). We then say that light falls off with the square of the distance, and that distance is therefore a critical element in the determination of apparent brightness, as compared to the actual brightness of a star. In order that all stars may be compared on an equal basis, let us suppose that they were all placed at a distance of 10 parsecs and then determine the magnitude that they would appear to have at that distance. By definition this is called their *absolute magnitude.* If our sun were placed at a distance of 10 parsecs, it would be a very dim object, just visible to the naked eye. Rigel, on the other hand, which is at a distance of 250 parsecs, if brought into 10 parsecs, would brighten to −7 mag. Rigel would then appear to be 625 times as bright as it now appears.

Apparent magnitude, absolute magnitude, and distance are related by the proportion

$$\frac{L(10)}{L(r)} = \left(\frac{r}{10}\right)^2$$

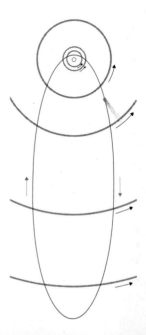

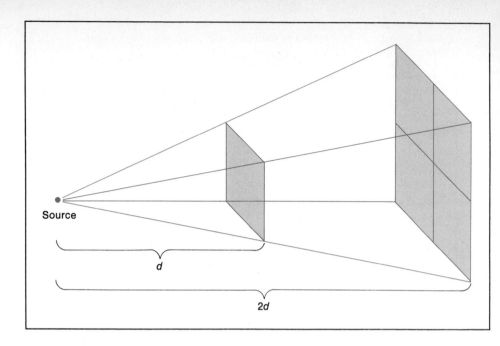

Figure 8.13 In traveling twice the distance, the light covers four times as much area. Therefore we would expect its intensity to be only one-fourth.

Distance (parsecs)	16	25	40	63	100	160
Difference between absolute and apparent magnitudes	1	2	3	4	5	6

Table 8.3 Difference in magnitude at various distances

where $L(10)$ is the brightness of a given star at 10 parsecs, $L(r)$ is its brightness at r, its distance in parsecs. Suppose that a star that is situated at 1000 parsecs is brought into 10 parsecs; what will be its change in magnitude? Letting $r = 1000$ in the above equation, we obtain the following brightness ratio:

$$\frac{L(10)}{L(r)} = \left(\frac{1000}{10}\right)^2 = \left(\frac{100}{1}\right)^2 = \frac{10,000}{1}$$

It would appear 10,000 times brighter. From Table 8.1 we see that this ratio of brightness corresponds to a change of 10 mag; thus if the

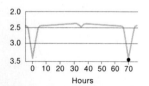

apparent magnitude of the star was +7, its absolute magnitude will be 7 − 10 = −3. (The absolute magnitudes of many stars are shown in Appendix 8.)

By similar calculations we may determine that a star situated at a distance of 16 parsecs will appear 1 mag dimmer than its absolute magnitude, that a star located at 25 parsecs will appear 2 mag dimmer than its absolute magnitude, and so on. This concept is summarized and extended in Table 8.3.

COLOR OF STARS

Stars radiate energy in a broad range of wavelengths. If we consider the total energy emitted in all wavelengths, we call this the star's *bolometric magnitude*. However, the astronomer is usually able to measure the magnitude of a star within only a limited range of wavelengths. If he uses a yellow-sensitive film, he gets a visual magnitude (m_v). This most closely resembles the magnitude as seen by the human eye. If a blue-sensitive film is used, the astronomer records a photographic magnitude (m_p). For most stars, m_v and m_p are different, and this difference is called the *color index* (C.I.) of a star, defined by

$$\text{C.I.} = m_p - m_v$$

The color of a star may be determined by this difference, as is shown in Table 8.4.

The color of a star is principally a function of its surface temperature, ranging from the very hot blue-white stars, with a surface tem-

Table 8.4 Spectral classes of stars

CLASS	COLOR	SURFACE TEMPERATURE	COLOR INDEX
O	Blue-white	50,000°K	−0.6
B	Blue	20,000°K	−0.3
A	White	10,000°K	0.0
F	White	7,000°K	+0.2
G	Yellow	6,000°K	+0.6
K	Orange	5,000°K	+0.8
M	Red	3,500°K	+1.5

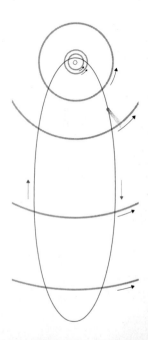

perature of approximately 50,000°K, to the very cool red star, with a temperature of approximately 3000°K. Invisible stars exist with temperatures as low as 1000°K, radiating only infrared wavelengths. A star may be placed on a scale according to color (see Table 8.4). Each spectral class is further subdivided into ten subdivisions as follows: B0, B1, B2, B3, B4, B5, B6, B7, B8, B9; A0, A1, A2, and so on.

As the light from distant stars travels through the dust clouds of space, it is reddened; therefore its original color may not be evident. We must depend upon more reliable means by which we may assess the surface temperature of a star. The spectra of stars give us a better indication, for some lines show up very clearly at certain temperatures and not at others (Figure 8.14). Stars were originally classified in order according to the strength of the hydrogen lines in their respective spectra. Class A has the strongest lines, Class B the next strongest, and so on to Class O. These classes were later rearranged according to temperatures, as is indicated in Table 8.4. Thus we see that this rather jumbled set of letters did in fact have an orderly beginning. Their present order may be remembered by the first letters of the words in "Oh, Be A Fine Girl, Kiss Me." At the extremely high temperature typical of the O-type star, the very energetic collisions that occur among the atoms often knock electrons entirely free of the atom, thus producing ions with their own characteristic spectra. At the other extreme—the lower temperatures—atoms may unite to form compounds such as titanium oxide, as evidenced in the spectrum of an M-type star. Table 8.5 shows samples of specific stars in each class, together with their typical spectra.

HERTZSPRUNG-RUSSELL
DIAGRAM

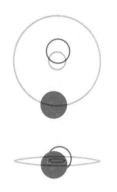

Early in the twentieth century a very important study concerning the relationship between the surface temperature of a star and its luminosity was made by two astronomers, Ejner Hertzsprung of Denmark and Henry N. Russell of America, working independently. The results of their work are shown graphically in Figure 8.15, known, in their honor, as the *H-R diagram*.

Stars of known distance have been plotted on the chart according to their spectral class (surface temperature) and their luminosity (absolute photographic magnitude). It is obvious at a glance that the stars are not evenly distributed over the entire chart, but rather seem to be grouped in several areas. We shall try to understand the significance of this grouping, but first let us see how several familiar stars are placed within it. Our sun is of the spectral class G2 and has an absolute magnitude of +5; hence, it is placed at point A on the diagram. *Betelgeuse* is of spectral class M2—a very cool star—but has an absolute

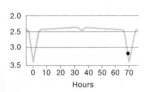

Type		Star
O6		λ Cephei
B3		η Aurigae
A0		δ Cygni
F2		β Cassiopeiae
G2		η Pegasi
K5		γ Draconis
M5		α Herculis

Figure 8.14 Examples of different spectral types. (Hale Observatories)

Table 8.5 Stellar spectra

CLASS	EXAMPLE	SPECTRA	SURFACE TEMPERATURE
O5	None visible to the naked eye	Ionized helium nitrogen, oxygen	50,000°K
B3	Achernar	H, He strong	15,000°K
A1	Sirius	H lines at maximum Ca lines weak	11,000°K
A3	Fomalhaut	H lines strong Ca lines stronger Metals weak	9,000°K
F0	Canopus	H lines weak Ca lines strong	7,600°K
F5	Procyon	Ca lines very strong Neutral metals	6,600°K
G0	Capella Sun	Ca lines at maximum Iron lines strong	6,000°K
K2	Arcturus	H lines weak Molecular bands present	5,000°K
M2	Betelgeuse	Neutral lines strong TiO molecules present	3,500°K

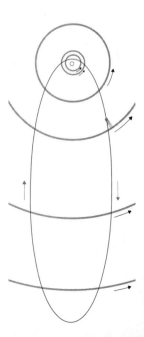

magnitude of −4, placing it at position B. We might ask ourselves how a cool star could possibly be so luminous. The answer is that it must be very large: therefore stars in this region of the chart will be called the *giants* and *supergiants*. *Spica* is of the spectral class B1 and has an absolute magnitude of −3, so it is placed at point C. The band of stars that pass through C and A are called the *main-sequence stars*. What characteristics must a star possess to be placed at point D? It must be a very hot (white) star and yet rather dim, hence a small star. Stars in this region of the chart are called *white dwarfs*.

This particular H-R diagram represents only a very limited number of luminous stars relatively close to the sun and should not be interpreted as an accurate picture of the distribution of all stars. Furthermore, it should not be inferred from the location of the sun on this diagram that it is a below-average star. If Figure 8.15 included all stars in a given region of space, we would recognize that less than

Figure 8.15 The H-R diagram. The points represent approximately 6700 stars of known absolute magnitude. (Yerkes Observatory)

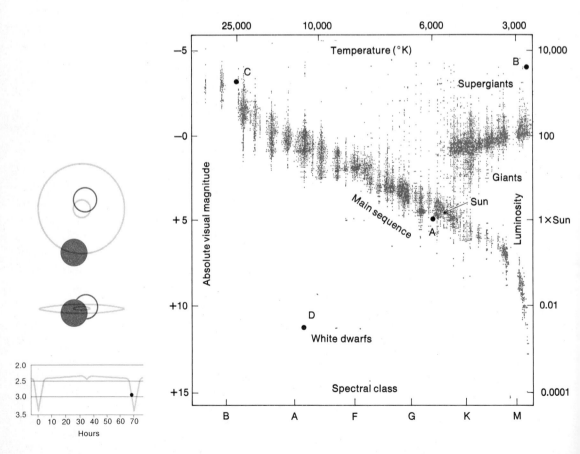

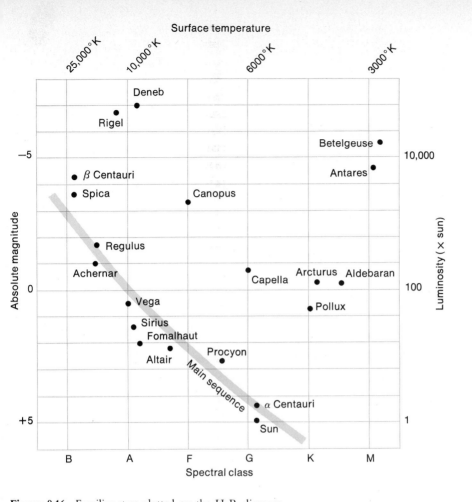

Figure 8.16 Familiar stars plotted on the H-R diagram.

5 percent of those stars are brighter than the sun, thus the sun is far above average among the stars. In order to plot the additional stars, the H-R diagram would have to be extended downward and to the right, because most of the unplotted stars are both cooler and dimmer than those shown. Such stars are now being revealed by infrared techniques. Some familiar stars are plotted in Figure 8.16.

A further subdivision of the giants and main-sequence stars may be made as follows (represented graphically in Figure 8.17):

Ia   Most luminous supergiants
Ib   Less luminous supergiants
II   Bright giants
III   Normal giants
IV   Subgiants
V   Main-sequence stars

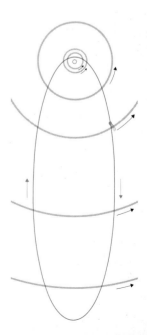

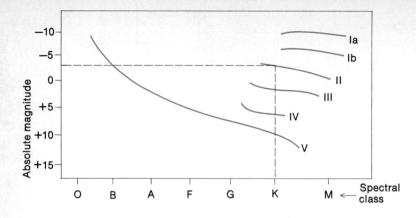

Figure 8.17 Subdivisions of H-R classifications.

Class Ia supergiants, because of their very large size, will have extremely low pressure and low density. The spectral lines of such a star will be very narrow (sharply defined). Each successive class represents stars of increasing pressure and density; this is shown by broader spectral lines. Accordingly, a star of unknown distance may be placed in its proper class and its distance inferred from its apparent magnitude. This method of determining distance is called *spectroscopic parallax.*

SPECTROSCOPIC PARALLAX

We have discussed the methods of geocentric and heliocentric parallax, but we are also aware of their very definite limitation to nearby stars. The method of spectroscopic parallax is limited only by our ability to see the star and photograph its spectrum. Let us take a step-by-step approach to this method.

Step 1. Place the given star in its proper category (Ia, Ib, II, III, IV, V) on the H-R diagram. To do this, you must look at its spectrum to see the degree to which its atmosphere has been ionized due to low pressure: Ia-type stars have lowest pressure because of their tremendous size; types Ib, II, III, IV, and V have progressively higher pressure because of their reduced size.

Step 2. Classify the star by spectral type, again using the spectrum as discussed earlier in this chapter.

Step 3. Run a vertical line upward on the chart corresponding to the spectral classification, extending it until it intersects the proper category line. For example, take a star of K1 type which is also in Category II and plot as is shown in Figure 8.17.

Step 4. From the point of intersection draw a horizontal line to the left-hand side of the chart and read out the corresponding absolute magnitude, which in this case is − 3.

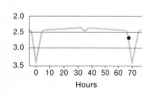

Step 5. Observe the apparent magnitude of the star, using the photographic method explained earlier.

Step 6. By comparing the absolute brightness of a star to its apparent brightness, its distance may be determined by

$$\frac{L(10)}{L(r)} = \left(\frac{r}{10}\right)^2$$

$L(10)/L(r)$ is the ratio of absolute brightness to apparent brightness.

SIZES OF STARS

We have been discussing the variety of sizes within the stellar population, ranging from the dwarfs to the supergiants. Most stars are at such a great distance that they appear as mere points of light in even the largest telescopes; however, as we observed in connection with the H-R diagram, a cool star that is also bright (in absolute magnitude) must be a large star. Let us see how these factors are related.

Suppose that the spectrum of a star indicates a surface temperature of 3000°K, exactly half that of the sun, and that the absolute magnitude of the star is zero, 5 mag brighter than the sun. A difference of 5 mag indicates that the given star is 100 times as luminous as the sun. It is also known that a star whose temperature is one-half that of the sun only radiates one-sixteenth as much energy over each square centimeter of its surface, as compared to the sun. Taking these two factors into consideration, we see that the given star must have 1600 (16 × 100) times as much surface area as the sun. Since the surface area of a sphere is proportional to the square of the radius, we may compute the radius by taking the square root of 1600, which is 40. Hence, the radius of the given star is 40 times that of the sun. Among the largest known stars is Betelgeuse, in the constellation of Orion, having a diameter 750 times that of the sun—a diameter which is greater than the diameter of Mars's orbit around the sun.

THE GREAT VARIETY
OF STARS

We have seen that stars vary greatly in size, surface temperature, color, and brightness, however we have not yet perceived the complete range of this variety because we have been considering only those stars which emit visible light. In other words, our entire discussion has centered around an extremely narrow portion of the electromagnetic spectrum.

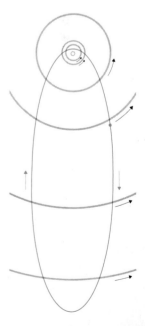

It may surprise you to discover that more than one-half the mass of stars in the Milky Way galaxy can not be detected using visible light; we must turn to other wavelengths and to other tools for detection of these objects.

First, let us consider a fundamental relationship between the surface temperature of a heated object and the wavelengths that it radiates. The curves in Figure 8.18 show that as an object is heated, it radiates

Figure 8.18   The radiation curves for stars of different temperatures.

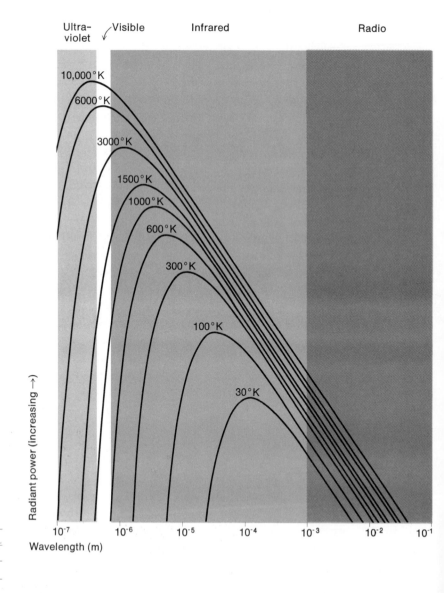

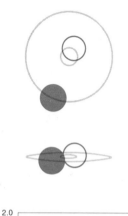

a broader range of wavelengths. The wavelength at which the maximum radiation occurs is related to the surface temperature by a simple mathematical statement known as Wien's law:

$$\text{Wavelength}_{\text{max.}} = \frac{3000}{T°}$$

where wavelength is measured in *micrometers* (abbreviated μm: $1\ \mu$m $= 10^{-6}$ m $= 1$ millionth of a meter); T is the surface temperature in degrees Kelvin. For example, the sun has a surface temperature of 6000°K and it radiates its peak energy at a wavelength of 0.5 μm because $3000/6000 = 0.5\ \mu$m. Note that 0.5 μm is the same as 5000 Å—near the center of the range of wavelengths called visible light. On the other hand, a star whose surface temperature is only 1500°K will radiate its maximum energy at 2 μm, which falls in the infrared range. Over 50 percent of the energy radiated at 2 μm will penetrate the earth's atmosphere, making this one of the better "windows" through which the astronomer may survey the infrared sky. The atmosphere is opaque to most of the infrared spectrum, and so Orbiting Astronomical Observatories are essential to the total infrared picture.

THE INFRARED SKY

A map of the infrared sky would look so entirely different from a map of the visible sky that we could not recognize familiar constellations. Compare the map of bright infrared objects in Figure 8.19 with the same region, namely that of Orion, shown for visible stars (see Appendix 12, *winter map*). Out of the many thousands of bright infrared sources which have been identified, only a few can be seen with the naked eye; thus infrared astronomy has provided a wealth of new information, but also new questions. What kind of objects are being detected? What kind of objects would have temperatures in the range of 300° to 400°K and thereby radiate primarily in infrared? (It is interesting to note that our own body temperature, 311°K, produces peak infrared radiation of approximately 10 μm.) These are relatively cool objects, some of which may be *protostars*—stars in the making. Stars are thought to condense out of huge clouds of gas and dust and one of the manifestations of such a condensation is heat. A condensation as cool as 100°K would radiate at 30 μm. Many such sources are large in angular diameter, which is consistent with the idea that they are clouds of gas.

Visible starlight is significantly scattered as it passes through dust which is concentrated near the center of our Galaxy, the Milky Way,

Motion of globular clusters

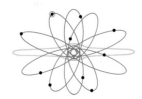

Rotation of the Milky Way

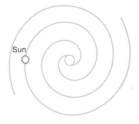

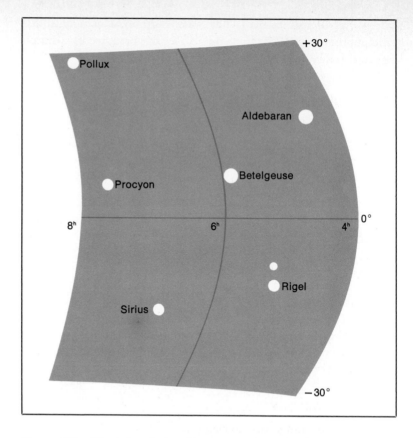

Figure 8.19 The infrared sky. If our eyes were sensitive to infrared wavelengths alone, we would recognize only a few familiar stars. Compare this infrared star map with the visible winter sky in Appendix 12.

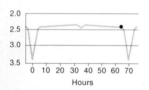

and this produces such severe loss of light that objects which are intrinsically bright in visible light may not be visible at all. On the other hand, infrared energy is not significantly scattered by that same interstellar media; therefore, bright infrared objects whose line of sight passes through the center of our Galaxy are readily detectable. This ability to penetrate gas and dust was the critical factor in the recent discovery of two new galaxies (Maffei I and Maffei II), for their line of sight passes near the center of the Milky Way.

Stars are also believed to cool off in their old age, and so old stars represent still another possible class of infrared objects. Several observers have speculated that a star may throw off a shell of gas and/or dust, and then the core will heat that shell to some temperature less than 1500°K.

Some infrared sources may radiate energy at levels exceeding that of the sun by a factor of 1000 or more, yet their rate of production per square meter of surface area is low. We must conclude, therefore, that such sources are extremely large.

X-RAY ASTRONOMY

At almost the other extreme from the cool, infrared object we see the very hot, X-ray object. From Wein's law we see that an object which has a surface temperature of 30 million degrees Kelvin would peak its radiation at a wavelength of 0.0001 μm (1 Å), in the X-ray portion of the spectrum. There are phenomena other than high-temperature effects, however, which produce X rays. Thus we cannot limit our discussion to hot stars alone.

X rays have been detected from what is thought to be an extremely small but dense rotating star (called a *pulsar*) in the Crab Nebula. Here the process of X-ray production is tied to a rapidly rotating object which accelerates electrons to speeds near that of light and sends them hurtling through a magnetic field. The Crab pulsar can be detected "beeping" on and off at radio wavelengths and also pulsating in X-ray wavelengths. The total picture of this and similar objects could never have been found without inspecting their characteristics over a wide range of wavelengths.

Thus, we see what has been happening throughout all of astronomy in recent years—the opening of virtually the entire spectrum to our "view."

QUESTIONS

1. How long is the base line used in the method of heliocentric parallax?
2. The method of heliocentric parallax can be used to determine the distances to stars up to ＿＿ parsecs.
3. Find the distance to a star whose heliocentric parallax is 0.50 second.
4. Which motion of stars appears to change the shape of the Big Dipper constellation?
5. The radial velocity of a star is indicated by what kind of observation?
6. Define the term *space velocity*. Why can this not be called the true velocity of a star?
7. The sun moves within the Milky Way galaxy at a rate of ＿＿ kilometers per second, due to the rotation of the Galaxy.
8. What do we know about a star whose peculiar velocity is zero?

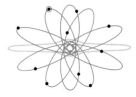

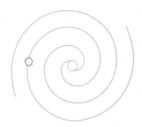

9. The computation of the tangential velocity of a star depends upon our knowledge of what two properties of the star's location and/or motion?

10. What was Hipparchus's system for categorizing stars by brightness?

11. List three means by which the apparent brightness of stars may be judged today.

12. A change of 1 in magnitude corresponds to a change of _____ in luminosity.

13. A star of −3 mag appears _____ times as bright as one of +2 mag.

14. True or false: Venus sometimes appears brighter than the brightest star.

15. True or false: The use of time exposures on film has extended the limiting magnitude of the Palomar 5-m telescope by several magnitudes.

16. The true brightness of two stars may best be compared by consideration of (a) their apparent magnitude; (b) their absolute magnitude; (c) neither of these. Which is true?

17. How is the apparent brightness of a star related to its absolute brightness and its distance from the observer?

18. Describe at least two ways by which the surface temperature of stars may be measured.

19. What is the general range of surface temperatures of stars? Can the surface temperature of a star be judged in even the roughest fashion by the naked eye? Explain.

20. What relationship is demonstrated by the fact that the majority of stars fall along the main sequence on the H-R diagram?

21. What advantage does the method of spectroscopic parallax have over that of heliocentric parallax for determining the distance to a star?

22. What is the range in star sizes as compared to the sun?

23. A 100-watt light bulb has a certain apparent brightness if viewed from a distance of 10 m. What will be the change in its apparent brightness if viewed from 20 m?—from 50 m?

24. An object as cool as 300°K will radiate its maximum energy in what part of the spectrum?

25. The wavelength at which a star emits its maximum energy is inversely proportional to its surface temperature. If a star whose temperature is like that of the sun (6000°K) has its maximum output at 0.5 μm, then find the wavelength for maximum output of a star whose temperature is 12,000°K. How will its color compare to that of the sun?

26. What increase in luminosity would accompany a change in temperature of a star from 3000°K to 6000°K: (a) assuming the diameter of the star remains the same; (b) assuming the diameter of the star is halved?

27. The sun appears to have a magnitude of −26.5, as seen from earth. What must be its magnitude as seen from Pluto, 40 times as far away?

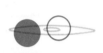

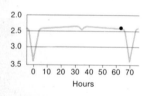

Hours

SUGGESTED READINGS

Giacconi, Riccardo, X-ray astronomy. *The Physics Teacher* **11** (3), 135–143 (1973).

Mihalas, Dimitri, Interpreting early-type stellar spectra. *Sky and Telescope* **46** (2), 79–83 (1973).

Neugebauer, G., and Becklin, Eric E., The brightest infrared sources. *Scientific American* **228** (4), 28–40 (1973).

Smith, E. P., and Jacobs, K. C., *Introductory astronomy and astrophysics.* Philadelphia: Saunders, 1973.

Strand, Kaj A. (ed.), *Basic astronomical data.* Chicago: University of Chicago Press, 1965.

Struve, Otto, Lynds, Beverly, and Pillans, Helen, *Elementary astronomy.* New York: Oxford University Press, 1959.

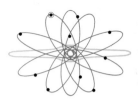

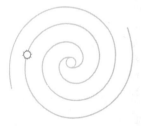

MULTIPLE
STAR
SYSTEMS

9

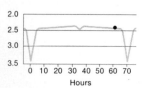

The casual observer would rarely suspect that more than one-half of

the stars that he sees with his naked eye are in reality multiple

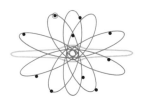

systems, systems that contain two, three, or more stars. The astron-

omer realizes that two stars may appear close to each other for two

basic reasons: they may actually be close to each other; or they may

just happen to line up from the observer's point of view, even

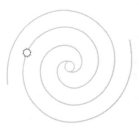

though one of the stars is in actuality much farther away from him

than the other.

291

Sir William Herschel, a famous observer of *binary* (double) *stars,* held to the theory that such stars differed greatly in distance because one star of the pair was often much dimmer than the other. In trying to prove his theory, he found himself to be wrong, for he discovered that most binary stars are in each other's gravitational field. By this he meant that they are close enough and massive enough so as to influence each other's motion directly. They literally revolve around some common point between them. In proving his original theory wrong, Herschel had made a very important discovery, and he continued his observations, cataloguing some 800 double stars by the year 1820.

OPTICAL AND VISUAL BINARIES

On the rare occasion that two stars appear close together from the observer's point of view but one is really much more distant than the other, they are called *optical binaries.* This is not a true binary system.

A much more common class of binary stars are those which are in each other's gravitational field and can be seen as doubles in a telescope. They are called *visual binaries* (Figure 9.1).

SPECTROSCOPIC BINARIES

If the components of a true binary system are so close together that they can not be *resolved* (separated) by a telescope, they may still be identified as a binary system by their spectrum. Consider a pair of binary stars, A and B, in mutual revolution around a point that is

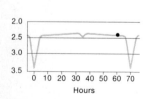

Figure 9.1 Stars may appear close together because (a) they are actually close or (b) they merely line up, from the observer's point of view.

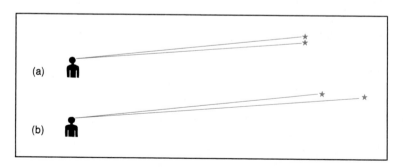

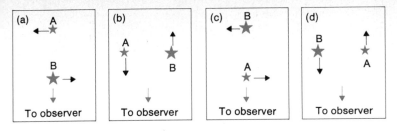

Figure 9.2 Spectroscopic determination of a binary system.

Figure 9.3 The double lines (B) as seen in the spectrum of a spectroscopic binary star system. The top band (A) shows no separation, since the two stars are in alignment with the observer. (Hale Observatories)

the center of the system, as in Figure 9.2. When the stars are in a position such as that shown in Figures 9.2(a) and 9.2(c), both stars have the same Doppler shift in their spectral lines. However, when they are in positions represented by Figure 9.2(b) or 9.2(d), one star is moving in a direction toward the observer and the other star is moving away; hence the spectral lines of one star will be slightly different from those of the other, producing a double line (Figure 9.3).

The periodic separation of the spectral lines then signifies that it is a binary system—more specifically, a *spectroscopic binary system.* The spectrum may reveal the binary nature of a system by exhibiting lines that are characteristic of both a cool and a hot star.

It is possible for you easily to identify a system of stars that illustrates both the visual and the spectroscopic types. You can see with your naked eye the two most obvious members of the system, Mizar and Alcor, in the handle of the Big Dipper. Several minutes of arc separate these stars (Figure 9.4).

Now, if you look at Mizar through a small telescope, you will discover that Mizar is itself a visual binary—its brighter component *Mizar A,* and its dimmer component *Mizar B.* Next, if you were to analyze this system spectroscopically, you would discover that Alcor, Mizar A, and Mizar B are each spectroscopic binaries. Thus the system is composed of six stars.

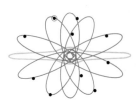

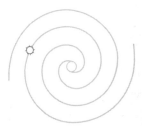

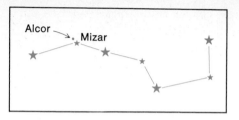

Figure 9.4 The Big Dipper.

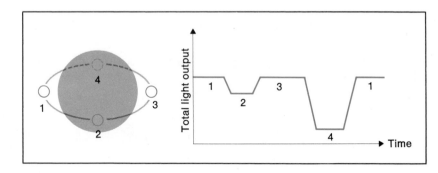

Figure 9.5 The light curve of a binary system.

ASTROMETRIC BINARIES

It is possible that the dimmer component of a binary system is so dim as to go unnoticed by any of the above methods, and yet its presence could be detected by the gravitational effect that it has on the brighter star, causing it to move along a wavelike path in the sky. Such a system is called an *astrometric binary system*.

ECLIPSING BINARIES

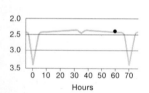

Some binary systems are oriented in such a way that one star passes in front of the other; that is, we see the system edge-on to its plane of orbit. These are known as *eclipsing binary* systems. As one star is eclipsed by the other, we expect some variation in the total light reaching us from that system. If we plot the variations in light received as these eclipses occur, we may discover a number of facts from such a light curve. First, consider a binary system composed of a large star and a small one, as in Figure 9.5, where the small star is the hotter of the two. When the small hot star is in position 1 or 3, we see the combined light output of both stars. When it is in position 2, we see an annular eclipse, with only slightly less light received, whereas when it is in position 4, we see a total eclipse of the hotter star, resulting in the least amount of light received. If the orbit of this system were tipped slightly more in our direction, then we might observe only partial eclipses, with a resultant change in the light curve, as in Figure 9.6. The left-hand flip pages beginning on page 390 depict an eclipsing binary system in motion and also the light curve being received.

Consider the light curve for a pair of stars that are so close together as to distort each other's shape by their mutual attraction, as in Figure 9.7.

Whereas we have first proposed a model of a given system and then deduced the light curve, in actual practice the astronomer first observes the light curve and then tries to build a model to fit that curve.

The light curve also gives an indication of the size of the stars in relation to their orbital size. A smaller star is very rapidly eclipsed,

Figure 9.6 Partially eclipsing binaries.

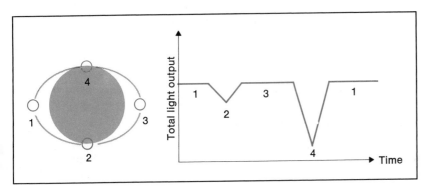

Figure 9.7 A binary system, distorted by gravitation.

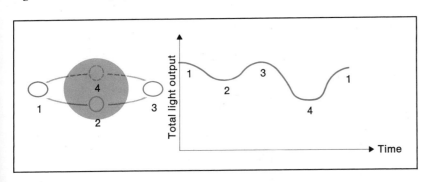

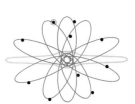

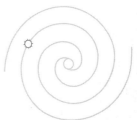

making the sides of the curve very steep. A larger star requires more time for an eclipse and thus produces a less steep curve.

CONTACT BINARIES

About one in a thousand stars is in reality a pair of stars that are so close to each other that the material of their atmospheres actually forms a bridge between them. Such stars are called *contact binaries*. These systems are usually composed of low–mass stars and have a period of 1 day or less. Many pairs of stars may have had a common origin; however, only those of lower total mass are believed to have stayed in contact. The stars of higher masses that had a common origin are now binary systems with greater separation.

DETERMINATION OF THE MASS
OF BINARY SYSTEMS

A binary system lends itself very well to the determination of mass, both of the system and of the individual members. Three basic factors of the system are related: the mass of each star (M_1 and M_2); the separation of the stars (r); and their period of revolution (p). This relationship, first expressed by Kepler and later refined by Newton, is stated thus:

$$M_1 + M_2 = \frac{r^3}{p^2}$$

where M_1 and M_2 are expressed in solar masses (masses as compared to the sun's mass), p in years, and r in astronomical units. Since p and r may be observed for a number of binary systems, the sum of their masses ($M_1 + M_2$) may be determined. Suppose that two stars were orbiting each other at an average separation of 5 A.U. and that their period of revolution were 10 years; then

$$M_1 + M_2 = \frac{(5)^3}{(10)^2} = \frac{125}{100} = 1.25 \text{ solar masses}$$

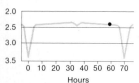

Figure 9.8 The barycenter of a binary system.

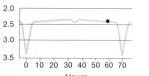

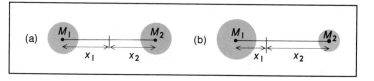

Figure 9.9 The path of a binary pair, Sirius A and Sirius B.

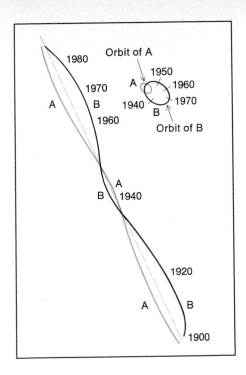

Since this gives us only the total mass, we must next try to determine how the mass of the system is distributed between the two stars. If the stars were equal in mass, they would orbit around a point midway between the two. This point is called the *barycenter* of the system. However, if one star is 3 times as massive as the other, we might expect the barycenter to be nearer the larger mass (Figure 9.8). These factors are related by the proportion:

$$\frac{M_1}{M_2} = \frac{x_2}{x_1}$$

By observing the displacement of the stars in a binary system, as compared with several nearby stars, it is possible to locate the barycenter of the system, after which the distribution of mass may be calculated.

Consider the case of Sirius, a binary system with its A component the brightest star we see, and its tiny B component the first white dwarf ever discovered. As this system moves through space, its barycenter marks a uniform path, as is indicated by the dashed line in Figure 9.9. The two components, on the other hand, oscillate in varying degrees to either side of this path.

The approximate period of this system has been observed to be 50 years, and the separation of its members, 20 A.U. The total mass of the system is computed to be 3.2 solar masses:

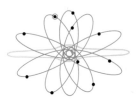

$$M_1 + M_2 = \frac{(20)^3}{(50)^2} = \frac{8000}{2500} = 3.2 \text{ solar masses}$$

Sirius B is observed to orbit 2.2 times as far from the barycenter as does Sirius A, therefore the combined mass must be distributed in the ratio of $1:2.2$. The mass of Sirius A is approximately 2.2 times that of the sun, and the mass of Sirius B is equal to that of the sun. The left-hand flip pages beginning on page 162 depict the earth and moon as a binary system. These objects may also be visualized as two stars in a binary system.

MASS-LUMINOSITY RELATIONSHIP

One of the most significant results of being able to determine the masses of binary stars becomes obvious when the masses of these stars are plotted against their absolute magnitudes (Figure 9.10).

It is evident that most of these stars fall within a narrow band running from upper left to lower right. Low-mass stars are also low in absolute magnitude. High-mass stars are high in absolute magnitude. This is called the *mass-luminosity* relationship. It is likely that all main-sequence stars satisfy this relationship. On the other hand, white dwarfs and red giants generally do not show this relationship. Figure 9.10 shows several such white dwarfs that do not fit within the narrow band. (Note the similarity between this graph and the H-R diagram.)

Once the mass-luminosity relationship had been established, it became a tool of the astronomer: he could estimate the masses of main-sequence stars by calculating their absolute magnitude, even though they were not part of a binary system.

ORIGIN OF BINARIES

Binary systems are so numerous that any theory concerning the origin of stars must account for these special associations. Theories concerning the origin of binary systems run somewhat parallel to those of the solar system.

One theory suggests that two stars became entrapped within each other's gravitational field as a result of passing very close to each other. The chance of such an encounter is so small, however, that this theory is hard put to explain the multiplicity of binary systems. A third mass is also essential in such a "capture" process.

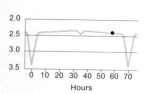

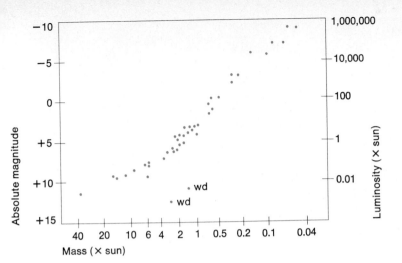

Figure 9.10 The mass–luminosity relationship.

A second theory suggests that a rapidly rotating star broke up into two or more parts. We might expect a rotating star to throw off some material from around its equator, but it is difficult to think of a star being torn in half by such a motion.

It is conceivable that, as a cloud of hydrogen gas began to condense to form a star, more than one center developed, eventually producing two or three stars within the same contraction. Such stars would possess a motion in common with the gas cloud out of which they formed. Thus, the existence of binary systems suggest a common origin.

CLUSTERS

No matter what part of the sky is observed, if seeing conditions are fair to good, even a pair of binoculars will usually reveal from a dozen to hundreds of stars within its field of view. However, there are certain regions that seem to "come alive" with stars when they are scanned. One such region is that of the *Pleiades cluster,* a group of stars visible to the naked eye but doubly spectacular in binoculars or in a low–power telescope. Hundreds of stars may be seen by using such an instrument, and yet we must look further to determine whether this is more than merely an accidental association. The answer to our question will be found in the motions of these stars. While each star differs slightly in speed and direction, there is a general trend toward the same direction and the same speed; hence they are a true *cluster.*

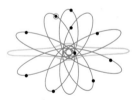

Figure 9.11 The Pleiades (Seven Sisters), a typical open cluster in Taurus. (Lick Observatories)

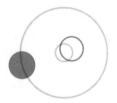

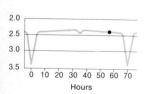

ORIGIN OF CLUSTERS

It is possible that most stars were formed in clusters. Some have lost their identity with a cluster while others have retained their identity. If the stars of an identifiable cluster did have a common origin, we may assume that they are all at about the same distance from us, so that their apparent magnitude is proportional to their absolute magnitude. In other words, a star that appears to be brightest among the group *is* in fact brightest. Recalling the apparent relationship between the luminosity and the mass of a star, we see that the more massive members of a cluster ought also to appear the brightest. When clusters are observed with these relationships in mind, it appears that the more massive members of a cluster tend toward the central region. Perhaps clusters were formed with this concentration of mass around the center; on the other hand, the more massive stars may gradually be moving to this central position.

CLUSTER TYPES

Typical of the *open cluster* are the Pleiades (Figure 9.11) and the cluster in Cancer (M67) as seen on page 291 (at the beginning of this chapter). Also known as *galactic clusters,* because they occur primarily in the disk of our Galaxy, the open cluster usually contains young, hot (O- and B-type) stars numbering in the hundreds. They form a rather loosely bound system that may disperse in a matter of a few million years due to the gravitational forces within the Galaxy as a whole. Thus, by the time such stars age, they are already separated by distances which no longer suggest a common origin. Almost 1000 open clusters are known in our Galaxy.

The *globular cluster* forms the second class. A cluster of this type usually contains thousands of stars that appear so tightly packed that the central regions cannot be resolved into individual stars, even with the largest telescopes (Figure 9.12). Just how close are these stars in

Figure 9.12   The globular star cluster in Hercules (M13). (Hale Observatories)

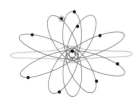

the center of a globular? Even in the most dense portion there are probably no more than 64 stars per cubic light-year (Figure 9.13). Within this distribution the average distance between stars would be such that light would require 3 months to travel from one star to the next, a distance of 2.4 trillion kilometers. By comparison, if we took a cubic light-year at random in our Galaxy, our chances of finding even one star within that space would be only 1 in 64.

Globulars seem to form a halo around the nucleus of the Galaxy (Figure 9.14). They do not participate directly in the revolution of the Galaxy, but rather seem to have elliptical orbits, moving in and out of the central region of the Galaxy in a rather random fashion. Their orbits and relationship to the Galaxy are somewhat similar to the orbits

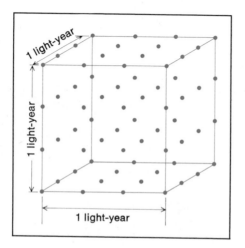

Figure 9.13 The density of stars near the center of a globular cluster.

Figure 9.14 The Milky Way galaxy, showing the halo, the nucleus, and the disk.

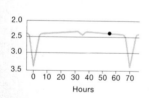

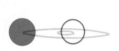

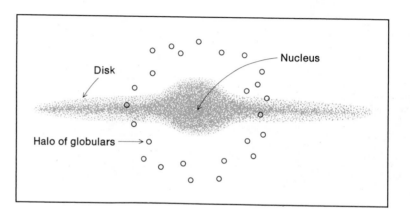

Figure 9.15 The double open cluster in Persei. (Lick Observatory)

and relationship of comets to the solar system.* The distance to these objects may be determined by the variable stars that they contain, called the RR Lyrae, or cluster-type variables (see Chapter 10).

Whereas the globular clusters typically contain thousands of stars and are usually found surrounding the nucleus of the Galaxy, the typical open cluster contains fewer than 1000 stars, and these are found in the spiral arms of the Galaxy.

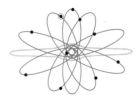

ASSOCIATIONS

Star types O and B are not distributed at random, but rather appear to be associated in groups. Almost 100 such *associations* are known in the Milky Way galaxy, and one such is situated in the region of the

*The right-hand flip pages beginning on page 285 demonstrate the motion of the globulars in the halo of the galaxy.

Orion Nebula. These high-luminosity stars are thought to be very young stars, lying close to the flattened disk portion of the Galaxy. We will see, in Chapter 13, how these very loose associations mark the spiral arms of the Milky Way as bright lights mark the streets of a city seen at night from the air.

QUESTIONS

1. Most of the stars we see as double stars are (a) two stars that are many light–years apart but just happen to line up from our point of view; (b) two stars that are close enough together so as to control each others' motion. Which is true?
2. How may a true binary system be recognized, even if the two stars cannot be separated by the largest telescope?
3. In the case of eclipsing binary stars, what properties of such a system can be determined from its light curve?
4. What is the single most important characteristic of stars that can be determined in a binary system?
5. What does the location of the barycenter of a binary system tell the astronomer?
6. When the mass of a star is plotted against its absolute magnitude, what becomes evident from the graph?
7. What does the fact that many stars of a cluster are moving in the same direction and at approximately the same speed suggest about their origin?
8. What is the most obvious difference between the open–type and the globular–type cluster?
9. Within the Milky Way galaxy, where are the globular clusters found?
10. Describe the motion of the globulars in relation to the Milky Way galaxy.

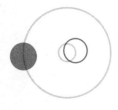

11. (a) Find the mass of each star in a binary system if their total mass is 10 solar masses and their respective distances from the barycenter are 2 A.U. and 3 A.U. (b) Find their period.
12. Find the total mass in a binary system which has a separation of 3 A.U. and a period of 3 years.
13. What change would accompany a reduction in the distance between two binary stars, say, if some unknown force shoved them closer together?

14. What assumption must be made about a star or star system if both the lines of ionized helium and the lines of molecules show up in the same spectrum?

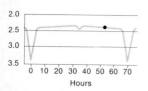

SUGGESTED READINGS

Baade, Walter, *Evolution of stars and galaxies,* Chapters 9, 10, and 12. Cambridge, Mass.: Harvard University Press, 1963.

Eggen, O. J., Masses of visual binary stars. *Annual Review of Astronomy and Astrophysics* **5,** 105–138 (1967).

Iben, Icko, Jr., Globular-cluster stars. *Scientific American* **223** (1), 26–39 (1970).

King, Ivan R., Dynamics of star clusters. *Sky and Telescope* **41** (3), 139–143 (1971).

Paczynski, B., Evolutionary processes in close binary systems. *Annual Review of Astronomy and Astrophysics* **9,** 183–208 (1971).

Popper, Daniel M., Determination of masses of eclipsing binary stars. *Annual Review of Astronomy and Astrophysics* **5,** 85–104 (1967).

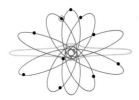

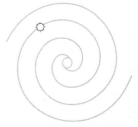

VARIABLE
STARS

10

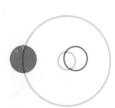

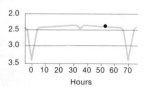

We have already seen a type of star system—the eclipsing binaries—that *appears* to vary in brightness; however, in the present chapter we shall be concerned with stars that *actually* vary in light output. The existence of such stars was recognized by Hipparchus in the first century B.C., and today thousands of variables have been catalogued.

The Cepheids, perhaps the most important class of variable stars, are named after a particular star, δ *Cephei,* the delta star in the constellation *Cepheus* (Figure 10.1). This notation is an example of a

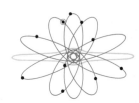

system that was initiated by Johann Bayer in his catalogue of stars published in 1603. With few exceptions, he assigned the Greek letter α (alpha) to the brightest star in a given constellation, β (beta) to the second brightest, γ (gamma) to the third, δ (delta) to the fourth, ε (epsilon) to the fifth, and so on.

The variable nature of δ Cephei was discovered by John Goodricke, a young British astronomer, in 1784. The light curve of δ Cephei, shown in Figure 10.2, indicates its period of 5.4 days.

CEPHEID VARIABLES

We can see from Figure 10.2 that the light of δ Cephei builds up rather rapidly from a magnitude of +4.3 to +3.6, a difference of 0.7 mag, which corresponds to a doubling of luminosity. This particular star appears twice as bright when at its maximum as compared to its minimum (Figure 10.3). Cepheids in general have periods of variation ranging between 1 and 50 days, and their light output varies over a range of 0.1 to 2 mag. Polaris, the North Star, is an example of a Cepheid that has only a small variation of 0.1 mag in a period of 4 days, not detectable by the naked eye. On the other hand, variations in δ Cephei are quite evident with the aid of binoculars.

We might wonder why certain stars fluctuate in their light output while others appear to be rather stable. What is happening to the star itself to cause these changes? The spectrograph will help us answer this question, for when a variable star is subjected to spectral analysis it becomes very evident that the star is pulsating—growing larger for a time and then smaller again. Let us assume, for example, that a particular star is moving away from us and therefore has a red shift in its spectral lines due to its radial velocity. As this star grows, its spectral lines will be shifted slightly from their normal red shift position back toward the blue, since the star's motion due to expansion is

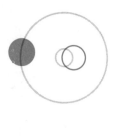

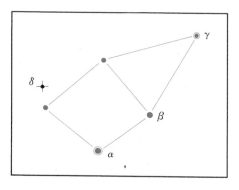

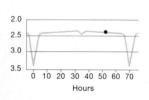

Figure 10.1 The constellation of Cepheus.

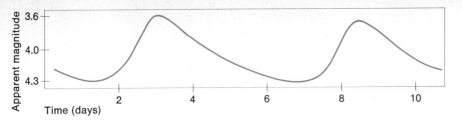

Figure 10.2 The light curve of δ Cephei.

Figure 10.3 A double exposure with slight displacement, showing the variable star WW Cygni at maximum and minimum brightness. The variable is located in the center of the photograph. (Hale Observatories)

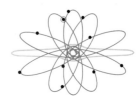

basically toward us. On the other hand, when the star is decreasing in size, both this motion and its radial velocity will increase the red shift. If we plot the rate of change in size, along with the light curve, we find a distinct relationship between the two. The actual size of the star at any given time is shown in Figure 10.4, bottom graph.

If a star were to behave simply like a "ball of gas," we might expect the time that it is brightest to correspond to its most condensed state, when the star would also be hottest due to its contraction; however, it is evident that the point of greatest light output follows shortly

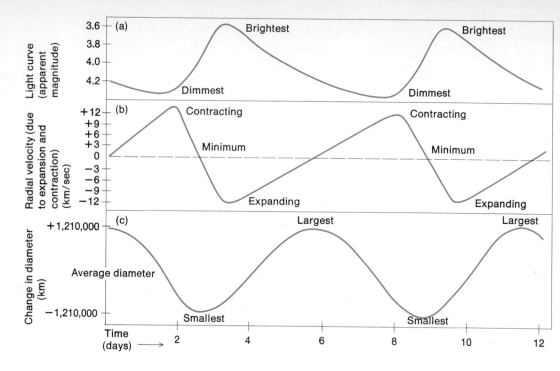

Figure 10.4 Graphs of a Cepheid variable. (a) Light curve. (b) Rate of change in size. (c) Change in size.

after this time of greatest contraction. The core of the star may actually put out most energy at the time of greatest contraction, but this effect does not reach the outer layers until later. Can we explain the variation in light by the change in size alone? δ Cephei has an average diameter of 40 million kilometers, with its expanded diameter about 2.4 million kilometers greater than its contracted diameter, representing a change of only about 6 percent. This in itself could not account for the doubling in luminosity; however, the spectrum of the star also reveals that accompanying a change of diameter is also a change of temperature. A small change in temperature creates a much more drastic change in energy output than does a corresponding change in diameter, and for this reason the variation in light output is primarily a function of temperature.

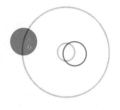

CEPHEIDS—

INDICATORS OF DISTANCE

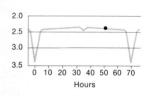

In 1912 Miss Henrietta Leavitt of Harvard College Observatory became interested in variables that had been discovered in the Small Magellanic Cloud (Figure 10.5). Traveling to the southern station of Harvard

Observatory in South Africa, she took many photographs of this Small Cloud near the south polar region. From these photographs she made a remarkable discovery: that there was a definite relationship between the apparent magnitude of the Cepheids and their period of variation. The longer-period Cepheids were also the most luminous. A plot of the stars that she studied is shown in Figure 10.6.

The very fact that these stars appear to lie along a diagonal line on this plot instead of being distributed randomly over the whole chart shows the relationship between the period and the apparent magnitude of these stars. The longer the period, the brighter the appearance of the star. Does it necessarily follow that, because of this relationship, there also exists a relationship between the period of a star and its absolute magnitude? Miss Leavitt reasoned that because all the stars in the Small Magellanic Cloud belong to the same group, they are all approximately the same distance from the observer. This supposition was later proven correct. When a group of stars is found to lie at approximately the same distance from the observer, their absolute magnitudes compare in precisely the same way as their apparent magnitudes. It is only necessary to find the distance to a few Cepheid-type

Figure 10.5 The Small Magellanic Cloud. (Mount Stromlo and Siding Spring Observatories, The Australian National University)

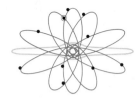

variables in order to make this conversion; however, at that time no Cepheids had been found within the limits of the method of heliocentric parallax.

Harlow Shapley and others joined Miss Leavitt in the search for Cepheids in our own neighborhood of stars, and by means of a method of statistical parallax, distances to a small number of Cepheids were found. Cepheids of a 1-day period were found to have an absolute magnitude of approximately zero, while those of a 50-day period were set at −4 in absolute magnitude; thus the latter were relatively luminous stars ranging from 100 times to 4000 times the luminosity of

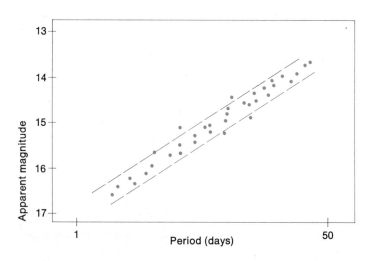

Figure 10.6 A plot of Cepheids in the Small Magellanic Cloud.

Figure 10.7 A plot of RR Lyrae and Cepheids.

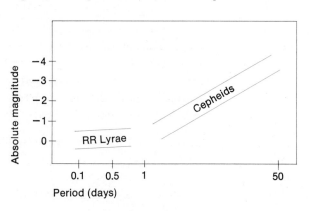

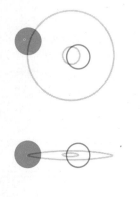

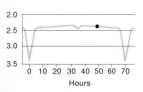

the sun. The Small Magellanic Cloud was recognized as being a very distant object, later to be established as another galaxy outside our own at a distance of more than 150,000 light-years.

NAMING OF VARIABLES

If in a given constellation a variable is found that already has a Greek-letter designation, as in the case of δ Cephei, it is retained. In the case of no previous designation, variables are given a prefixed letter, in the order of their discovery within a given constellation, according to the following scheme: R, S, T, . . . Z; RR, RS, RT, . . . RZ; SS, ST, SU, . . . SZ; and so on until ZZ is reached; then AA, AB, AC, . . . AZ; BB, BC, BD, . . . BZ; CC, CD, . . . CZ; through QZ, with the letter J omitted. Up to this point, 334 different designations are possible. If additional designations are needed in any given constellation, the prefix V335, V336, and so on, is used, always followed by the name of the constellation. Examples include RR Lyrae and V335 Herculis. The scheme by which variables are named has evolved over a period of time and now represents a blend of several schemes.

RR LYRAE STARS

A class of variables was found with periods ranging from a few hours to 1 day. These are called the RR Lyrae type, and each group member is estimated to have an absolute magnitude of zero; thus the group seems to be a continuation of the Cepheid type. Using this supposition, Walter Baade of Mt. Wilson and Palomar Observatories in 1952 conducted a search for variables in the Andromeda galaxy. He was able to photograph a variety of Cepheids in the galaxy, including those of 1-day period; however, he could find no RR Lyrae type, even though it should have been of equal magnitude. Let us review the latter fact by referring to Figure 10.7. Notice that both the 1-day Cepheid and the RR Lyrae stars were thought to be of zero absolute magnitude.

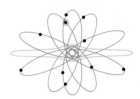

The fact that Baade could not find RR Lyrae stars in the Andromeda galaxy made him suspicious of Shapley's calibration of the absolute magnitudes of the Cepheids. Further study revealed that there are actually two types of Cepheid variable stars: Type-I Cepheids, which are found in the disk of spiral galaxies like our own; and Type-II Cepheids, found in globular clusters. Baade made numerous observations using the 5-m telescope at Mt. Palomar, and he calibrated the 1-day, Type-I Cepheids as having an absolute magnitude of -1.5, which was 1.5 mag brighter than the Type-II Cepheids Shapley had

observed. This was equivalent to a fourfold change in luminosity. Since the old Cepheid calibration had been used to determine the distance to nearby galaxies, and then the nearby galaxies had been used to estimate distances to other galaxies (and ultimately the size of the universe), a fourfold increase in luminosity estimates produced a doubling of all distance estimates. In other words, when Baade realized that the Type-I Cepheids he had been observing in the disk of the Andromeda galaxy were really four times as bright, he was forced to conclude that they were twice as far away. Remember that the apparent brightness of any source falls off with the square of its distance.

After the period-luminosity relationship of both Type-I and Type-II Cepheids was determined with greater accuracy, these stars came to play a vital role in measurement of distances to galaxies. Let us see how this has been accomplished. Suppose that the astronomer can isolate a Type-I Cepheid in the disk of a spiral galaxy and that he observes its period to be 10 days. He can read off its absolute magnitude as -4 (Figure 10.8). Now suppose that same star has an average apparent magnitude of $+21$; representing its luminosity as L, he may use the following proportion to determine its distance (r):

$$\frac{L(10)}{L(r)} = \left(\frac{r}{10}\right)^2$$

Apparent magnitude	$+21$
Absolute magnitude	$- 4$
Difference	25

A change of 25 mag is equivalent to a change in luminosity of 10^{10} (see Table 8.1); therefore,

$$\frac{10^{10}}{1} = \frac{r^2}{10^2} \quad \text{and} \quad r^2 = 10^{12}$$

Thus,

$$r = 10^6 = 1 \text{ million parsec} = 3.26 \times 10^6 \text{ light-years}$$
$$(\text{or } 3.26 \text{ million light-years})$$

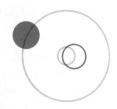

IRREGULAR VARIABLES

A variable star may be irregular in both its period and the amplitude of its variations. The light curve of Mira Ceti is shown in Figure 10.9. We see that its magnitude at maximum is between 3 and 5 and that at minimum it is between 8 and 10. Its period averages about 330 days; however, this does not mean that any single maximum is predictable.

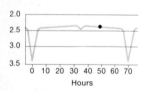

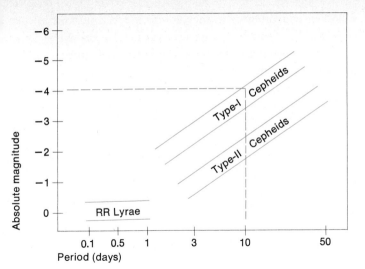

Figure 10.8 A modern period-luminosity graph of variables.

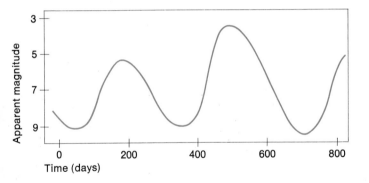

Figure 10.9 The light curve of Mira Ceti, an irregular variable.

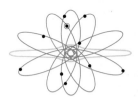

What kind of changes in a star can produce a 5-mag (hundredfold) change? Mira is an M-type star with a surface temperature, at minimum light, equal to about 2000°K and rising to only about 2600°K at maximum. Such an increase in temperature can produce only about a threefold increase in total light output, not the hundredfold increase observed. The second factor that may be considered is a change in size. Mira Ceti is one of the relatively few stars whose diameter may be computed by direct observations using an interferometer. Its diameter is approximately 300 times that of the sun, and during pulsations it increases to 360 solar diameters, an increase of 20 percent. This in turn produces almost a 50 percent increase in surface area, yet this in itself is not sufficient to explain the total variation in light output. While the final explanation is not certain, it is felt that the atmosphere of the star must also undergo drastic changes, and it may hold additional clues concerning the large light variations.

Betelgeuse is still another example of an irregular variable with a single magnitude variation for every period of 5 to 6 years. Its diameter varies between 500 and 750 solar diameters. The T Tauri stars form still another group of irregular variables, and they are characterized by their very rapid variations. This type of star is usually found in young clusters and often has a certain amount of uncondensed gas (nebulosity) in its vicinity. This suggests that the T Tauri stars are probably very young, still contracting and not yet stabilized as main-sequence stars. T Tauri stars can also be identified by a strong H_α (hydrogen-alpha) emission line in their spectra that is not characteristic of older pulsating stars.

RECURRENT NOVAE

To witness the "birth" of a *nova* (new) star would indeed be a spectacular event in a man's life (Figure 10.10). Ancient observers thought that this was happening when from time to time a star would suddenly appear where no star had been visible before. Far from being a new star, the nova is probably a star nearing its old age, having already passed through a pulsating state. It is a star that suddenly brightens without warning, increasing in light output perhaps a thousandfold—an occurrence which may be repeated. A typical prenova is a small blue or white dwarf star of about the same magnitude as the sun (+5). When it brightens, its outer layers expand very rapidly, 1600 km/sec, and its magnitude may reach −7, that is, a change of 12 mag, or a 60,000-fold increase in luminosity. The expanding shell of gas, which may be detected spectroscopically, gives a clue to its distance, for if both its rate of linear expansion and its rate of change in angular diameter can be observed, then its distance may be determined. Figure 10.11 graphically depicts the light curve of a typical nova, showing its variability even at minimum.

The eruption may take place in only a few hours, then require several weeks, months, or years to subside. The nova usually returns to its prior luminosity or only slightly less than that, indicating that the explosion was a superficial one, involving only its upper atmosphere. Probably less than one-ten thousandth of its mass is lost. Nova Aquilae 1918, for instance, increased in brightness 13 mag (from +5 to −8),

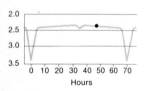

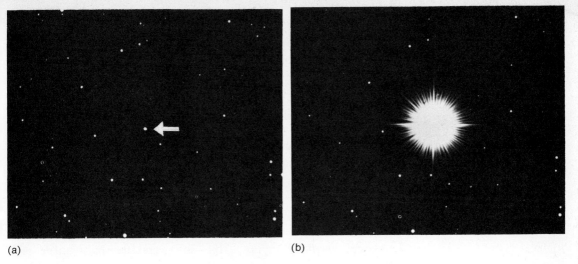

(a)   (b)

Figure 10.10 Nova Herculis 1934, showing the large change in brightness between (a) March 10, 1935, and (b) May 6, 1935. (Lick Observatory)

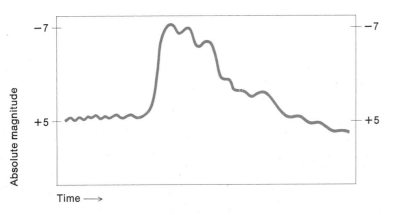

Figure 10.11 The light curve of a typical nova.

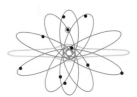

and a shell of gas was thrown off at a velocity of 1700 km/sec. At a distance of about 1200 light-years, this shell appeared to increase in diameter about 1 second of arc per year.

By what mechanism can a star expel a shell of gas and then return to its former brightness? Suppose that a hot dwarf star is a member of a binary pair in which the other member is a star that is expanding to a giant stage. As the star expands, some portion of its outer layer approaches the dwarf star close enough to experience its stronger gravitational force; as a result, some of the material of the cool giant will be transferred to the dwarf. Such a renewal of hydrogen-rich gases pouring onto the dwarf, which has used most of its hydrogen in thermonuclear reactions, may trigger a renewed reaction. Thus, a shell of gas would become heated and would then expand to produce the nova phenomenon. In this model, the dwarf star may then return to its former dim state until another such reaction occurs. Some observers believe that a binary association is essential for nova-type reactions to occur. By contrast quite a different model is presented for the supernovae, discussed next.

SUPERNOVAE

The name *supernova* implies a big nova, and the light curve of a supernova may superficially resemble that of a nova—but that is where the similarity ends. The record of supernovae suggests that they are very rare occurrences: only one has been recorded in the past 4 centuries in the Milky Way galaxy (in 1604). Furthermore, a supernova does not return to its former state after an explosion but rather is a reaction

Figure 10.12 Supernova in NGC 5236 (a) before and (b) after brightening in 1972. (Hale Observatories)

(a)
(b)

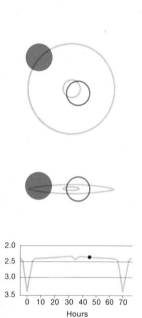

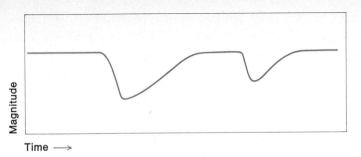

Time $\longrightarrow$

Figure 10.13 The light curve of R Coronae Borealis.

that occurs in the very heart of the star, one in which significant amounts of mass are thrown off (Figure 10.12). Most stars could not sustain repetition of gigantic experiences such as this, and therefore the supernova is considered a major step in the evolution of a star. We shall return to this subject later in Chapter 12.

R CORONAE BOREALIS STARS

A class of variable stars that seems to have a light curve that is almost upside down from those that we have studied is the R Coronae Borealis type (Figure 10.13). Not having a predictable period, these stars suddenly drop several magnitudes and then slowly return to normal brightness. When at a minimum, some reveal a small shell of gas surrounding the star; the spectrum of this shell is suprisingly similar to that of a planetary nebula. Furthermore, the distribution of these stars is quite similar to that of the planetary nebulae. We can not be sure of this relationship, but the R Coronae Borealis stars form an interesting group and constitute at least a possible predecessor to the planetary nebulae (to be considered in Chapter 12).

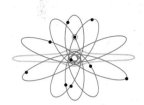

FLARE STARS

The final class of variable stars to be discussed is exemplified by UV Ceti, a flare star. We have discussed flares that occur on the sun, and this may be the same kind of phenomenon which causes certain stars to brighten periodically. It is a localized hot spot on the sun. For stars that are in reality very bright, it is difficult to spot a flare since the proportionate increase in light output is small. On the other hand, a

flare on an intrinsically faint star, say, an M-type dwarf, is much more apparent. Typically, the flaring process creates a very rapid variation in light output, lasting only minutes. If this phenomenon in a star is similar to the localized flare on the sun, it represents a tremendous release of energy in a very short period of time, hence a real explosion—perhaps much more violent than that we observe on the sun.

We have studied a number of special types of stars, some of which surely represent different stages in the life cycle of stars in general. In Chapter 12 we shall try to discover an evolutionary progression for these various types.

QUESTIONS

1. How much variation in brightness is shown by δ Cephei?
2. True or false: Of all the different types of variable stars, the Cepheids can be distinguished by their light curve.
3. What physical change appears to produce the variations of brightness in the Cepheids?
4. What relationship makes the Cepheids a valuable distance indicator?
5. What characteristic of the RR Lyrae stars makes them good distance indicators?
6. The discovery that there are really two types of Cepheids (Type I and Type II) led to a reevaluation of the size of the known universe. Explain this reevaluation.
7. What circumstances are thought to have produced the Crab Nebula?
8. What evidence suggests that a planetary nebula bears little or no relationship to a nova?
9. There is some indication that stars may evolve through several variable stages. Is the T Tauri group thought to be composed of young or old stars? What evidence supports your answer?
10. What distinguished the light curve of the R Coronae Borealis stars from that of other variable types?
11. Why is it thought possible for novae to recur over and over again whereas a supernova probably represents a one-time event for a star?
12. RR Lyrae stars are classified as Type-II variables. Explain the meaning of this classification and tell where the RR Lyrae stars are usually found.
13. The period-luminosity graph of Figure 10.8 tells us that a 1-day, Type-II Cepheid has an absolute magnitude of -1. Suppose this same star had an apparent magnitude of $+14$, find its distance.
14. True or false; A flare star can be recognized as showing a variation in its light output only if it is a rather cool star.

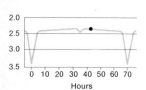

2.0
2.5
3.0
3.5
0 10 20 30 40 50 60 70
Hours

SUGGESTED READINGS

Glasby, J. S., *Variable stars.* Cambridge, Mass.: Harvard University Press, 1969.

Smak, Jozef, The long-period variable stars. *Annual Review of Astronomy and Astrophysics* **4,** 19–34 (1966).

Smith, E. P., and Jacobs, K. C., *Introductory astronomy and astrophysics,* Chapter 16. Philadelphia: Saunders, 1973.

Struve, Otto, *The universe,* Chapter 5. Cambridge, Mass.: MIT Press, 1962.

Warner, Brian, and Nather, R. E., High-speed photometry of cataclysmic variables. *Sky and Telescope* **43** (2), 82–85 (1972).

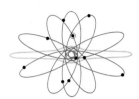

INTERSTELLAR
MEDIA

11

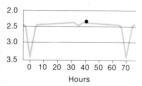

Although the space between the stars was once thought to be almost entirely empty, astronomers now realize that it may hold more material of an uncondensed nature than all the condensed matter in the galaxies themselves. *Condensed matter* manifests itself in the form of stars, planets, moons, comets, and meteoroids. We will consider *uncondensed matter* to consist of particles that are too small to be readily visible to the naked eye. Such uncondensed matter includes the general—but sparse—distribution of gases throughout the universe, the

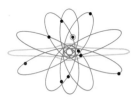

clouds of more highly concentrated gases, the clouds of dust, and the particles that constitute the cosmic rays. Recent observations are pointing more conclusively than ever before to the fact that the total mass of such matter exceeds the total mass of all stars, planets, and lesser bodies.

INTERSTELLAR GASES

While an *interstellar gas cloud* is almost transparent under normal conditions, it may manifest its presence in a number of ways. The most obvious visible form is the emission nebula. Atoms that constitute the gas are excited by nearby stars. This is to say that their electrons receive energy from the light of nearby stars, producing upward transitions, and then, when the downward transitions follow, visible light is produced. If the stars nearby are very hot, a large part of their radiation is in the form of ultraviolet light, which has enough energy to free the atoms of some electrons completely, leaving the atoms ionized and producing temperatures in the order of 10,000°K within the gas. This is called *photoionization*. The free electrons are then attracted to the positive ions. Upon recombination of these particles, light and radio emissions are produced. We see examples of emission nebulae in ionized regions, called *H II regions,* in the Orion Nebula and in the Lagoon

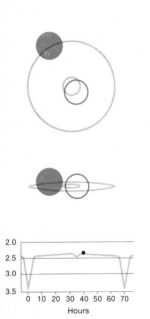

Figure 11.1 The Orion Nebula, NGC 1976 with NGC 1977. (Lick Observatory)

Figure 11.2 The Lagoon Nebula in Sagittarius, NGC 6523 (M8). (Lick Observatory)

Nebula (Figures 11.1 and 11.2). Very hot stars may cause photoionization as far away as 400 light-years.

Radio emissions are a very significant way in which gas clouds reveal their existence; in much the same way that different elements produce their own characteristic set of spectral lines, these gas clouds also produce a characteristic set of radio "lines"—they emit certain wavelengths. Neutral hydrogen, for example, emits a radio signal at the 21-cm wavelength. This is accomplished when the electron in a hydrogen atom flips its spin axis. Picture a hydrogen atom in which the spin axis of the electron has the same direction as the spin axis of the proton. When the electron flips its spin axis, the atom gives up a very small amount of energy. This energy is emitted in the form of a radio signal of 21-cm wavelength. If a radio astronomer tunes his receiver to accept the 21-cm wavelength, rejecting all other wavelengths, he may record the presence of interstellar clouds of neutral hydrogen. Since large concentrations of hydrogen gas seem to be located in the spiral arms of our Galaxy, a study of the distribution of neutral hydrogen, using the 21-cm wavelength, helps us to paint a picture of the Galaxy (Figure 11.3).

By means of this 21-cm wavelength, huge clouds of neutral hydrogen have also been discovered rushing toward the galactic plane at velocities of about 240 km/sec.

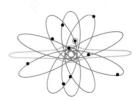

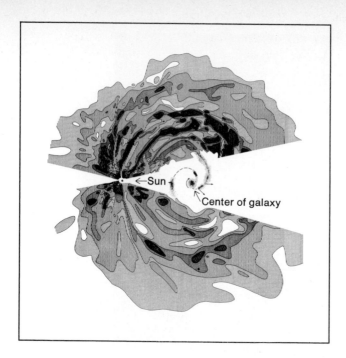

Figure 11.3 The spiral nature of the Milky Way galaxy as constructed from 21-cm, neutral-hydrogen observations made at Leiden Observatory, Netherlands, and at Radio Physics Laboratory, Sydney, Australia.

Figure 11.4 A multiple-line spectrum indicating several clouds between the source and the observer, each with slightly different line-of-sight velocities. (Kitt Peak National Observatory)

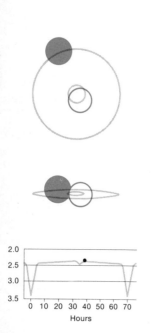

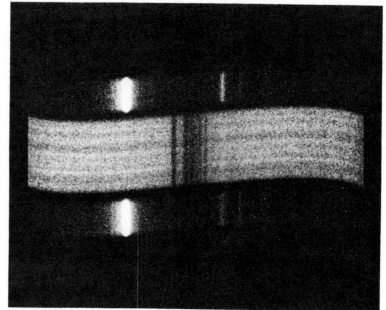

Certain elements present in gas clouds also create absorption lines in the visible spectrum, and these too exhibit shifts due to motion. On a single spectrum of a star may be superimposed the absorption lines of hydrogen from gas clouds that are in between that star and the observer. These absorption lines often appear as multiple lines, each line representing a separate cloud with a slightly different velocity. Thus, spectroscopic study of absorption lines has also become a powerful tool for analyzing the presence of a given gas and its motion within the Galaxy (Figure 11.4). Other elements which have been identified in interstellar gases include calcium, sodium, helium, oxygen, nitrogen, and carbon.

INTERSTELLAR MOLECULES

The first hint that molecules exist in interstellar gas came in 1937 with the recognition of certain spectral lines associated with the methylidyne radical, an atom of carbon linked to an atom of hydrogen (CH), and the cyanogen molecule, a combination of carbon and nitrogen (CN). The real breakthrough came with the advent of radio astronomy, which ultimately revealed some very complex molecules inhabiting the regions between the stars. One of the reasons that radio telescopes are so effective in the study of molecules in space is because radio energy penetrates the dust clouds that are opaque to visible light. It is within such dust clouds that molecules are generally found.

Furthermore, the characteristic wavelengths of many molecules exist in the radio portion of the spectrum: molecules have certain inherent abilities to release radio wavelengths, which independent atoms do not have. This is due to rotational and vibrational motions common to molecules, and changes in these motions release wavelengths that are characteristic of the given molecule. In addition to these changes, molecules may also radiate radio energy due to electron transitions. Table 11.1 lists some of the known interstellar molecules with their characteristic wavelengths. Spectroscopists have given the radio astronomer the knowledge of what wavelengths are associated with a given molecule. They have said, in effect, "If you want to find methyl alcohol in space, tune your radio telescope to 35.9 cm."

We should recognize the fact that some of these molecules have only been found in a few locations. Even when they are found, they represent only trace amounts when compared to the hydrogen present. Estimates suggest that for every 10,000 atoms of hydrogen there are only four of oxygen, two of carbon, one of sulfur, and one of nitrogen. Such estimates are based on the strengths of the respective spectral lines,

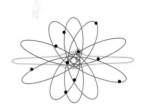

Table 11.1 Interstellar molecules and their characteristic wavelengths

MOLECULE	FORMULA	CHARACTERISTIC WAVELENGTH
Methylidyne	CH	4300 Å
Methylidyne (ionized)	CH$^+$	3958 Å
Cyanogen radical	CN	3875 Å, 2.6 cm
Hydroxyl radical	OH	18.0, 6.3, 5.0, 3.7, 2.2 cm
Ammonia	NH$_3$	1.3, 1.2 cm
Water	H$_2$O	1.35 cm
Formaldehyde	H$_2$CO	6.6, 6.2, 2.1, 1.0, 0.2 cm
Hydrogen (gas)	H$_2$	1.060 Å
Carbon monoxide	CO	2.7 cm
Methyl alcohol	CH$_3$OH	35.9 cm
Hydrogen cyanide	HCN	3.4 mm
Cyanoacetylene	HC$_3$N	3.3 cm
Formic acid	HCOOH	18.3 cm
Silicon monoxide	SiO	2.3, 3.4 mm
Carbon monosulfide	CS	2.0 mm
Formamide	NH$_2$CHO	6.5 cm
Carbonyl sulfide	OCS	2.5 mm
Methyl cyanide	CH$_3$CN	2.7 mm
Isocyanic acid	HNCO	1.36 cm, 3.4 mm
Methylacetylene	CH$_3$CCH	3.5 mm
Acetaldehyde	CH$_3$CHO	28.1 cm
Thioformaldehyde	H$_2$CS	9.5 cm
Methanimine	CH$_2$NH	5.8 cm
Hydrogen sulfide	H$_2$S	1.8 mm

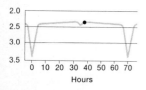

as judged by the heights of the peaks in a radio spectrogram. Figure 11.5 shows the radio emission associated with ammonia.

Molecules that contain carbon are called *organic molecules,* indicating their vital role in living organisms. In our search for carbon-containing molecules that may have prepared the way for life on earth, we see many examples in Table 11.1.

How are molecules formed? Some observers believe that atoms may simply stick together; that is, they may bond as they do on earth when they are brought close together under the proper conditions. A dust cloud may present the proper conditions due to its cool, dense state. Dust particles themselves may play a key role, forming a base upon which complex molecules can form, gathering together by a process of accretion.

INTERSTELLAR DUST

Interstellar dust consists of solid particles of appreciable size when compared to molecules. Their size and shape represent the critical factors in the effect they have on light. One of the ways that dust exhibits itself is in the *reflection nebula*. For example, the Pleiades are enveloped in a nebulosity that might be mistaken for an emission nebula (Figure 11.6); however, the spectrum of the nebulous material

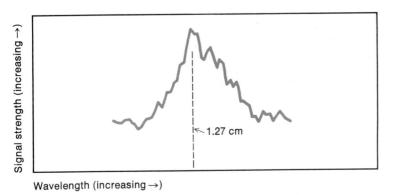

Figure 11.5 A radio spectrogram showing one of the emission lines of ammonia. [From Turner, Barry E., Interstellar molecules. *Scientific American,* **228** (3), 50–69 (1973)]

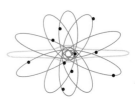

Figure 11.6 The nebulosity surrounding the Pleiades is thought to be primarily dust. (Hale Observatories)

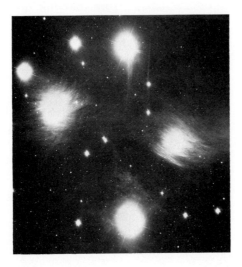

Figure 11.7 The Horsehead Nebula in Orion. The dark "horse-head" figure represents a dust cloud that obscures the light from behind. (Hale Observatories)

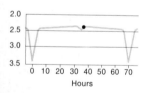

is almost the same as that of the stars that it surrounds. This indicates that the nebulous material is merely reflecting the light and so must be of the nature of dust. Gas molecules are not large enough to reflect light, nor can they effectively absorb light over the continuous spectrum. Gas clouds absorb a limited number of wavelengths to produce an absorption spectrum, but this does not appreciably dim the light from a source beyond the cloud. Dust clouds, on the other hand, do in fact appreciably dim such objects. The Horsehead Nebula is an example of such a cloud (Figure 11.7).

The North American Nebula is an emission nebula; however, the portion roughly corresponding to the Gulf of Mexico is an absorption nebula, basically consisting of cosmic dust (Figure 11.8).

The dark central regions of the Milky Way, near the constellation Sagittarius, were once thought to be "windows" through which the observer might look to the other side of the Galaxy. Now it is known that these regions are clouds of cosmic dust that obscure our view of almost all objects that fall behind them. Early observers called this region the "Zone of Avoidance," for no galaxies are evident in that direction. Modern astronomers are penetrating this zone by use of infrared techniques. Infrared wavelengths are not appreciably affected by dust, and recently new galaxies have been discovered in infrared photographs near the center of the Milky Way (see Chapter 14). The presence of obscuring clouds makes the sky look spotty in many regions, and what appears to be a lack of stars in a given area of the sky may only signal the presence of such clouds. Concentrations of dust may appear as small black globules against the background of a glowing nebula (Figure 11.9).

In addition to dimming the light of objects beyond these obscuring clouds, cosmic dust also reddens the light that does penetrate. This indicates that dust is also selective in that it absorbs and scatters blue light better than red (short wavelengths better than long wavelengths), thus leaving the light reddened.

Interstellar reddening affects our entire picture of the galaxy in regard to the distribution of stars. We judge the distance to a star by its apparent brightness; however, the presence of dust in the line of sight causes a star to appear dimmer than it would otherwise. A correc-

Figure 11.8 The North American Nebula in Cygnus. (Lick Observatory)

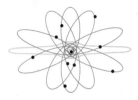

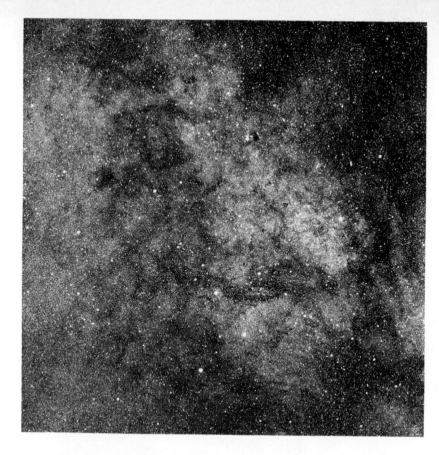

Figure 11.9 The Milky Way near Sagittarius. (Lick Observatory)

tion must be applied by saying that the star is really closer than it appears on the basis of brightness alone. The amount of correction depends upon the amount of reddening, and this can be judged by comparing the spectral class of the star as determined from its spectrum to its spectral class as determined from its apparent color. In other words, if a B-type star looks like an A-type, then the observer can compute the amount of reddening and make allowance for this factor in determining distance. Such striking effects of interstellar dust would seem to suggest that it must constitute a significant part of interstellar material; but, on the contrary, the total mass of dust represents only about 1 percent of the mass of the interstellar gas clouds.

Still another effect that the dust has on light is *polarization,* causing its oscillations to be oriented predominantly in one plane. In order to polarize light, the grains of dust must be elongated, needlelike, or flattened objects. Spherical objects can not produce polarization according to our present understanding of the phenomenon. Furthermore, these elongated grains must be aligned, or must possess a spinlike motion with their spin axes aligned, in order to produce polarization. Any material with an electrical property similar to a metal can be aligned by a magnetic field; such fields are believed to exist in space. The study of polarization due to interstellar dust shows concentrations in the spiral arms of the Milky Way galaxy. We may be searching for a metallic grain or metal-like conglomerate of atoms. Such material, of course, responds to a magnetic field and aligns itself accordingly. In addition to silicates and iron structures, carbon—which can take on the form of tiny flat platelets, or even the form of diamond dust—has been suggested as the principal component of cosmic dust. A definitive answer concerning the composition and origin of this interstellar dust must await further investigation.

Cosmic dust seems to play a significant role in star formation, as is exemplified in the following ways. Dust clouds are often associated with hot blue, presumably young, stars. The Pleiades are an example of this. Furthermore, dust clouds are characteristic of the spiral arms of our Galaxy, the regions of stellar formation. Dust is conspicuous by its absence in the globular clusters, the older members of the Galaxy, which are located in the halo surrounding the Galaxy nucleus. It is possible that they too possessed clouds of gas and dust in early stages of stellar formation, only to have these constituents swept out, later to form into the flattened disk of the Galaxy.

COSMIC RAYS

Cosmic rays constitute a principal component of the universe, ranking almost on a par with the stars themselves. The term itself is a misnomer that reflects an earlier idea of the nature of these particles. A *cosmic ray* is really a charged atomic particle that has been accelerated to nearly the speed of light. It may consist of an electron, a positron, a proton (hydrogen nucleus), an alpha particle (helium nucleus), or other heavier nuclei. Hydrogen nuclei account for almost 90 percent of all cosmic rays; helium nuclei represent about 9 percent, with the remaining particles supplying the other 1 percent. These accelerated particles carry a very large amount of kinetic energy (energy due to their motion). It is the motion of these particles, together with their mass, that makes cosmic rays out of otherwise normal atomic particles.

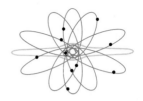

In order to determine the source for such energetic particles, we must make several observations. When detection devices are lowered into the ocean, the count of cosmic particles decreases. When counters

are carried aloft in balloons or rockets, the count increases up to about an elevation of 20,000 m. These facts do not point to the earth as the source of cosmic rays, for if it were, the readings would be reversed. Next, we might look to the sun, for there is some evidence of increased cosmic radiation on the occasion of solar flares; however, it is doubtful that the sun is the major source. The sun does not produce enough high-energy particle radiation to account for that which strikes the earth; furthermore, cosmic radiation is sensed on the earth's surface almost equally from every direction, hence it is not localized in the sun. The particles seem to permeate space, and it is believed that if it were not for the solar wind blowing the less energetic of the cosmic particles away from the earth, perhaps three times as many would strike the earth. The solar wind, however, has little effect on the more energetic particles.

A clue to the source of cosmic radiation may be found in the small percentage of particles consisting of accelerated electrons. When high velocity electrons pass through a magnetic field, synchrotron (radio) radiation results. There are only a few types of sources that yield synchrotron radiation: these are the supernovae, other explosive reactions in the core of our Galaxy, and radio sources outside our Galaxy. If the source were outside our Galaxy, the radiation would have thinned out so much before reaching us that it would be almost undetectable. Current thinking favors sources within our own Galaxy, with heavy emphasis on the supernovae. A supernova represents a huge explosive reaction which could provide the necessary acceleration for these particles. Periodic explosions replenish the total energy in cosmic particles. A charged particle that encounters a magnetic field will be accelerated; the particles, being charged, would not be expected to travel in a straight line as they encountered different magnetic fields in space, and thus it is possible that the particles occupy the entire Galaxy.

Noting Albert Einstein's statement that our perception of space is influenced by the distribution of matter that produces gravitational fields, we realize that it may also be influenced by the distribution of electrical charges—a distribution which produces electrical and magnetic fields. We are now in a better position to appreciate the opening statement of this chapter. There may be more material dispersed in the space between the stars than within stars themselves.

QUESTIONS

1. By what process does an interstellar gas cloud emit its own light?
2. By what process may a nebula produce a radio spectrum?
3. How can the astronomer distinguish a reflection nebula from an emission nebula?

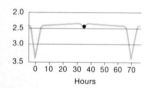

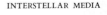

4. Describe the effects that interstellar dust clouds have upon light passing through them.

5. In what sense is the term "cosmic ray" a misnomer?

6. What are possible sources of cosmic rays?

7. What protection does the earth have from continual bombardment by cosmic rays?

8. What did early observers mean by the term "Zone of Avoidance"?

9. How has the modern astronomer penetrated the "Zone of Avoidance" to discover new objects beyond the central bulge of the Milky Way galaxy?

10. How does neutral hydrogen generate a 21-cm radio signal?

11. Looking at Table 11.1, list the individual elements of which these compounds are formed.

12. Can you explain how molecules found in interstellar space may be distinguished from each other?

13. How is polarization related to the study of dust between the stars?

14. Although cosmic "rays" are charged atomic particles (like protons and electrons), what distinguishes them from ordinary atomic particles?

SUGGESTED READINGS

Bok, Bart J., The birth of stars. *Scientific American* **227** (2), 49–61 (1972).

Lynds, B. T. (ed.), *Dark nebulae, globules and protostars.* Tucson: University of Arizona Press, 1971.

Middlehurst, Barbara M., and Aller, Lawrence H. (eds.), *Nebulae and interstellar matter.* Chicago: University of Chicago Press, 1968.

Middlehurst, Barbara M., and Aller, Lawrence H. (eds.), *Stars and stellar systems.* Chicago: University of Chicago Press, 1968.

Shu, Frank H., Spiral structure, dust clouds and star formation. *American Scientist* **61** (5), 524–536 (1973).

Smith, E. P., and Jacobs, K. C., *Introductory astronomy and astrophysics,* Chapter 17. Philadelphia: Saunders, 1973.

Soloman, Philip M., Interstellar molecules. *Physics Today* **26** (3), 32–40 (1973).

Turner, Barry E., Interstellar molecules. *Scientific American* **228** (3), 50–69 (1973).

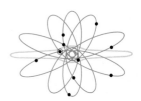

STELLAR
EVOLUTION

12

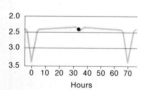

Our study has revealed that stars vary greatly in size, mass, temperature, color, and luminosity. Does this great variety indicate that stars are basically different from one another, or does it indicate that stars are merely in different stages of a life cycle, throughout which their appearance drastically changes? While stars differ widely in their masses, and this influences their life cycle, the fundamental reason for variety lies in the fact that they do change. Like man, stars go through stages which could be termed pregnancy, birth, youth, adulthood, old age,

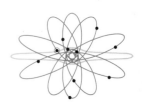

337

and death. Only under the rarest circumstances may an astronomer hope to witness a transition from one evolutionary stage to another, for the life cycle of an average star extends over 10 billion years; and so the astronomer must be content to observe stars in different stages and try to arrange them in the proper order. It is as though an intelligent being from another planet had only one day to spend on the earth and that he had no prior knowledge of the life cycle of man. What approach might he use to develop a theory concerning the order of man's aging process? Obviously he could observe man in all stages of his development—but how could he determine which stage came first? He might judge the size of man at various ages; or he might consider vigor, metabolism, condition of skin, speech qualities, and so on. As a result of these observations, he might deduce the proper life cycle. In a very similar way, the astronomer observes various stars in different stages of their life cycle and attempts to place these in their proper order. To complete this analogy, we must make two assumptions: that stars, like man, have been and are being created continually and hence are of different ages; and that stars do change with time, however slowly. The pieces of our puzzle include the main-sequence stars, the dwarfs, the giants and supergiants, the pulsating variables, the novae, and so on—but which came first? Let us approach this problem from a theoretical point of view. We assume that a star is a ball of gas and that, under prescribed conditions, it should behave like a gas.

GAS LAWS

In our discussion of stellar evolution, we will see that factors such as volume, density, pressure, and temperature play a very significant role in determining the nature of a star at any point in time. Let us see how these factors are interrelated by performing several simple experiments. Consider a certain number of gas particles (atoms or molecules) in a container with a plunger-type top. Such particles are always in motion. In fact the temperature of the gas is a measure of their average velocity (the small arrows in Figure 12.1 indicate their direction of motion, and length of the arrows indicates speed). Now if the plunger were lowered to reduce the volume but the temperature remained the same [Figure 12.1(b)], then the pressure would increase. You can visualize this increase in pressure by noticing that the particles would be closer together and hence collisions would be more frequent. This experiment illustrates Boyle's law:

The pressure of a gas at constant temperature is inversely proportioned to its volume.

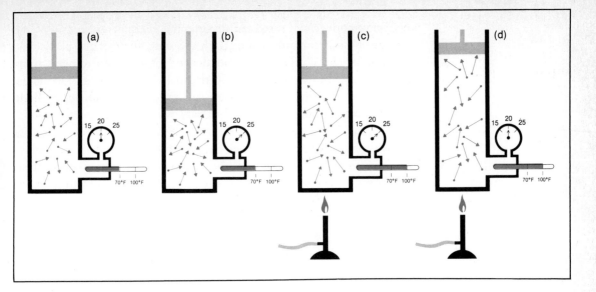

Figure 12.1 Operation of the gas laws: (a) large volume and low temperature produces low pressure; (b) reduced volume and same temperature yields higher pressure; (c) increased temperature and same volume as in (a) yields higher pressure; (d) high temperature and expanding volume results in reduced pressure.

Next, let us start again with the container as in Figure 12.1(a) and heat the gas as in Figure 12.1(c). As the temperature rises, the particles move faster on the average (as indicated by longer arrows), and this increases the tendency for particles to collide, producing an increase in pressure. Alternately, if the plunger were lifted as in Figure 12.1(d), the increase in temperature could produce an increase in volume leaving pressure constant. This illustrates Charles's law:

> *Pressure (at constant volume) is proportional to temperature, and volume (at constant pressure) is proportional to temperature.*

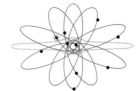

Figures 12.1(a) and 12.1(d) illustrate the fact that when a star is heated it will tend to expand as long as it behaves like a gas. But before we can consider this idea, or speculate as to the birth of a star, we must recognize the star's initial source of energy.

EFFECTS OF GRAVITATION

The very fact that the particles of a gas cloud are spread out over a given volume and that they attract one another gravitationally represents a form of energy called *potential energy*. If that cloud contracts, it is

339

capable of converting some of this potential energy into *kinetic energy* (energy associated with motion) by speeding up the gas particles—heating the gas. Thus, as a gas cloud condenses it not only gets more dense but also increases in temperature due to energy conversion. Then, as is true of the sun, if temperature and pressure are sufficiently high, other sources of energy (thermonuclear) will also become activated.

With a knowledge of the interrelationship among all these factors, the astrophysicist has been able to build hypothetical star models which start with a huge cloud of dust and gas; by computer-assisted analysis, he can trace the evolution of this hypothetical star from birth to death. We will look at the predictions that are derived from this model regarding evolutionary changes in the star and test out these predictions against actual observations.

FORMATION
OF A STAR

We know that great amounts of interstellar gas and dust remain in an uncondensed state, for example, in the disk of our Galaxy (see Chapter 11). This material provides the possible building blocks for stars. Let us attempt to theorize as to how a star might be formed and then search for evidence to see if we are correct. The temperature within an average interstellar gas cloud is estimated to be $100°K$ ($-373°C$). At such a temperature the atoms and molecules are moving about in random fashion and fast enough so that there is little chance that their mutual gravitational attraction will arrest their motion. However, there are certain regions where dust grains also abound, and such regions are thought to be very cold, perhaps as low as $5°K$ ($-268°C$), because dust obscures most of the ultraviolet radiation of nearby stars. At this low temperature the average speed of the molecules is greatly reduced, permitting the weak gravitational forces to arrest their motion and begin to build a "knot" (*condensation*). Once started, such condensations will continue to accrete (gather in) material from the surrounding region of the nebula as the force of gravity increases in each growing knot.

How might these dust regions be observed? They would most likely be dark areas revealed against the background of a glowing nebula or obscuring the stars which would normally be seen beyond the dust cloud. You will find a number of such regions in Figures 12.2, 12.3, and 12.4. If condensations are actually forming in these dust clouds, they may exhibit themselves in still another way, for two significant changes would be taking place. The condensation of the gas cloud or a portion of it is equivalent to a reduction in volume and an increase in density. Furthermore, some of the gravitational (potential) energy

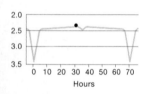

Figure 12.2 The dark globules in this nebula (IC 2944), in the constellation of Centaurus, suggest regions of cool gas and dust, perhaps regions of star formation. (Cerro Tololo Inter-American Observatory)

Figure 12.3 Dark globules in the Lagoon Nebula (M8). (Lick Observatory)

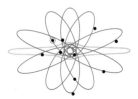

of the cloud is being converted to kinetic energy, heating the cloud. By the time the temperature has reached several hundred degrees Kelvin, it will radiate in infrared wavelengths. With the development of modern methods of infrared detection, the existence of such infrared sources has been proven and tends to confirm our suppositions as to this point.

At this stage, these infrared sources can not yet be called stars. Until temperatures and pressures increase sufficiently to initiate a ther-

Figure 12.4 An enlarged section of the nebula in Monoceros, showing dark regions. See Figure 12.6 for a view of the entire nebula. (Hale Observatories)

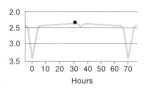

monuclear fusion reaction, these objects must still be termed *protostars* (stars in the making).

As the condensation knot grows and a temperature of about 1500°K is reached, the protostar may become visible on red–sensitive film. The photo record of condensations in the Orion Nebula actually shows growth over a period of only a few years (Figure 12.5). This may represent one of those rare examples of a crucial stage in stellar evolution occurring on a time scale which man can witness. Of course, we are seeing only a very brief segment of a star pregnancy in these photos, for the average time needed for a star (like the sun) to reach this stage is in the order of a million years. After all, time is required for a gas cloud more than 1 trillion kilometers in diameter to shrink down to one which is 80 million kilometers in diameter.

To this point the only force which has been acting is that of gravity, shrinking the cloud to smaller and smaller diameters. Where will this condensation be halted and by what force? The force which tends to counter that of gravity is pressure, and already we have noted that pressure is gradually increasing with the decrease in volume. Furthermore, the protostar is about to reach that significant point at which its central temperature has built up to 10 million degrees Kelvin and its central pressure is a billion times that of the earth's atmosphere. When the "critical" point igniting the thermonuclear process is attained, an enormous amount of energy is released and pressure is significantly increased.

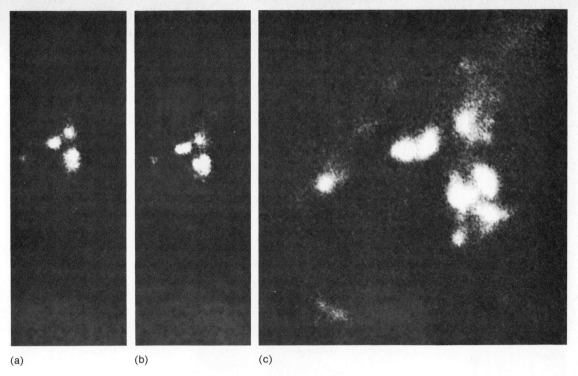

(a)   (b)   (c)

Figure 12.5 Herbig-Hara objects in Orion, taken (a) in 1947, (b) in 1954, and (c) in 1959, showing growing concentrations. (Lick Observatory)

A STAR IS BORN

With the ignition of thermonuclear fusion, we may truly say that a star has been born. However, it will continue to contract until the outward force of pressure exactly balances the inward force of gravity—a condition called *hydrostatic equilibrium.* This stabilized state probably does not occur as a simple halting of contraction but rather may be accompanied by a period in which the star pulsates in size and appears to vary in its light output. When the astronomer observes certain regions of gas and dust, such as in the Monoceros cluster (Figure 12.6), he sees a type of variable star which we have already studied—the T Tauri type. These stars show rapid, irregular variations and may be recognized by their typical emission spectra. Like the sun, most stars have absorption spectra. A plot of these stars on the H-R diagram seems to suggest that the T Tauri stars may represent an evolutionary stage just preceding the stable "main-sequence" stage, for most of them appear just to the right and above that stable group. In Figure 12.7 the T Tauri stars in the Monoceros cluster (NGC 2264) are shown by the "plus"

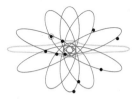

343

Figure 12.6 Nebulosity seen in Monoceros. (Hale Observatories)

Figure 12.7 A plot of the stars in NGC 2264.

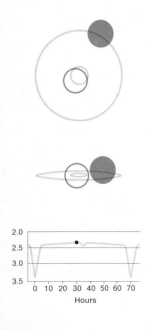

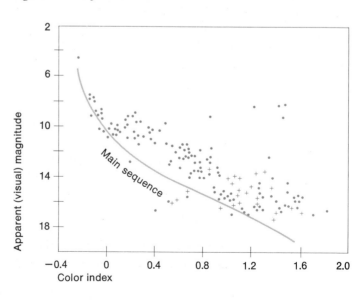

(+) symbol. Margherita Hack has drawn the early evolutionary tracks of stars of various masses, as shown in Figure 12.8. The numbers associated with each track represent the star's mass, measured in units of *solar mass*. (The mass of the sun is equal to one such unit.) From the mass-luminosity relationship considered earlier (see Figure 9.10), we expect stars of greater mass to stabilize higher on the main sequence.

As you view these evolutionary tracks in Figure 12.8, and others which follow in this chapter, keep in mind what changes on the H-R diagram mean. Vertical changes mean either a brightening (up) or a dimming (down); horizontal changes mean either an increase in surface temperature (left) or a decrease (right): Thus, when an evolutionary track slopes upward to the left, we interpret this to mean an increase in luminosity (brightening) accompanied by an increase in surface temperature. This is what we might expect of a star that is heating up but not changing its size appreciably. What must be happening when a track is horizontal, moving to the left? The surface temperature is increasing, but surface area must be decreasing at the same time—the one tending to counter the other; therefore luminosity remains unchanged. Note how the condensation tracks of the stars of lower mass seem to end on the main sequence, indicating that they have passed through the T Tauri stage.

Figure 12.8 The evolutionary track of stars of different masses. (Diagram prepared by Margherita Hack)

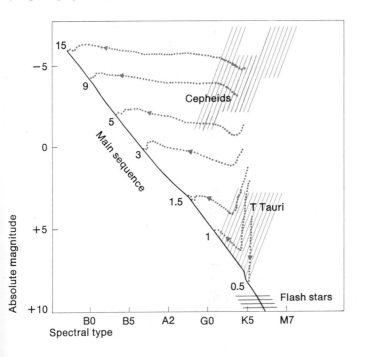

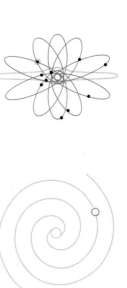

MAIN-SEQUENCE STAGE

When the star finally stabilizes to the point of hydrostatic equilibrium (discussed earlier), its size, surface temperature, and luminosity are basically determined for the major portion of its life cycle. What evidence do we have that stars spend at least 95 percent of their visible life on the main sequence? The answer lies in the fact that on a H-R plot of any large number of stars selected at random we find the majority of stars on the main sequence, and there is a direct correlation between the number of stars found in any stage and the length of time stars spend in that stage.

To clarify this, let us return to our analogy of the intelligent being from outer space who comes to the earth and tries to decipher the life cycle of man in one day: He would find less than 1 percent of mankind in cribs, and he would therefore conclude the crib stage to be very short. He would find perhaps 3 percent of preschool age, another short period in man's life. Then, if he grouped youth and adulthood into one stage, this would account for about 90 percent of the population, hence 90 percent of man's life cycle. (The remaining 6 percent would be the elderly and the dying.) The combined youth and adulthood stage would correspond to the main-sequence stage in a star.

It is in the main-sequence stage that thermonuclear fusion converts hydrogen to helium. Energy is now released at a slightly increased rate. The *proton-proton cycle* (described in Chapter 8) is the process whereby stars similar to the sun produce energy. However, as the core of the star continues to heat, another cycle may operate concurrently with the proton-proton cycle—yielding the same net output of energy. In this cycle, called the *carbon cycle,* carbon merely acts as a catalyst (an initiator of a reaction that is neither created nor destroyed). Note that four hydrogen atoms (^1_1H) are used to make one helium atom (^4_2He) with the same conversion of mass as occured in the proton-proton cycle. This cycle depends upon carbon (C) being present in a star, and nitrogen (N) and oxygen (O) are intermediates in the process:

$$^{12}_6C + {}^1_1H \rightarrow {}^{13}_7N + \text{gamma ray}$$
$$^{13}_7N \rightarrow {}^{13}_6C + \text{positron} + \text{gamma ray}$$
$$^{13}_6C + {}^1_1H \rightarrow {}^{14}_7N + \text{gamma ray}$$
$$^{14}_7N + {}^1_1H \rightarrow {}^{15}_8O + \text{gamma ray}$$
$$^{15}_8O \rightarrow {}^{15}_7N + \text{positron} + \text{gamma ray}$$
$$^{15}_7N + {}^1_1H \rightarrow {}^{12}_6C + {}^4_2He$$

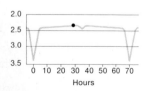

Throughout the main-sequence stage the star is building a helium core, and it is this fact which finally leads to rather drastic changes. As the supply of hydrogen available in the core is depleted, the rate of energy production decreases. The resulting reduction in pressure allows the core to contract under the force of gravity, and this contraction releases gravitational energy to produce a significant rise in temperature. The hot helium core supplies sufficient heat to the surrounding shell of hydrogen gas so that the fusion process is initiated at this outer level, and instead of the star getting dimmer it actually pours out more energy as a result of the shell converting hydrogen to helium at a faster rate than was true of the core.

The additional energy does two things: initially, the greater part is expended in the expansion of the outer layers of the star; later, it creates an increase in total luminosity which outranks anything the star has achieved before. How are these two factors related? First an expansion of gases is generally associated with a cooling—a movement to the right on the H-R diagram. With such a cooling, say, from 6000°K to 3000°K, the rate at which energy is radiated for each square meter of surface area drops to one-sixteenth of its previous level, for the luminosity of a star is proportional to the fourth power of temperature; [in our example, the temperature is decreased by one-half: $(\frac{1}{2})^4 = \frac{1}{16}$]. This drop in luminosity could be compensated for with only a fourfold increase in size—since the luminosity of a star is directly proportional to the square of any increase in radius. Thus, a star like the sun would need only a fourfold increase in radius in order to balance the loss of surface temperature. Observations of some large nearby stars like Betelgeuse show diameters ranging up to 750 times that of the sun, and so it is not hard to see how the net output of an expanding star could increase despite its loss in surface temperature. Furthermore, we can see the massive star taking up new positions on the H-R diagram —moving to the right as it cools, but also moving upward as its total output of energy increases. Because such a star is cool on the surface (red), and because it is very large, this kind of star has been dubbed a *red giant*.

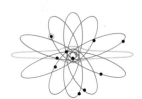

THE RED GIANT

Margherita Hack has plotted the evolution tracks for the more massive stars (Figure 12.9). Since the massive stars go through each step of their life cycle more rapidly, more observational evidence exists for these stars. This is to say that not very many stars of one solar mass have had time to evolve to the red-giant stage, but many stars of three or more solar masses have already reached that stage. Proof for these statements come when we plot the stars of an old globular cluster onto the H-R diagram. Take, for instance, the globular cluster listed as M3 (NGC 5272). This cluster is composed of stars of varying masses but all about the same

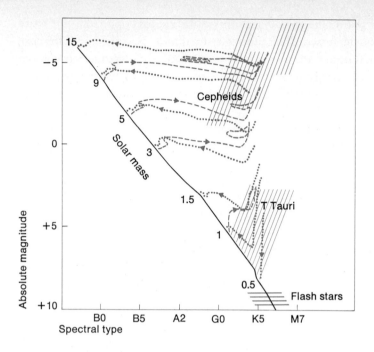

Figure 12.9 Evolutionary track of the more massive stars. (Diagram prepared by Margherita Hack)

Figure 12.10 A plot of the stars in M3. (After H. C. Arp, W. A. Baum, and A. R. Sandage)

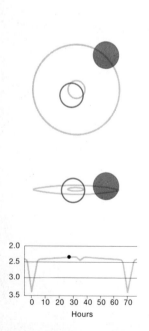

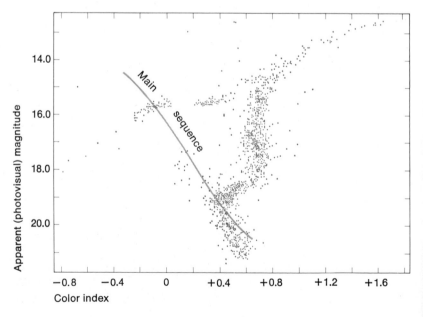

age. We know that the more massive stars plot high on the main sequence, and it is obvious from Figure 12.10 that most of these stars have already evolved away from the main sequence to become red giants. There is a strong possibility that they have followed the tracks outlined in Figure 12.9; in fact, some may have evolved to still later forms which we have not yet discussed. The stars of one solar mass or less evolve so slowly that even in an old cluster like M3 (Figure 12.11) they still remain on the main sequence. A plot of younger open clusters in the disk of the galaxy (Figure 12.12) shows the same tendency for the more massive stars to evolve away from the main sequence first. With the exception of M67, these clusters are so young that not even their most massive stars have become red giants.

We must not forget that within the red giant lurks a core that is still increasing in temperature due to further contractions, a core now so dense that our normal picture of atoms must be modified: here, the nuclear parts are pushed close together, and electrons are no longer associated with particular atoms. When the temperature of such a core rises to the order of 100 million degrees Kelvin, helium fusion takes place; that is, helium atoms begin to produce still heavier elements, such as beryllium (Be), carbon (C), oxygen (O), neon (Ne), and magnesium (Mg). The most plausible processes are the following:

$$^4_2He + {}^4_2He \rightarrow {}^8_4Be + gamma\ ray$$
$$^8_4Be + {}^4_2He \rightarrow {}^{12}_6C + gamma\ ray$$
$$^{12}_6C + {}^4_2He \rightarrow {}^{16}_8O$$
$$^{16}_8O + {}^4_2He \rightarrow {}^{20}_{10}Ne$$
$$^{20}_{10}Ne + {}^4_2He \rightarrow {}^{24}_{12}Mg$$
$$etc.$$

Figure 12.11 The globular cluster NGC 5272 (M3). (Lick Observatory)

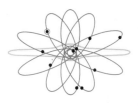

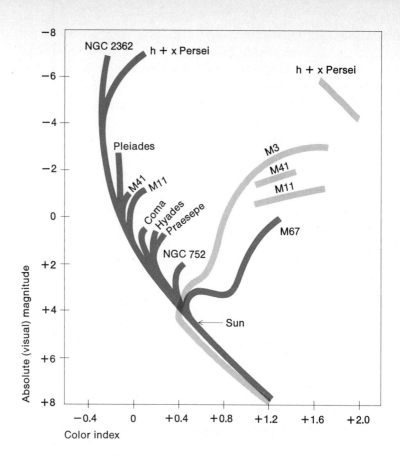

Figure 12.12 The evolutionary tracks of several familiar galactic clusters superimposed on the track of M3.

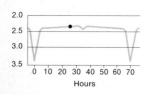

With the fusion into heavier elements, energy is released and the core temperature rises still more. If that core were like a gas it would expand with the increased temperature and start to cool down, acting like a safety valve controlling the rate of energy production. The dense nature of the core no longer responds like a gas, however, and without a safety valve the core continues to heat up until the thermonuclear process literally runs away with itself and explodes. This explosion is called the *helium flash.*

Is this the end of the red-giant stage? Not necessarily—for while the star may suffer a temporary halt to the nuclear fusion following the helium flash, it will contract once again under the influence of gravity. This contraction may produce still higher temperatures, leading to further explosive flashes and the production of still heavier elements. The zigzag nature of the evolutionary tracks in the upper-right-hand corner of Figure 12.9 show the changes in the star during these several flashes. A flash is not seen by an observer at such times because most of the energy is absorbed within the star itself. The time scale for the red-giant stage together with these later manifestations is in the order of 10 to 100 million years.

CEPHEIDS
AND RR LYRAE STARS

There is no direct evidence as to when a star may take on the characteristics of a Cepheid or RR Lyrae variable star. However, a plot of these variable stars on the H-R diagram places them very near to plots of stars which have just experienced helium flash. The pulsations of these stars are caused by the pendulumlike effect of gravity playing against pressure. Because of gravity, a star is heated; it produces more energy, then expands due to increased pressure, then cools due to expansion, then shrinks because of gravity; and this cycle repeats again and again. Could these be the symptoms of a star settling down after the explosive nature of a helium flash?

DYING STARS

We see that with the development of first a helium core and then a carbon core, higher and higher temperatures are required to ignite nuclear fusion. Eventually the star will simply not have sufficient gravitational force to ignite any further thermonuclear processes, and so this nuclear source of energy is lost.

The star still has a few sources of energy left: what remains of its gravitational force will produce limited heating through contraction; and its rotational energy may still contribute to production of radiation.

The mass of a star appears to be a very significant factor in determining the way a star dies. Stars of approximately one solar mass are thought to have a rather nonviolent type of demise. Their cores continue to be heated by the conversion of gravitational energy to kinetic energy as they continue to shrink in size. These cores become very dense. In fact, they become as dense as their atomic nature will allow without destroying the separate existence of protons and electrons. The modern physicist suggests that a star of less than 1.2 solar masses does not have sufficient mass to push its condensation beyond this state. Thus a star of one solar mass would shrink to the size of the earth but would have a density of 2×10^6 g/cm^3 (about 34 tons/in.^{3}).

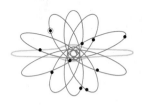

In a star of this nature, heat from the core is conducted very readily to the surface, the surface temperature ranging from 50,000°K to 100,000°K.

THE WHITE DWARF

The star is now hot (white) and relatively small, hence a *white dwarf*. This represents a drastic change in the nature of the star, for its tenuous atmosphere (outer layers) has been shed—but by what mechanism?

Many white dwarfs have been observed, and some of these have large slowly expanding shells of gas surrounding the hot core. These objects are called planetary nebulae, because when they were first discovered in a small telescope they resembled the disklike image of a planet. Modern views of two such "planetaries" are shown in Figures 12.13 and 12.14. Measurements reveal that one single planetary nebula would dwarf our entire solar system, being 20,000 to 200,000 A.U. in diameter. Often they appear somewhat like a ring because our line of sight near the center passes through less of the shell's thickness, but in reality the shell is spherical in nature. More than 500 planetary nebulae are known, and their distribution in the Milky Way galaxy resembles a flattened sphere surrounding the nucleus of the Galaxy, somewhat similar in distribution to the RR Lyrae stars. This suggests

Figure 12.13 The planetary nebula in Aquarius, NGC 7293. (Hale Observatories)

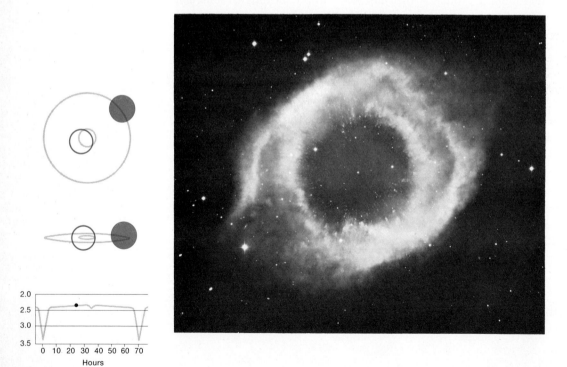

Figure 12.14 The Dumbbell Nebula, a planetary nebula in Vulpecula. (Lick Observatory)

that planetary nebulae and the stars with which they seem to be associated are older objects, well along in their evolutionary development.

We suspect that at least some stars on their way to becoming a white dwarf have shed their outer layers this way, thus explaining how a red giant could turn into a white dwarf. The mechanism whereby the star sheds its outer layers is not absolutely clear. A helium flash may produce such drastic expansion in the star that its outer layers attain the velocity necessary for escape from the core's gravitational field. This shedding may also be assisted by increased energy in the shell produced by the familiar process of ions combining with free electrons, causing downward electron transitions.

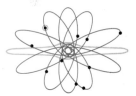

The evolutionary track of a star moving from the red-giant stage to the white dwarf is shown in Figure 12.15. The star is plotted further to the left on the H-R diagram as the hotter surface temperature of the core is revealed. But then as the star shrinks in size its luminosity decreases and it gradually cools, sending it downward to the right on

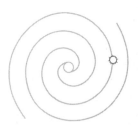

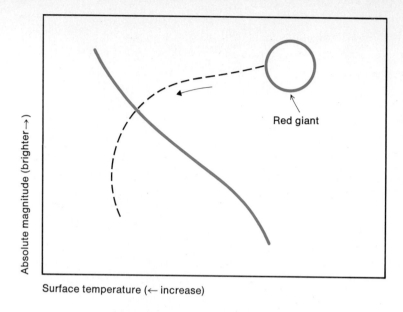

Figure 12.15 The evolutionary track of a star moving from the red-giant stage to the white-dwarf stage.

the H-R diagram, downward into what will eventually be a yellow-, red-, and black-dwarf death. This final cooling process is thought to be slow—in the order of a billion years.

MORE MASSIVE STARS

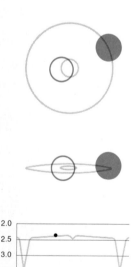

Stars of several solar masses have followed quite different evolutionary paths from that of the sun. They not only are generally brighter than the sun and evolve faster, but we will now see how their additional mass affects their development of a central core and its partial destruction. A star of greater mass also possesses greater potential (gravitational) energy: where a star of one solar mass fell short of having enough potential energy to ignite the core beyond helium fusion, a star of several solar masses may generate the temperature of 600 million degrees Kelvin necessary for carbon fusion (in which the products are oxygen, neon, magnesium, and so on). The net result will be the production of most elements up to iron, Fe (with 56 nuclear parts—*nucleons*). Up to that point in the fusion of heavier elements, energy has been released, but to produce elements heavier than iron energy is required. Hence this is a natural stopping point in such a chain reaction. The reaction has been so violent to this point that its cessation allows a tremendous collapse to occur—an *implosion,* producing a supernova (see Chapter

10). It is at this time that elements heavier than iron may be created by the capture of additional nucleons (protons and neutrons). Some of these nucleons are ejected to become the cosmic rays which seem to permeate the universe (Chapter 11).

THE SUPERNOVA

The major result of this implosion of the core and superheating and fusion within the outer layers is a gigantic explosion that sends a large part of the mass of the star out into interstellar space, providing a mixture of every element to enrich the hydrogen gas found there. At the same time the core collapses beyond the limiting density of the electron–ion combination discussed earlier, the electrons being forced into such close proximity to the protons that the electrical charges neutralize to form an extremely dense star composed largely of *neutrons*.

A supernova may increase in brightness by 17 to 25 magnitudes in a very short time, and if seen in one of the less luminous galaxies may temporarily outshine that entire galaxy. The remains of a supernova recorded in A.D. 1054 by the Chinese are still visible as the Crab Nebula, which continues to expand at the rate of more than 1300 km/sec. From this velocity of expansion, together with its apparent increase of size over the years, its distance from the earth has been determined to be more than 4000 light-years (Figure 12.16). In some supernovae, velocities of expansion may approach 5000 km/sec, representing a much more violent reaction.

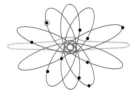

Figure 12.16 The Crab Nebula, the remains of a supernova first seen in A.D. 1054. (Hale Observatories)

THE NEUTRON STAR

Let us suppose that a star originally contained four solar masses and one half of its mass was expelled in a supernova-type explosion, leaving a remnant core of two solar masses. If such a core were to contract to only 32 km in diameter, what would be its density? *Answer:* 200,000,000,000,000 g/cm^3 (200 trillion g/cm^3)! To conceive of the meaning of such a density, let us first visualize a greatly enlarged model of the ordinary hydrogen atom. Imagine a single golf ball placed at the center of a football field. This represents the single proton of the hydrogen atom. Now imagine a gnat flying around the outside of the huge stadium which surrounds the field. This represents the one electron. The fact is that an ordinary atom is mostly empty space, and its mass is concentrated in a very small volume of space at the center. Furthermore, two atoms in an interstellar gas cloud might be separated like two stadiums in adjoining towns. But in the neutron star, virtually all empty space has been taken up, and the gnats (electrons) have been forced inside the golf balls (protons), producing neutral golf balls (neutrons), which are also packed so closely together as to touch. Should stars such as this exist, how would they be likely to manifest themselves? Perhaps as pulsars.

PULSARS

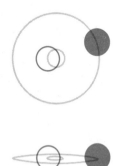

While investigating certain sources of radio energy, a small group of British astronomers at the University of Cambridge discovered a weak radio signal that appeared as pulses at very regular intervals. Speculation immediately suggested the possibility that intelligent beings were trying to contact the earth, and they were soon dubbed LGMs (Little Green Men). But this possibility was soon eliminated, for many other similar sources were then found. Their extraterrestrial origin, proved by the fact that they move with the stars, also eliminated the possibility that these signals originated in mechanical devices on earth, a constant source of interference for the radio astronomer. Because of their pulsing output they are called *pulsars,* the first being called CP 1919, meaning "Cambridge Pulsar located at 19 hr 19 min right ascension." The first nine pulsars to be discovered are listed in Table 12.1.

A search was made for a visible counterpart to these pulsars, but none was found, and early speculation concerning the origin of these pulsed radio signals took many forms. Most theories suggested either

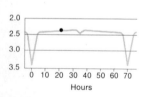

Hours

Table 12.1 Pulsars[a]

PULSAR	RIGHT ASCENSION	DECLINATION	PERIOD (SEC)	DISTANCE (PARSECS)
CP 1919	$19^h 19^m 37^s$	$+21° 47'$	1.337301	126
CP 0950	$09^h 50^m 29^s$	$+08° 11'$	0.253065	30
CP 1133	$11^h 33^m 36^s$	$+16° 08'$	1.187911	50
CP 0834	$08^h 34^m 22^s$	$+06° 07'$	1.273764	128
HP 1506	$15^h 06^m 50^s$	$+55° 41'$	0.739678	200
CP 0328	$03^h 28^m 52^s$	$+54° 23'$	0.714463	270
CP 0808	$08^h 08^m 50^s$	$+74° 42'$	1.292231	60
PSR 1749	$17^h 49^m 49^s$	$-28° 06'$	0.562645	500
PSR 2045	$20^h 45^m 48^s$	$-16° 28'$	1.961663	115

[a]CP indicates Cambridge Pulsar; HP, Harvard Pulsar; PSR, Pulsar; h is hours; m, minutes; s, seconds.

a pulsating star, a rotating star, or a revolving system. Theoretical models were devised to account for the very rapid recurrence of the signal; most of these models were of very small dense stars or systems.

Then, in 1969, a team of astronomers working at Steward Observatory, University of Arizona, realized that a star that was clearly visible in the Crab Nebula was actually a pulsar. This was Pulsar NP 0532, with a period of about 0.0333 sec—one of the shortest known—and hence the flashing of its optical counterpart was too rapid to be detected by the eye. However, a special rotating aperture was perfected that allowed astronomers at Lick Observatory to photograph this pulsar, showing that it is "on" part of the time and "off" part of the time (Figure 12.17). Pulsar NP 0532 is an 18-mag object, and its flashes are equivalent to 15 mag. Its light curve is indicated in Figure 12.18.

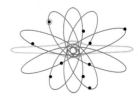

Observers now feel more confident that pulsars are high-density neutron stars, perhaps as massive as the sun and yet only 15 km in diameter, their pulses being emitted in step with their rotation. Perhaps a strong magnetic field associated with these stars tends to beam their radiations, causing them to act as a rotating beacon.

With the continued contraction of a dying star, the original magnetic field appears strengthened to such a degree that electrons

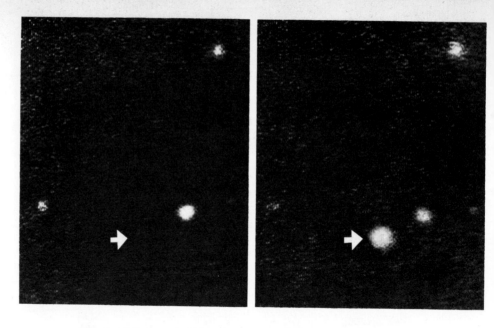

Figure 12.17 Pulsar NP 0532 in the Crab Nebula, photographed using a special rotating disk, showing the pulsar "off" in the left-hand view and "on" in the right-hand view. This object blinks on and off approximately 30 times per second. (Lick Observatory)

Figure 12.18 Light curve of NP 0532. [From R. Lynds, S. P. Maran, and D. Trumbo, Optical identification and observations of the pulsar NP 0532. *Astrophys. J.* **155**, L121 (1969). © University of Chicago Press; Kitt Peak Observatory]

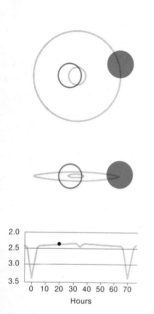

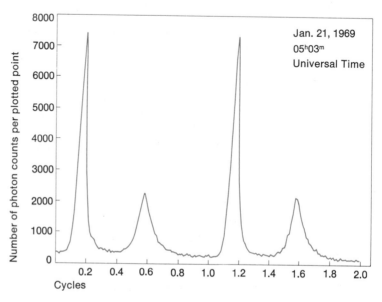

which are ejected with high velocity through that magnetic field produce light, radio, X rays, and gamma rays. When radiant energy is produced by this process, it is called *synchrotron radiation*. The ejected particles and their radiations are concentrated, by the same magnetic field, into two beams or cones of emission. If this model of a pulsar is correct, the presence of such a star will be sensed only if the observer's line of sight falls within one of these cones (Figure 12.19). Perhaps only 10 percent of all neutron stars that fit this model are aligned in such a way as to be sensed from the earth's position in space.

The periods of the pulsars seem to be increasing, which indicates that these objects are rotating more slowly as time passes, giving up some of their rotational energy to the outflow of electrons; this in turn produces the radiation. Based on these observations, the duration of the stage of evolution represented by the pulsars is seen to be relatively short, in some cases as little as 1 million years. Since the primary source of energy for the pulsar is its rotation, when that rotation stops it will no longer radiate energy, and the last stage in the evolution of such a star has been reached. In several cases, pulsars have been known to suddenly speed up. This sudden increase in rotational velocity may indicate that the star has contracted to a smaller volume, which would necessitate a rearrangement of the neutrons (somewhat like the collapse of a crystalline structure). This could be termed a "starquake." The star would respond to such a reduction of size by an increase in rotational velocity in order to preserve its angular momentum.

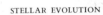

Figure 12.19 The rotating neutron–star model of a pulsar.

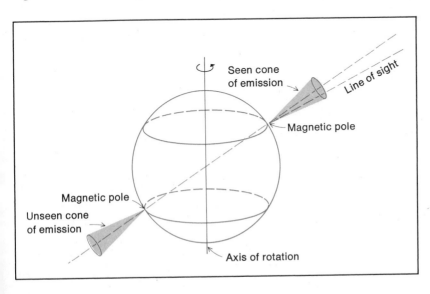

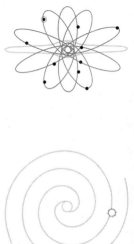

Some stars are many times as massive as stars we have discussed up to this point. The life cycle of such stars parallels closely those already traced to neutron stars, but they possess even higher levels of gravitational force. This means that temperatures may be developed in their carbon cores on the order of 1 billion degrees Kelvin, and elements as massive as iron may be produced before the collapse of the core occurs. Under the extremely large gravitational forces associated with 10 to 20 solar masses, the collapse of such an iron core transcends anything discussed to this point. Not only are elements heavier than iron produced, a shell of enriched gas thrown off as a supernova, but the implosion of a significant portion of the total mass creates momenta in the condensing core which cannot be stopped by neutron forces— forces which dictate the stable size of a neutron star. At this point the forces of gravity are dominant. In fact, nothing can stop the collapse of such a star, and its inevitable fate is a *black hole*.

Albert Einstein predicted the possibility of such a collapse in his general theory of relativity (published in 1915), and Karl Schwarzschild worked out some of the consequences of this theory in 1916. Schwarzschild said that when a star collapsed to a certain size (dependent upon its mass only), the radiation from that star could no longer escape due to the enormous gravitational forces which would ensue. For example, if a star of 3 solar masses were to collapse to become a black hole, this discontinuance of radiation would occur when the radius was reduced to 9 km. This does not mean that the collapse would stop at that point, for the collapse is thought to continue into a condition approaching infinite density and infinite tidal forces. This condition is called a *singularity*.

The Schwartzschild radius defines a sphere within which particles and radiation can only fall toward the singularity. In fact, if a particle were approaching a black hole, its radiation would cease as it passed through this sphere and the event could no longer be witnessed (Figure 12.20). Prior to reaching this sphere, a particle would experience rapid acceleration and heating, perhaps to 1 billion degrees Kelvin, so that a portion of its radiation could be expected to fall in the X-ray spectrum.

These speculations led astronomers to reexamine known X-ray sources and ask questions as to the most likely circumstances under which material would be available to be sucked into black holes. One very natural suggestion is that of a binary star system in which one member is a black hole and the other member is a red giant. The surrounding envelope of the red giant might well extend close enough

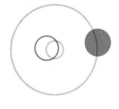

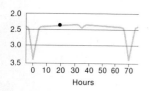

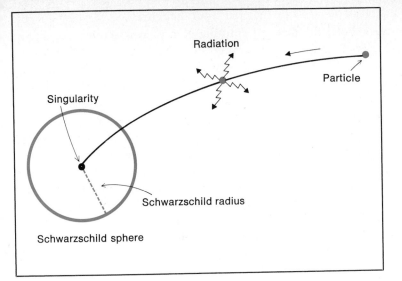

Figure 12.20 As a particle passes within the sphere defined by the Schwarzschild radius, on its way toward the singularity, the particle's radiation ceases because it can not escape the gravitational field of the black hole.

Figure 12.21 Mass exchange in a binary pair. The very strong gravitational field of the black hole attracts material from the outer portions of the expanded red giant.

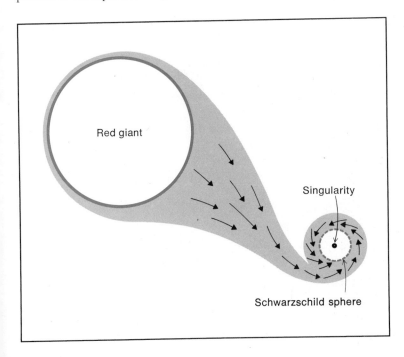

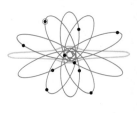

to the black hole so that material from that envelope would spiral into the black hole, the material emitting X rays as it accelerated (Figure 12.21). Some astronomers suspect that this explains what they are observing in Cygnus X-1, a source of X rays in which the visible star behaves as though it were a member of a binary system, with the unseen member having a mass of more than 3 solar masses.

Another possible method of detection of black holes uses the fact that the collapse of a very dense star core is believed to generate gravitational waves of sufficient strength to be detected on earth. The attempts to perfect a device for sensing such gravitational waves was considered in Chapter 2 (see Figure 2.61). Disturbances have been sensed which seemed to relate to sources outside the earth; however, the results are not conclusive.

Figure 12.22 Rotating black hole. A particle that enters the ergosphere (shaded) may split into two, one part passing through into the Schwarzschild sphere and the other being ejected back outside the ergosphere with more mass-energy than the original particle had.

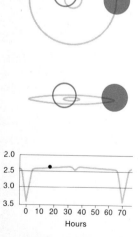

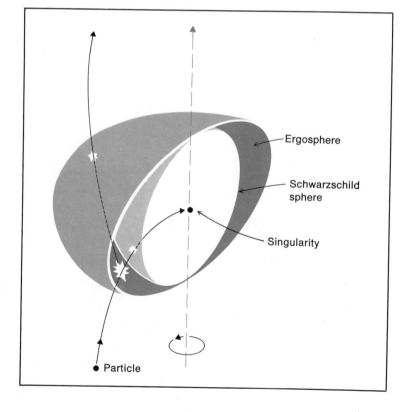

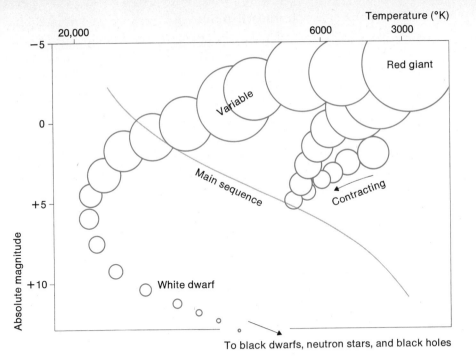

Figure 12.23 Proposed evolutionary life cycle of a star.

Temperature (°K) scale: 20,000 6000 3000

Red giant

Variable

Main sequence

Contracting

White dwarf

Absolute magnitude: −5, 0, +5, +10

To black dwarfs, neutron stars, and black holes

ROTATING BLACK HOLES

From our discussion to this point, it is difficult to imagine a black hole giving up some if its energy to the outside universe. However, this may be true for a rotating black hole. As a spinning ice skater pulls in her arms, she spins faster and faster, conserving angular momentum. Likewise a rotating star will spin faster as it collapses. As a consequence of this rotation, a deformed region called an *ergosphere* develops outside the black hole (Figure 12.22). If a particle enters the ergosphere, it is possible for that particle to split into two parts—the one part entering the black hole, but the other part being ejected with more mass-energy than the original particle had. The additional mass-energy is derived from the rotational energy of the black hole. Could this be the source of energy for some of the unexplained phenomena of the universe, such as quasars and certain types of galaxies? We will consider these objects in Chapter 14.

Table 12.2 compares the various ways in which a star may end its life cycle. The critical factor which determines the form of death of stars appears to be their mass.

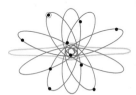

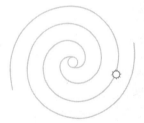

Table 12.2 Final forms a star may take

	WHITE DWARF	NEUTRON STAR	BLACK HOLE
Radius[a]	13,000 to 32,000 km	16 to 32 km	10.5 to 180 km
Density	2×10^5 g/cm³	2×10^{11} g/cm³	Infinitely large at singularity
Mass[b]	Up to 1.2	1.2 to 3.5	3.5 to 60

[a] Refers to Schwarzschild radius.
[b] Expressed in units of solar mass.

In this chapter, we have seen that stars form and evolve in response to the fundamental force of gravity, together with the reactions which it produces: condensation, high temperature, high pressure, energy produced by thermonuclear fusion, and the continual dissipation of that energy (cooling). Figure 12.23 summarizes this evolutionary cycle on the H-R diagram.

QUESTIONS

1. Describe a likely birthplace of stars and the process that is thought to bring them into being.
2. What evidence suggests that certain stars are relatively young?
3. Not all stars are thought to evolve at the same rate. Which kind appear to evolve most rapidly?
4. Of the following, which stage in evolution appears to be the longest and which the shortest: variable, T Tauri, white-dwarf, red-giant, main-sequence, or neutron star? State evidence for your answer.
5. Describe a neutron star.
6. How does the astronomer sense that he is receiving energy from a pulsar, as compared to other types of stars?
7. What changes have already been observed in the pulsars?
8. When the evolutionary life cycle of a star is shown on an H-R diagram, a change in location on the diagram does not indicate a change in location in the sky. What does such a change on the diagram indicate?
9. If a star increases in temperature, what change must take place if its internal pressure remains substantially the same?
10. In a gas cloud, gas molecules and dust particles have a certain form of energy which may be converted to heat (kinetic energy) upon collapse of the cloud. Name this form of energy.

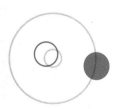

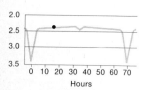

11. What is the role of dust in creating a condition in which a star is more likely to form?
12. Name at least two ways in which dust is revealed visually.
13. What role does carbon play in the carbon cycle in stars?
14. Interpret a horizontal movement to the left on an H-R diagram.
15. What evidence do astronomers have that stars spend a large percentage of their time in the main-sequence stage?
16. What is thought to trigger the evolution of a star from the main-sequence to the red-giant stage?
17. What evidence do we have that the T Tauri variables are associated with very young stars and not with old stars?
18. How is it possible for a star that is getting cooler also to get brighter?
19. When a star runs out of available hydrogen in the core, it should cool down, but instead it heats up significantly. Why is this true?
20. How are the elements heavier than iron manufactured in stars?
21. Compare the densities of a white dwarf, a neutron star, and a black hole.
22. Explain what is meant by the terms *singularity* and *Schwarzschild radius* in relation to a black hole.
23. Why is it *not* thought possible for the sun to ever become a black hole?
24. Why is it *not* thought possible for the sun to fuse elements as heavy as iron?
25. How may a black hole be recognized?

SUGGESTED READINGS

Bok, Bart J., The birth of stars. *Scientific American* **227** (2), 48–61 (1972).

Chiu, H. Y., and Muriel, A. (eds.), *Stellar evolution*. Cambridge, Mass.: MIT Press, 1972.

Gorenstein, Paul, and Tucker, Wallace, Supernova remnants. *Scientific American* **225** (1), 74–85 (1971).

Harrison, B. K., Thorne, K. S., Wakano, M., and Wheeler, J. A., *Gravitation theory and gravitational collapse*. Chicago: University of Chicago Press, 1965.

Maran, Stephen P., The gum nebula. *Scientific American* **225** (6), 20–29 (1971).

Misner, C. W., Thorne, K. S., and Wheeler, J. A., *Gravitation*. San Francisco: Freeman, 1973.

Penrose, Roger, Black holes. *Scientific American* **226** (5), 38–54 (1972).

Ruderman, Malvin A., Solid stars. *Scientific American* **224** (2), 24–31 (1971).

Ruffini, Remo, and Wheeler, John A., Introducing the black hole. *Physics Today* **24** (1), 30–41 (1971).

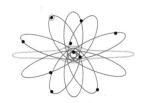

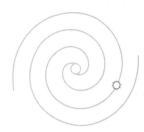

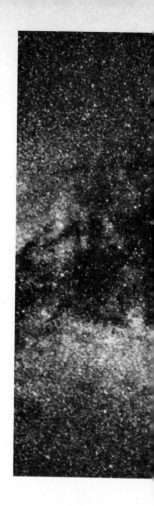

THE
MILKY
WAY

13

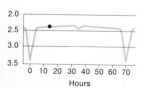

Man's accurate perception of the universe took a giant leap forward

when he realized that the nearby collection of stars, of which the

sun is one, is really only an example of a fundamental unit in the

universe, the *galaxy*. By the late eighteenth century, Messier had cat-

alogued more than 100 nebular objects without ever suspecting that

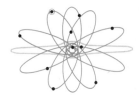

some of them were in reality collections of stars completely separated

from our own collection, the Milky Way galaxy. By the early nineteenth

century, more than 5000 nebulae had been identified, largely as a result

367

of the work of Sir William Herschel and his son John. The latter published the *General Catalogue of Nebulae* in 1864. By 1908 almost 15,000 nebulae had been listed in a volume called the *New General Catalogue,* together with its supplement called the *Index Catalogues.* Objects in Messier's list also carry NGC numbers; for example, M31 is represented by NGC 224 in the later work.

The term *nebula* then referred to any object which appeared fuzzy in the telescopes of that time. Sir William Herschel did express his belief that certain objects that he found were collections of stars separated from our own, but lacking proof he did not pursue the idea. As late as 1912 Miss Henrietta Leavitt, in her work with the Cepheids in the Magellanic Clouds, did not realize that these "clouds" were galaxies outside our own.

With the installation of the 2.5-m telescope on top of Mt. Wilson in 1917, together with the photographic methods available by that time, individual stars were being resolved in the nearer galaxies (Figure 13.1), and novae were discovered in them. It was reasoned that if these novae were as bright as some that had been discovered in our own Galaxy, and yet appeared very dim to the observer, they must be at very great distances. However, the matter was not settled until 1924, when Edwin Hubble, working at the Mt. Wilson Observatory in California, discovered Cepheid variables in several nearby galaxies. From the periods

Figure 13.1 The Andromeda galaxy, a spiral galaxy considered to be very much like the Milky Way galaxy. (Hale Observatories)

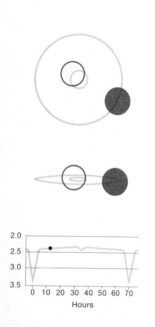

Figure 13.2 The Milky Way from Sagittarius to Cassiopeia. (Hale Observatories)

Figure 13.3 Counting stars.

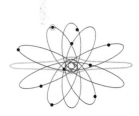

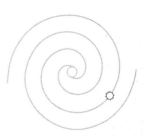

of these stars their absolute magnitude may be computed, as explained in Chapter 10. They appear as such faint objects that they are undoubtedly outside our own Milky Way galaxy.

By this time astronomers realized that galaxies exist in a wide variety of shapes. Just a glance into the first few pages of Chapter 14 will show spherical, elliptical, and flattened galaxies, none of which have arms, as well as the spiral galaxies, and barred spirals with arms, and the irregulars. It seems reasonable to suspect that the Milky Way galaxy looks something like one of these types; but since the sun and the earth are situated within the Milky Way galaxy, the problem is not as simple as viewing another galaxy.

If the Milky Way galaxy is spherical in shape, then we might expect a rather even distribution of stars within it. Let us perform a simple experiment to see if this is the case. Cut out a small cardboard frame with a square opening of 5 cm. Hold the frame at arm's length and count the stars that you see within the frame. Repeat this for different parts of the sky, recording the location and number of stars counted on each occasion. It will become apparent that the distribution of stars is not uniform and that there are higher concentrations of stars in certain parts of the sky. Try the region near Sagittarius or that near Orion (Figures 13.2 and 13.3); in fact, try any area through which runs the fuzzy band of light we refer to as the Milky Way. What are

369

Figure 13.4 The Milky Way as shown by Martin and Tatjana Keskula. Sagittarius is in the center, and the two bright objects in the lower right portion are the Magellanic Clouds. (Lund Observatory, Sweden)

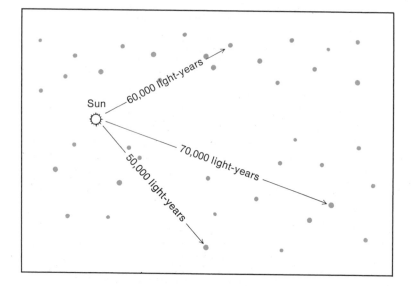

Figure 13.5 Distribution of the globulars in relation to the sun.

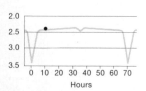

we really looking at when we see this milky band on a clear dark night? A small telescope or even a pair of binoculars will begin to reveal the fact that the band is composed of millions of stars. If we observe the Milky Way over a period of several months, we realize that it forms a complete circle in the sky (Figure 13.4). This suggests that we are part of a flattened system of stars, but where are we in that system? The globular clusters will help us to answer that question. Recall that

370

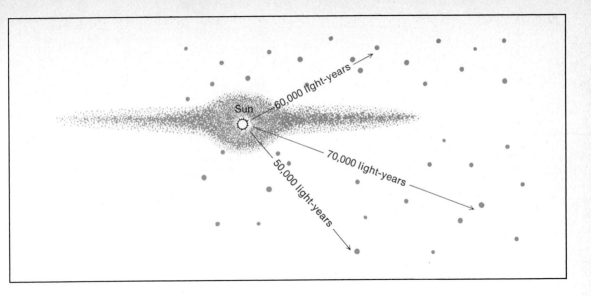

Figure 13.6 If the sun were located at the center of the Milky Way galaxy, the globulars would be thrown off center in relation to the Galaxy.

globulars contain RR Lyrae-type variables with absolute magnitudes very close to zero. By comparing this absolute magnitude to the apparent magnitude which was observed for each, astronomers have determined their distances and plotted their position in relation to the sun (Figure 13.5).

Suppose we were to assume that the sun is located at the center of the Milky Way galaxy; then the picture would look like Figure 13.6. However, it seems logical to assume that the globulars are distributed symmetrically with respect to the Galaxy (Figure 13.7). Thus, the sun and its planets are thought to be located in the flattened disklike portion of the Galaxy, approximately 30,000 light-years from its center and the overall diameter of the Galaxy is placed at 110,000 light-years.

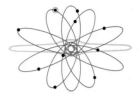

The center (or *nucleus*) of the Galaxy is further identified by the high concentration of stars toward the constellation of Sagittarius. When you view the Milky Way band near Orion, you are looking out through the disk toward the outer edge of the Galaxy (Figure 13.8). The Milky Way band is indicated on the star maps in Appendix 12.

The next question we might ask is whether the Milky Way galaxy has arms like the many spiral galaxies we can view, or is its disk more uniformly populated with stars? By observing other galaxies of the spiral type, astronomers have noticed that very young O- and B-type stars (hot stars) populate the arms and leave spaces in between them. These hot stars are easily recognized as bright dots in the photograph of the

371

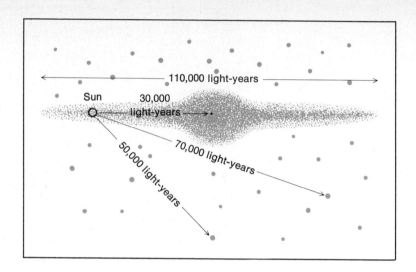

Figure 13.7 A view of the Milky Way galaxy.

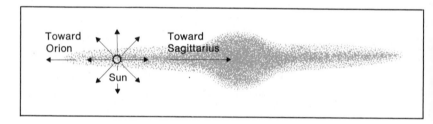

Figure 13.8 The Milky Way from our own point of view (edge-on).

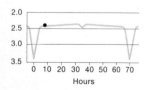

Whirlpool galaxy (Figure 13.9). Note how the bright stars outline the spiral arms in this particular galaxy. Furthermore, we would suspect that gas and dust would accompany these bright young stars because gas and dust are the building blocks of stars.

Turning this knowledge toward the Milky Way galaxy, astronomers have determined the distance to numerous O- and B-type stars, and a plot of these stars strongly suggests a spiral nature for our Galaxy (Figure 13.10). This finding was soon confirmed and expanded to a much larger portion of the Galaxy by radio astronomy. The presence of dust in the Milky Way galaxy obscures much of the starlight; however, the Galaxy is much more transparent to radio wavelengths. In fact radio signals characteristic of neutral hydrogen may be received from almost the entire Galaxy.

Figure 13.9 The Whirlpool galaxy, showing bright O- and B-type stars outlining its spiral arms. (Lick Observatory)

Figure 13.10 The optical pattern of the Milky Way galaxy based on a plot of O- and B-type stars in the vicinity of the sun.

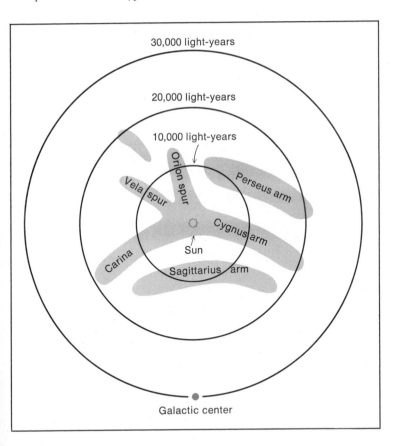

30,000 light-years

20,000 light-years

10,000 light-years

Orion spur

Vela spur

Perseus arm

Cygnus arm

Carina

Sun

Sagittarius arm

Carina

Galactic center

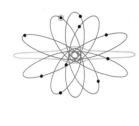

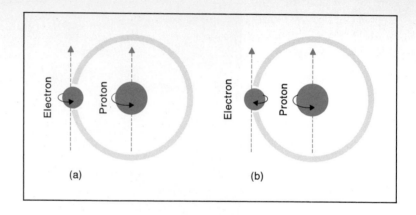

Figure 13.11 Electron spin reversal in the hydrogen atom. When the spin axes of the proton and the electron are aligned (a), the atom contains more energy than when they are opposed (b). When the electron flips from state (a) to state (b), it emits a 21-cm radio signal.

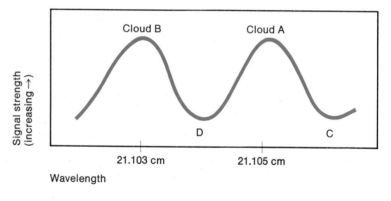

Figure 13.12 A radio scan of two hydrogen clouds showing wavelengths which have been shortened because the clouds are moving relative to the sun.

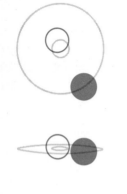

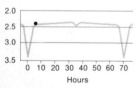

We have seen how hydrogen, when excited, produces certain characteristic wavelengths in the visible spectrum—for example, the H_α (hydrogen-alpha) line produced by a downward transition of the electron. Neutral hydrogen also produces a characteristic radio "line" which has a wavelength of 21.11 cm and which is simply referred to as the 21-cm signal of hydrogen. The process whereby the hydrogen atom can emit or absorb this particular wavelength is associated with the spin of its nucleus and the spin of its electron. The electron may *align* its spin axis with that of the proton, in which case it has more energy than when it *opposes* the spin axis of the proton. Thus, when the electron flips over from an aligned orientation to an opposed orientation, it *emits* energy corresponding to the 21-cm radio signal. When it flips in the reverse direction, it *absorbs* the same wavelength (Figure 13.11).

As an astronomer tunes his radio receiver to this 21-cm wavelength, much as we would tune in a local station on an ordinary radio, he can detect hydrogen in the Galaxy. However the hydrogen clouds are in motion relative to the sun, as demonstrated by the fact that the typical 21.110-cm signal is not always detected by our receivers at exactly that wavelength but is Doppler-shifted to a shorter wavelength if the cloud is moving toward the sun. Figure 13.12 shows the wavelength of cloud A shortened by 0.005 cm and that of cloud B shortened by 0.007 cm, making it possible to compute their relative velocity toward the sun. This is a powerful tool in determining the rotation and structure of the Galaxy. If we assume that, like the planets, the hydrogen clouds which are closer to the center of the Galaxy move faster and those farther away move slower, then the Doppler shifts of these clouds will reveal their position. Based upon this assumption, the astronomer translates the radio scan of Figure 13.12 into a theoretical physical model shown in Figure 13.13, cloud B being closest to the center of the Galaxy because it showed the largest Doppler shift, and cloud A being farther from the center of the Galaxy because it showed a smaller Doppler shift.

Suppose the radio astronomer had scanned along a different line of sight, say, to the other side of galactic center, as in Figure 13.14. He would have found the wavelengths associated with hydrogen clouds in this direction lengthened, indicating that the materials which composed these arms are receding relative to the sun. Plotting their positions (E and F), he would not only find a spiral structure beginning

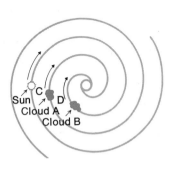

Figure 13.13 A model of the Milky Way galaxy in which clouds A and B are assumed to be located in the arms and points C and D represent spaces between the arms.

Figure 13.14 When viewed along this line of sight, hydrogen clouds show a lengthening of their normal wavelength (indicating recession), thus confirming the clockwise rotation of the Milky Way galaxy (see text).

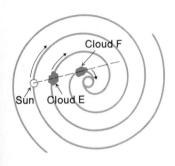

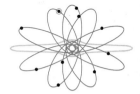

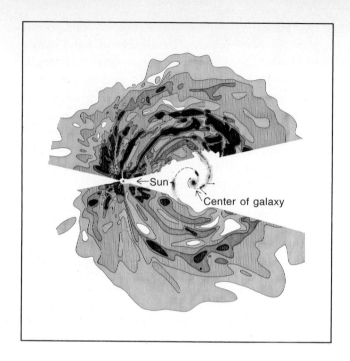

Figure 13.15 The structure of the Milky Way galaxy, in the 21-cm radio signal of neutral hydrogen. The darker regions represent higher concentrations of hydrogen. (Leiden Observatory, Netherlands, and Radio Physics Laboratory, Sydney, Australia)

to develop but would confirm the fact that the Galaxy is turning in a clockwise direction (as viewed looking in a northerly direction, relative to the earth). Using this method, a more complete mapping of the Galaxy's structure is shown in Figure 13.15. Let us see if we can specify its rate of rotation using the sun's motion as an indicator.

VELOCITY OF THE SUN
WITHIN THE GALAXY

In Chapter 8 we considered the various reference systems within which we might describe the motions of stars, including space motions relative to the sun and peculiar motions relative to the local standard of rest. To describe the motion of the sun within the Galaxy it is necessary to relate that motion to a standard of rest for the Galaxy. The globular clusters do not seem to participate in the rotation of the Galaxy but rather have a motion that crosses the galactic plane at right angles. The in-and-out motion of these objects, as shown in the right-hand flip pages

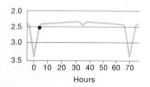

beginning on page 285, helps to establish a zero reference. This reference may also be established by galaxies outside our own. In other words, we may view the sun's motion from a distant point in space, for instance, on the northerly side of the galactic plane. We find that the sun is revolving clockwise in a nearly circular orbit around the center of the Galaxy and has a velocity of approximately 250 km/sec, making one revolution in about 200 million years.

MASS OF THE GALAXY

While the actual determination of the mass of the Milky Way galaxy is beyond our immediate scope, the basis for its calculation still rests with the way in which the mass of our Galaxy affects the motions of the sun. An oversimplification of the problem might assert that most of the mass of the Galaxy is concentrated in its central nucleus, hence the problem reduces essentially to a two–body problem like that of the sun and a planet; an approximation may be sought using Kepler's law:

$$m_{gal} + m_{sun} = \frac{(r_{sun})^3}{(p_{sun})^2}$$

where r is measured in astronomical units and p in years. The distance between the galactic center and the sun is approximately 30,000 light–years, which is equivalent to 2×10^9 A.U. and the period of the sun is 2×10^8 years. Since the mass of the sun is negligible in comparison to that of the Galaxy, the term m_{sun} may be dropped:

$$m_{gal} = \frac{(2 \times 10^9)^3}{(2 \times 10^8)^2} = \frac{8 \times 10^{27}}{4 \times 10^{16}} = 2 \times 10^{11} \text{ solar masses}$$

Thus, the total mass of the Galaxy would appear to be 200 billion times the mass of the sun. But since the luminosity of the sun is far more than that of the average star, we can conclude that its mass is likewise above average. Thus, we are led to believe that the number of stars in the Milky Way galaxy must exceed 200 billion and may be as great as 1 trillion stars.

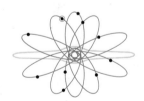

DISTRIBUTION OF STARS
IN THE MILKY WAY GALAXY

We have characterized the Milky Way galaxy as being a flattened spiral, and this is its most apparent shape; however, observation of certain types of stars within the Galaxy reveal that it really has three shapes. As we

trace these shapes, let us see if they give us a clue as to the process whereby our Galaxy became a flattened spiral.

First, consider those star types thought to be oldest, stars typical of the globular clusters. We have already established the advanced age of such clusters upon the evidence that they have already used up their gas and dust in star formation and, further, that their more massive stars have evolved off the main sequence. Astronomers refer to stars which inhabit the globulars as Population II objects. These include RR Lyrae and Type-II Cepheids, and long-period variables. The globular clusters form an almost spherical halo around the Galaxy, and they may still preserve the earlier shape of the cloud from which the Milky Way galaxy formed (Figure 13.16; see the halo labeled A).

An intermediate system exists between the spherical halo of globulars and the flattened disk where new stars are forming. The intermediate system is illustrated in Figure 13.16 as the semiflattened halo labeled B. It consists of semilong-period variables, subgiants, white dwarfs, G- to M-type dwarfs, and planetary nebulae. These types of objects are also believed to be of moderately old age and may represent by their distribution the shape of the galactic cloud when it was still in the process of flattening due to rotation.

Figure 13.16 The distribution of stars in the Milky Way (see text).

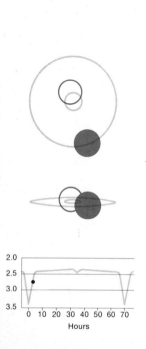

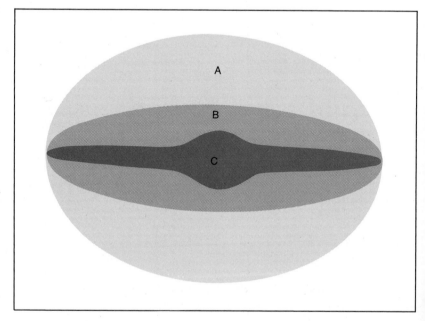

(a)   (b)

Figure 13.17 Population I and II stars. (a) Andromeda Nebula, photographed in blue light, shows giant and supergiant stars of Population I in the spiral arms. The hazy patch at the upper left is composed of unresolved Population II stars. (b) NGC 205, companion of the Andromeda Nebula, photographed in yellow light, shows stars of Population II. The brightest stars are red and 100 times fainter than the blue giants of Population I. The very bright, uniformly distributed stars in both pictures are foreground stars belonging in our own Milky Way system. (Hale Observatories)

Finally the flattened disk system (labeled C in Figure 13.16) is characterized by very hot, young (O-, B-, and A-type) stars, Type-I Cepheids, supergiants, open clusters, and interstellar gas and dust. Each of these types represent young stars or the material from which they are formed.

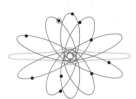

Does this progression of shapes represent *evolution* of galaxies in the usual sense of the word—that elliptical galaxies evolve into spirals, or vice versa as some would suggest? Perhaps not, but it surely suggests that in its very early stages, the Milky Way galaxy was spherical in shape and due to rotation it flattened significantly in the first billion years of its existence as a separate entity in space.

379

HOW OLD IS
OUR GALAXY?

If we assume that the original matter of the universe was pure hydrogen and that the heavier elements have been "manufactured" by a process of nuclear reactions within the stars, then the age of the Galaxy may be estimated. In order to do this, we must know how rapidly the elements are being formed and also what proportion of hydrogen has been converted. In order to have produced the proportion of heavier elements that is present today, the age of the Milky Way galaxy must be between 8 to 15 billion years. Cosmologists have estimated the age of the entire universe, based on its rate of expansion, to be within that same range. Most astronomers tend to agree that the galaxies were formed early in the expansion of the universe, perhaps within the first 100 million years. Thus, the Milky Way galaxy emerged within the same range of time as the universe itself, 8 to 15 billion years ago.

QUESTIONS

1. The term *nebula* includes what kinds of objects in addition to gas clouds?
2. What evidence does the casual (naked–eye) observer have that the Milky Way galaxy is not simply a sphere (ball) that surrounds us?
3. What role did the globular clusters have in helping us to find our true location in the Galaxy?
4. How much time would be required for light to travel from a point on the outer edge of our Galaxy to the opposite edge?
5. How do we know that our Galaxy is of a spiral nature? Specifically, how do we know it has "arms"?
6. The sun participates in the rotation of our Galaxy. What is its speed because of this rotation?
7. If the Milky Way galaxy contained 100 billion stars, and the average mass of these stars was twice the mass of the sun, find the total mass of the Galaxy.
8. Indicate whether each of the following would be found in the halo (h) of the Galaxy or in its disk (d): (a) open clusters; (b) globular clusters; (c) Type-II Cepheids; (d) Type-I Cepheids; (e) interstellar gas; (f) interstellar dust; (g) very hot stars (O and B type).
9. Do you think it is more reasonable to assume that the center of the distribution of globular clusters is the center of the Milky Way galaxy, or is it more probable that the sun is the center of the Galaxy? Why?

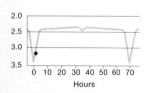

10. An optical picture of the spiral arms of the Milky Way galaxy has been made by a plot of what kinds of stars?

11. Why is the radio picture of the Galaxy more complete than the optical picture?

12. Why should a star in one of the arms of the Galaxy which is closer to the central nucleus appear to us to have the larger Doppler shift in relation to the sun?

13. What evidence do we have that the Milky Way galaxy was once more like a sphere and then later flattened to become a spiral?

14. What factor probably influenced the Milky Way galaxy to become a flattened system?

SUGGESTED READINGS

Blaauw, A., and Schmidt, M. (eds.), *Galactic structure*. Chicago: University of Chicago Press, 1965.

Bok, B. J., and Bok, P. F., *The Milky Way,* 4th ed. Cambridge, Mass.: Harvard University Press, 1973.

Gingerich, Owen (ed.), *Frontiers of astronomy,* Introduction to Chapter 5. San Francisco: Freeman, 1970.

Mavridis, L. N. (ed.), *Structure and evolution of the galaxy*. Dordrecht, Netherlands: Reidel, 1971.

Sanders, R. H., and Wrixon, G. T., The center of the galaxy. *Scientific American* **230** (4), 66–77 (1974).

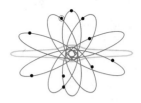

THE COSMOS

14

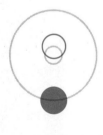

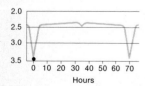

Suppose that we had the rare privilege of using the Palomar 5-m telescope to take a time-exposure photograph of the sky. Upon development of the film, numerous star images would be apparent. If we selected a small portion of the film and enlarged it sufficiently, we would likely see more galaxies than individual stars (Figure 14.1). For every star in our Galaxy (over 100 billion) there is one galaxy within the range of the 5-m telescope, and there are many more beyond its range, each containing billions of stars.

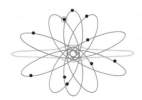

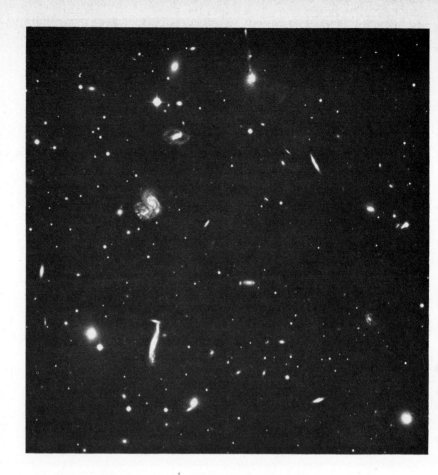

Figure 14.1 Cluster of galaxies in the constellation of Hercules.
(Hale Observatories)

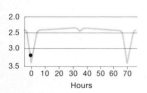

CLASSIFICATION
OF GALAXIES

The Milky Way galaxy represents only one of the many forms in which galaxies are found. Hubble, in his early work with galaxies (1920s) devised an extremely simple classification system for them. While some refinements are being suggested, his system remains in use to this day, essentially unchanged. The three main categories of galaxies include the *elliptical* type, the *spiral* type, and the *irregular* type (Figure 14.2).

The elliptical galaxies are subdivided in groups according to the eccentricity of their shape. A spherical galaxy is designated E0, and galaxies which are more and more eccentric are designated successively E1, E2, . . . , E7. You will see examples of E0 and E5 ellipticals in Figure 14.3.

(a)   (b)   (c)

Figure 14.2 Types of galaxies: (a) elliptical, NGC 4486; (b) spiral,
NGC 2841; (c) irregular, NGC 3034. (Hale Observatories)

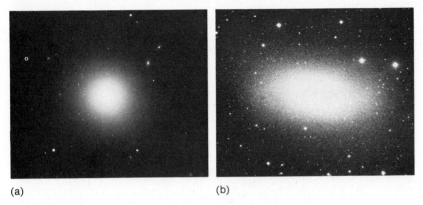

(a)   (b)

Figure 14.3 Elliptical galaxies of (a) the E0-type and (b) the
E5-type. (Hale Observatories)

A further subdivision of elliptical galaxies is the dwarf systems,
of which there are numerous examples within 1 million light-years
of the Milky Way galaxy. They are intrinsically dim (luminosity about
0.001 that of the Milky Way), sparsely populated collections of stars,
and yet they represent one of the most common types of galactic
systems in the universe.

The spiral galaxies are flattened systems that suggest rotation by
their appearance. Those with a very large, bright nucleus and tightly
wound arms are called Sa-type spirals. The Milky Way galaxy is an
example of the second classification, the Sb-type, in which the brightness is more evenly distributed between the nucleus and distinct arms.
The third classification, type Sc, has a much smaller nucleus and bright,
open arms. In fact most of the light of an Sc-type galaxy is concentrated
in its arms. These three types are illustrated in Figure 14.4(a,b,c).

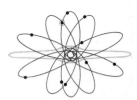

385

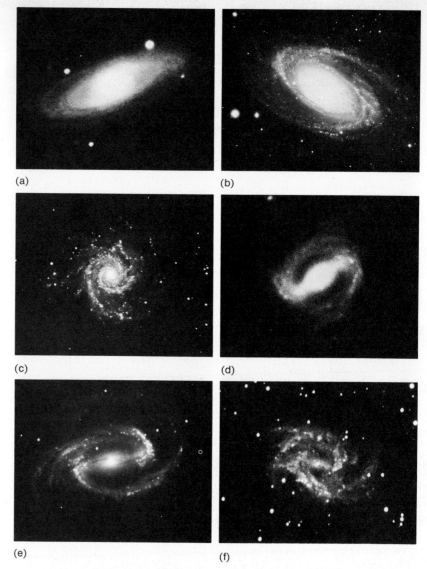

(a)

(b)

(c)

(d)

(e)

(f)

Figure 14.4 Spiral galaxies: (a) Sa, NGC 2811; (b) Sb, NGC 3031; (c) Sc, NGC 628. Barred spiral galaxies: (d) SBab, NGC 175; (e) SBb, NGC 1300; (f) SBc, NGC 2525. (Hale Observatories)

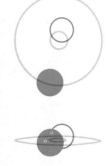

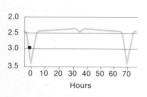

Within the general spiral class fall the barred spirals, a type which appear to have a barlike distribution of brightness running through their nuclei. The same general classification for spirals applies here. Those with high concentration of brightness in the bar and nucleus and tightly wound arms are called SBa, whereas the brightness of the SBb type is more evenly distributed between the arms and the nucleus.

The SBc type may have a less distinct nucleus, but it has a bright barlike structure and open arms [Figure 14.4 (d,e,f)]. Note that the SBab type shown in Figure 14.4(d) is midway between the SBa and SBb.

The S0-type galaxy shown in Figure 14.5 may at first glance resemble an elliptical type, yet if we could see this galaxy from an edge-on view, it would resemble the spiral type (Sa). Closer examination, however, reveals vast differences from either type. The S0 type shows no hint of arms, and it shows no gas or dust which is characteristic of the spiral. The S0-type galaxy does seem to bridge the gap between the ellipticals and the spirals. However, this should not be taken as an indication that it is an intermediate step in the evolution of galaxies from elliptical to spiral types, or vice versa. It is not firmly established that galaxies evolve at all. Some observers have speculated that the S0 type may represent a galaxy that has passed through another galaxy. Had this happened, individual stars would have been so far apart compared to their size that they would not have collided, nor would their gravitational interaction have been apparent, but any gas and dust which they possessed would have interacted and been swept from both galaxies. Since S0 galaxies are found in regions of space where other galaxies are relatively close, this appears to be a plausible explanation for their lack of gas and dust. This absence of gas and dust clouds leaves the S0 type with predominantly type-II (old) stars.

The irregular type galaxies are so named because they have no symmetry or structure which can be specified. They fall into two

Figure 14.5 An S0-type galaxy, NGC 1201. (Hale Observatories)

Figure 14.6 The Large Magellanic Cloud. (Lick Observatory)

Figure 14.7 An Irregular II galaxy, NGC 3034, showing filaments extending 25,000 light-years outward from the nucleus. (Hale Observatories)

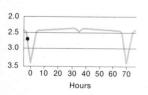

subtypes: Irregular I, illustrated by the Large Magellanic Cloud (Figure 14.6); and Irregular II, like NGC 3034 (Figure 14.7). Irregular I galaxies are characterized by O- and B-type stars and regions of ionized hydrogen, and a few examples have a suggestion of spiral arms. Irregular II galaxies are characterized by the fact that their stars can not readily be resolved in the telescope, hence they must be composed of

388

dim stars; yet they show spectroscopic evidence of gas and dust and eject material at high rates of speed (as shown by the filaments that we see extending outward from the nucleus in Figure 14.7).

HUBBLE'S CLASSIFICATION

Edwin Hubble suggested the orderly classification of galaxies as shown in Figure 14.8, and some observers have taken this as a supposed evolutionary pattern as well. Some would suggest that galaxies evolve from right to left in Hubble's diagram, and others would suggest the reverse order; however, we will present evidence shortly which seems to suggest virtually no evolution at all.

THE LOCAL GROUP

Our own local group of galaxies consists of 17 or 18 members that fall within a sphere approximately 3 million light-years in diameter. As can be seen in Figure 14.9, the Milky Way galaxy is not the center of the group but is nevertheless placed at the center of the diagram in order to aid in visualizing distances to the various other members. Table 14.1 presents the variety of different types included in the local group in order of absolute magnitude.

Within the local group we see almost every type of galaxy represented except the S0 type, and the general range of mass, diameter, and luminosity represented in the local group is almost the same for the entire universe.

Figure 14.8 Hubble's classification of galaxies.

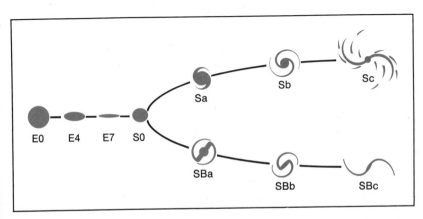

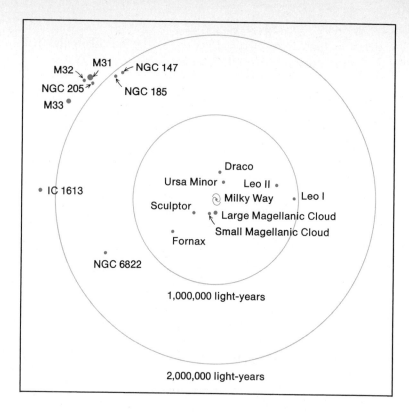

Figure 14.9 The local group of galaxies.

DISTANCES TO NEIGHBORING GALAXIES

Distances to galaxies within our local group are relatively easy to determine. Recalling Miss Henrietta Leavitt's work with Cepheid variables and the calibration of the period-luminosity relationship by Harlow Shapley and Walter Baade (Chapter 10), we understand that the distance to any galaxy may be determined if both the period and apparent magnitude of a single Cepheid in that galaxy can be determined. If a Cepheid can not be isolated, then other methods must be used. If we assume that a supernova in another galaxy has approximately the same absolute magnitude as a supernova in our Galaxy, then we can estimate distance by observing its apparent magnitude using the following equation:

$$\frac{L(10)}{L(r)} = \left(\frac{r}{10}\right)^2$$

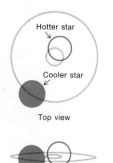

An eclipsing binary system

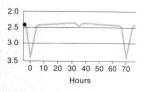

Light curve

Table 14.1 The local group of galaxies

GALAXY	TYPE	ABSOLUTE MAGNITUDE	DISTANCE (MILLION LIGHT-YEARS)	DIAMETER (LIGHT-YEARS)
M31 (Andromeda)	Sb	−21	2.2	100,000
Milky Way	Sb	−20	—	100,000
M33	Sc	−19	2.3	—
Large Magellanic Cloud	Irr	−18	0.16	30,000
Small Magellanic Cloud	Irr	−17	0.18	25,000
NGC 205	E5	−16	2.2	5000
NGC 221 (M32)	E3	−16	2.2	8000
NGC 6822	Irr	−15	1.5	9000
IC 1613	Irr	−15	2.2	16,000
NGC 185	E2	−15	1.9	8000
NGC 147	E6	−15	1.9	10,000
Fornax System	E3 (Dwarf)	−13	0.6	22,000
Sculptor System	E3 (Dwarf)	−12	0.27	7000
Leo I System	E4 (Dwarf)	−10	0.9	5000
Draco System	E2 (Dwarf)	−10	0.33	4500
Leo II System	E0 (Dwarf)	−10	0.75	5200
Ursa Minor System	E4 (Dwarf)	−9	0.22	3000
Maffei 1	E4	?	3.0	?

where L is luminosity and r is distance. If a typical supernova has an absolute magnitude of -15 and an apparent magnitude of $+10$, then it would show an increase (brightening) of 25 mag if brought to 10 parsecs, and this is equivalent to an increase in luminosity of 10^{10}. Substituting and solving for r, we get:

$$\frac{10^{10}}{1} = \frac{r^2}{10^2}$$

$$r^2 = 10^{12}$$

$$r = 10^6$$

$$r = 1 \text{ million parsecs (3.26 million light-years)}$$

Furthermore, when we consider clusters of galaxies, we may consider the average absolute brightness of the 10 brightest galaxies

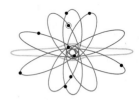

in one cluster to be the same as the average for the 10 brightest galaxies in another, and we can thereby judge distance from their apparent magnitude—the dimmer the galaxies, the farther away the cluster.

HUBBLE'S RED-SHIFT LAW

In 1929 Edwin Hubble made a startling discovery. As he recorded the spectra of many galaxies, he noticed a relationship between the amount by which the spectral lines were red-shifted and the apparent magnitude of the galaxies. In general, the dimmer galaxies had larger Doppler shifts toward the red end of the spectrum. Looking only at the photographs and spectrograms in Figure 14.10, you will see this relationship. The red shift of each is shown by a horizontal arrow on the spectrograms—very short in the first, but lengthening with each successive spectrogram.

In an attempt to refine this relationship, Hubble made two assumptions. He assumed that the red shift of each galaxy is due to its motion away from the observer and that the larger red shifts represent proportionately greater recessional velocities. He also assumed that the dimmer galaxies are farther away. Converting red shift to velocity of recession and estimating the distance to nearby clusters of galaxies, he plotted several points on a graph similar to Figure 14.11. A relationship is evident from the diagonal distribution of these points; however, he had made an error in assessing the distance to the nearby clusters of galaxies, and as a consequence he obtained an incorrect value for the expansion rate, namely, 165 km/sec for each million light-years. This value turned out to be about 10 times too large, based upon a modern determination of distances. Figure 14.11 shows this modern determination, and as you can see it indicates a rate of recession of 15 km/sec for each million light-years. This is called *Hubble's constant;* this is a misnomer, however, because its value is subject to change with time. If the expansion of the universe is slowing down, then the value of Hubble's constant will be smaller in the future. Furthermore, its present value is subject to an accurate determination of the distance to certain clusters of galaxies. For instance, if the distance to the Virgo cluster is not 80 million light-years, as shown in Figure 14.10, then Hubble's constant is not 15 km/sec for each million light-years. Hubble's relationship can be expressed very simply as

$$H = v/r$$

where v is the velocity of recession and r is the distance to the cluster of galaxies. Hubble's red-shift law expresses the fact that the distance

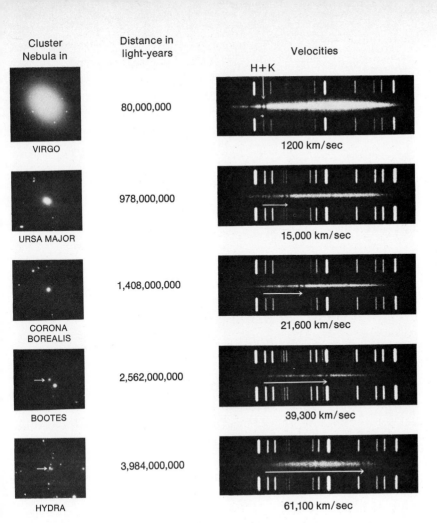

Cluster Nebula in	Distance in light-years	Velocities
VIRGO	80,000,000	H+K 1200 km/sec
URSA MAJOR	978,000,000	15,000 km/sec
CORONA BOREALIS	1,408,000,000	21,600 km/sec
BOOTES	2,562,000,000	39,300 km/sec
HYDRA	3,984,000,000	61,100 km/sec

Figure 14.10 Photographs of successively more distant galaxies; their distances are estimated by their apparent magnitude and thus are subject to reevaluation. The spectrogram of each galaxy is shown (on the right) with the Doppler shift, due to recessional velocity indicated by the arrows. Arrows indicate shift for calcium lines H and K. (Hale Observatories)

to any given cluster of galaxies appears to be directly proportional to its velocity of recession (based upon its red shift). While there is good confirmation for this relationship, in the case of normal clusters of galaxies a modern-day controversy exists as to whether the red-shift law applies to quasars, objects whose red shifts would indicate recessional velocities near the speed of light if Hubble's red-shift law applies. (This topic will be considered later in this chapter under the heading of quasars.)

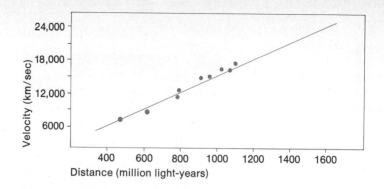

Figure 14.11 The relationship between red shift and distance.

Figure 14.12 Cygnus A, a radio galaxy. (Hale Observatories)

RADIO GALAXIES

It was in 1931 that engineer Karl Jansky of the Bell Telephone Laboratories accidentally discovered radio signals coming from outer space. Did these signals merely represent a general background of radio noise, or were they associated with separate sources? This question was answered by Walter Baade in 1951 when, using the 5-m telescope at Mt. Palomar, he identified a definite source of radio energy at Cygnus A, a galaxy some 700 million light-years distant. The nature of this source was not realized until Baade's identification. This opened a new era for astronomy, the era of *radio observation*.

Cygnus A is a highly unusual galaxy, for its radiation in radio wavelength is about one million times greater than that of a normal galaxy. Yet to be discovered is the source of this prodigious outpouring

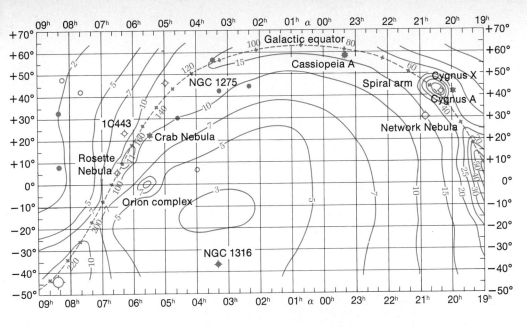

Figure 14.13 Radio map of the sky showing intense sources near the galactic equator. (Ohio State University Radio Telescope)

of energy—perhaps a gravitational collapse or an enormous explosion is taking place (see Chapter 12). The emissions seem to arise from two regions about 50,000 light-years to either side of Cygnus A (Figure 14.12).

Radio sources can be classified as extended or compact according to their apparent diameter. Extended sources are those which have an angular diameter of over 1 second of arc, and they would probably range in diameter from 10 to 100 parsecs. Compact radio sources have angular diameters less than 1 second of arc and actual diameters less than 10 parsecs (Figure 14.13).

Thousands of discrete radio sources have been found, many of which have been identified with visible galaxies. A *normal radio galaxy* emits about one-millionth as much radio energy as it does optical energy. A *peculiar radio galaxy* emits about 100 times as much radio energy as the normal radio galaxy: NGC 4486 (Figure 14.14) is an example of an elliptical galaxy that emits approximately 100 times as much radio energy as the normal emitter NGC 1068. The radio emission seems to come from two regions at equal distances on either side of the galaxy. A short-exposure photograph shows a jetlike appendage, the light from which is highly polarized, indicating a synchrotron emission, a result of high-energy electrons moving in a magnetic field.

Figure 14.14 An elliptical galaxy in Virgo, NGC 4486, with a jetlike appendage. (Lick Observatory)

Figure 14.15 A Seyfert galaxy, NGC 4151. (Hale Observatories)

SEYFERT GALAXIES

In 1943 Carl K. Seyfert of Mt. Wilson Observatory described a class of galaxies that superficially resembled a normal spiral (Figure 14.15). The characteristics that seemed to separate these particular spirals included a very small, bright nucleus that showed bright emission lines within its spectrum. This is unusual since the spectra of most galaxies show only broad absorption lines.

The light of several Seyfert galaxies has been observed to vary greatly in a period of only a few months. Several Seyferts are also strong radio emitters, again showing distant variations in output. These properties, together with their general starlike appearance, suggest that they are very compact sources. The energy distribution of Seyfert galaxies over a wide spectrum of wavelengths is shown in Figure 14.16. Notice how similar this output curve is to that of a quasar.

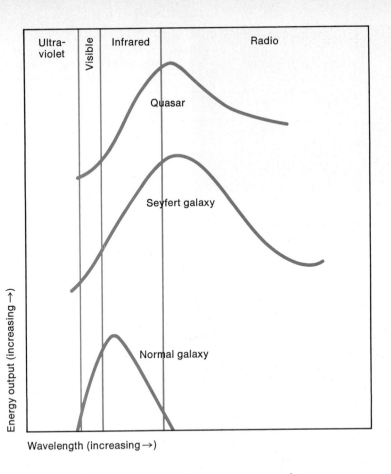

Figure 14.16 The energy output of a quasar as compared to a
Seyfert galaxy and a normal galaxy.

QUASARS

With the methods of radio astronomy firmly established, the search
for new radio objects continued. Early in the 1960s observers discovered
a type of radio source that appeared to be more starlike in dimension
than galactic. These sources were termed *quasi–stellar radio sources*
(contracted to *quasars*). The first such object was called 3C273 (Number
273 in the *Third Cambridge Catalogue of Radio Sources*). Attempts were
made to find the optical image of 3C273; however, the ability of a
radio telescope to pinpoint a source is rather limited. Because the radio
wavelengths are long compared to light, the resolution of even the larger
radio telescopes is rather poor (see Chapter 2). A unique approach to
locating 3C273 precisely was used by Cyril Hazard of Parkes Radio
Observatory in Australia. On a certain day when the moon was to pass
directly in front of the radio source, blocking the radio signals, Hazard

Figure 14.17 Quasar 3C273. (Hale Observatories)

observed the exact time of eclipse and reappearance of the radio source, and, with his knowledge of the exact position of the moon at all times, he pinpointed the radio source. As soon as this information reached Maarten Schmidt at Palomar, he was able to locate 3C273 on earlier photographs. It was starlike in size but fuzzy, and it had a jet extending out a distance almost equal to its diameter (Figure 14.17).

Schmidt was puzzled by the spectrum of this object that showed an unfamiliar placement of spectral lines. Finally, after weeks of work, he hit upon the idea that he was seeing lines of hydrogen that should appear in the blue portion of the spectrum but that had been red-shifted so far that they appeared in the red portion.

If the red shift of the spectral lines can be explained entirely as a phenomenon related to the speed with which an object is receding from the observer, then Schmidt had found an object receding at a rate of 45,000 km/sec. Furthermore, if this object was to fit Hubble's general pattern of red shift among the distant galaxies, then it had to be placed at a distance of 3 billion light-years.

Schmidt's analysis of the red shift was soon confirmed by his colleague Beverly Oke, who showed that the H_α (hydrogen-alpha) line, normally a red line, had been shifted into the infrared portion by an amount equal to Schmidt's estimate. But this was only the beginning, for today several hundred quasi-stellar objects are known, and the spectra of more than 100 have been photographed. In the case of quasar OH471 such a large red shift has been found in the spectra as to indicate a recessional velocity that is 90 percent of the speed of light. If this object is to fit the Hubble red-shift pattern, then it must be placed at a distance of 18 billion light-years away.

These observations set the stage for a controversy to last many years. On the one hand, some astronomers believed that they were seeing the most distant objects ever seen by man, objects so far distant that they were looking backward in time to what was perhaps almost the beginning of the present universe (Figure 14.18). And yet, if this was the case, then they were also looking at the brightest objects ever witnessed. In fact, they were hard pressed to explain a source of energy so great that it could be recorded 10 to 18 billion light-years away. No ordinary process in nearby galaxies could match the outpouring of energy necessary to be detectable at such distances—an energy output which must be 1000 times that of a normal galaxy. Those who represent the other extreme in the controversy say that these objects are nearby and therefore need not be so bright. They reason that the apparent red shift is not an indicator of great distance but perhaps a result of these objects being expelled in an explosion within our own Galaxy or in a relatively nearby galaxy. There is some evidence that several radio sources do align with certain "peculiar" galaxies, galaxies which may have exploded, ejecting the radio sources from their midst. If quasars are objects from other galaxies, then we would expect some of them to be moving toward us, hence to exhibit a blue shift in their spectra. But no quasars have been found with blue shifts.

Let us return, then, to the idea that quasars are distant objects, apparently very small in size. Some have suggested sizes ranging from $\frac{1}{25}$ to $\frac{1}{100}$ the size of a normal galaxy, yet radiating energy up to 1 million times greater than the average galaxy. Quasars have been seen to vary in energy output, and the conclusion is that they must be relatively small in order to show this variability. Theoretically an object which shows variations in as little as a week can not be over 1 light-week in diameter, or such variations would be smoothed out. One light-week is equivalent to approximately 15 times the diameter of the solar system.

How can such small objects emit the tremendous amount of energy indicated, if they are in fact situated at distances of 10 to 18 billion

Figure 14.18 (a) Source of radio noise, 3C295, in the constellation of Bootes. (b) Its very large red shift of spectral lines may indicate that it is one of the more distant objects of the known universe. (Hale Observatories)

(a)

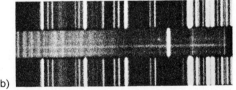

(b)

light-years away? Thermonuclear reactions that take place in the stars of any normal galaxy simply do not release sufficient energy to be seen at these vast cosmic distances. We must look for more energetic reactions. One such source of energy that could be released in a relatively short period of time is gravitation. If the core of a supermassive galaxy collapsed, with the nuclear particles falling together, huge amounts of energy would be released in a very short time. The result of such a collapse could be the ejection of surrounding materials such as is suggested by jets emanating from several quasars. Electrons ejected by such an event, if moving within a magnetic field, generate electromagnetic waves called *synchrotron radiation*. This process is capable of releasing large amounts of energy.

An important factor always to remember when talking of objects which are 10 to 18 billion light-years away is that we are also looking backward in time 10 to 18 billion years: we are seeing those objects as they existed at that time, and therefore we may be seeing galaxies in their initial stages of formation. The average density of the universe is thought to have been much greater at that time, a condition which may have permitted the formation of such dense galactic cores that they were in essence huge black holes (see Chapter 12). The gravitational collapse which would be a part of this picture could release energies in the amounts observed in quasars. Carrying this idea to the extreme, a quasar may be a galaxy which is collapsing into one gigantic black hole. Some observers have gone so far as to suggest that stars falling into such a black hole may appear in another space–time frame (see the following section on cosmology). If such a phenomenon can take place, these objects may then be termed *white holes,* and they may explain the very energetic reactions which have been observed in the centers of relatively nearby galaxies.

One further theory, which is not limited in the same sense as those above, offers the possibility that the universe may possess *antimatter* as well as matter as we know it. The *positron* is such a particle of antimatter. It is similar to an electron but of the opposite charge. When a positron and an electron come in contact, they annihilate each other, converting their masses to energy according to the formula $E = mc^2$.* Suppose that pockets of antimatter exist within the Galaxy and that matter sometimes comes in contact with this antimatter. Such contact would result in the complete annihilation of opposite masses, protons and antiprotons, neutrons and antineutrons. Such annihilation of mass results in a production of energy which may be adequate to explain the quasar energies, which are much greater than normal thermonuclear reactions.

*Energy equals mass times the speed of light squared.

These are rather imaginative theories, but they represent the type of thinking that may eventually lead to a solution to this fascinating problem.

EVOLUTION OF GALAXIES?

We have seen the great variety of galactic shapes, and it is only natural to suspect that galaxies evolve because stars do. This may be inferred from Hubble's classification scheme (see Figure 14.8), for it looks like a natural progression from E0- to Sc-type, or from Sc- to E0-type; however, there is little evidence to support evolution in either direction. Let us summarize the physical properties of each type of galaxy (see Table 14.2) and then ask the question: Could one type have evolved into another?

As would seem reasonable, there appears to be a correlation between the shape of a galaxy and its rate of rotation. The E0 type shows virtually no rotation, whereas the E1 through E7, S0, Sa, Sb, and Sc types show successively higher rates of rotation. This factor may have determined their shape from the very beginning, and it is difficult to see how the rotation rate could have changed enough to permit evolution of an elliptical into a spiral form, or vice versa. This does not preclude the possibility, however, that a spiral galaxy may have had an initial spherical shape during its protogalaxy stage. It does suggest

Table 14.2 Summary of the physical characteristics of elliptical galaxies as compared to spiral galaxies

ELLIPTICALS	SPIRALS
A wide range of mass (10^5 to 10^{13} solar masses)	A narrower range of mass (10^9 to 5×10^{11} solar masses)
A wide range of diameters (1000 to 200,000 parsecs)	A narrower range of diameters (5000 to 50,000 parsecs)
Less luminous in relation to mass	More luminous in relation to mass
Little or no rotation	Faster rotation
Little or no hydrogen gas	1–10% hydrogen gas
Little or no dust	Dust present
Primarily old-type stars	Both old and new stars
Found in dense clusters of galaxies	Found in sparsely populated clusters of galaxies

that there probably is not a slow evolutionary change from one type to another.

There are several additional factors which suggest that the shape of a galaxy is determined by conditions at the time of its formation and does not evolve. The most massive elliptical galaxies are approximately 50 times as massive as the most massive spirals, and we see an even greater contrast between the masses of the dwarf ellipticals and the smallest spirals. There is no known mechanism by which the initial mass of a galaxy can be substantially changed. Furthermore, the star types are basically different in the two types of galaxies. The ellipticals contain primarily Type-II and older Type-I stars, whereas the spirals contain both these types and the youngest Type-I stars. This may suggest that the ellipticals were formed earlier than the spirals, or it may merely suggest that star production and evolution proceeded faster in the elliptical galaxies. This line of reasoning is further strengthened by the lack of hydrogen gas in the ellipticals. With the rate of star production diminished because of this lack, the overall luminosity of the elliptical is less than that of the spiral, when compared to their masses. Today we find ample hydrogen gas in the spirals to sustain star production. Many observers believe that the gas is concentrated primarily within the arms of such galaxies because of the rather strong magnetic field they possess. An interesting speculation centers around the possibility that this magnetic field may direct a flow of new gases from the galaxy nucleus into the arms, replenishing this region as new stars are formed.

One further observation which tends to suggest that ellipticals may have been formed at a time and place of higher density is that they are seen today as members of dense clusters of galaxies, whereas the spirals are members of more sparsely populated clusters. Now let's test the ideas presented in this section against concepts of how it all began.

COSMOLOGY

Cosmology is the study of the universe as a whole—its large-scale structure, its organization, and its history. In a sense, some of the models of the universe which we considered in Chapter 1 represent early cosmologies; however, they were very limited views. What was the chain of events by which man expanded his view of the cosmos and gained hope that he might discover its history? In 1915, Albert Einstein gave science one of its most profound theories—*the general theory of relativity*. This theory says many things, but those parts which are most pertinent to our discussion of cosmology are the following: (1) In order to describe an event, both the three dimensions of space and the fourth dimension of time must be used; hence, we live in a four-dimensional world of space-time. (2) Gravity is determined by the distribution of mass (and energy). (3) Space-time has a curvature which is dependent upon the distribution of mass (and energy). Einstein proposed a cosmology which embodied a static universe and, knowing that gravity tends to make anything smaller, he introduced the idea of a cosmic force of repulsion which just balances the force of gravity. He soon abandoned this latter concept, however, recognizing that experience does not verify the presence of a repulsive force. While Einstein did not perfect a cosmological model, at the heart of every productive model which followed is his description of gravity.

In 1922, Alexander Friedmann suggested that the universe was extremely compact at some time in the remote past (in other words, an *initial singularity;* see Chapter 12). He further proposed an *expanding universe,* changing with time, These predictions preceded any observational evidence for an expanding universe by several years. Friedmann's model, with appropriate refinements, developed into what is known today as the "big bang" theory. His "initial singularity" has also been referred to as the "primeval atom." It is thought that this superdense and superhot "atom" exploded, producing the "primordial fireball." The first few seconds of this explosion were dominated by intense radiation (very-high-energy photons), which prevented the formation of nuclei; however, rapid expansion ensued, accompanied by rapid cooling, thus permitting nuclei of hydrogen and helium to form. Probably within the first 1000 sec, the primary supply of these elements was created. This universe, now dominated by matter (hydrogen and helium gas) continued to expand. Eventually clusters of galaxies formed, and these clusters still demonstrate the expansion of the universe today. In the big bang theory, it is assumed that the galaxies formed in the first 100 million years or so.

It was in 1923 that Edwin Hubble first demonstrated the existence of galaxies outside our own, when he recognized that the Andromeda Nebula was not a part of our own Galaxy. This is to say that only within the last half century has man known that the universe is composed of clusters of galaxies, the Milky Way being only one member of a cluster of which there are many. In 1929, Hubble discovered the red-shift law (discussed earlier), a relationship which plays an essential role in testing cosmological models. Hubble was joined by men like M. L. Humason and N. U. Mayall in his study of the red shifts of distant clusters of galaxies, and by 1936 two additional discoveries had been made, both of which were essential to the development of cosmological models:

(1) These observers noticed that the brightest elliptical galaxies of one cluster had virtually the same absolute magnitude as the brightest ellipticals of any other cluster. This was significant because these brightest

ellipticals could be used as an accurate distance indicator—the dimmer they appeared, the more distant they were. With knowledge of both their absolute magnitude and their apparent magnitude, solution of the equation

$$\frac{L(10)}{L(r)} = \left(\frac{r}{10}\right)^2$$

was expected to provide the distance. (See the discussion earlier in this chapter.) But certain corrections must be applied, as we shall see, and the process is not as simple as it may appear.

(2) In all the astronomers' searching, clusters of galaxies appeared to be randomly distributed with regard to distance and with regard to direction. Clusters of galaxies do not favor one part of the universe over another part. This was the first observational evidence that the universe, on a large scale, appears to be *homogeneous* (similar in density throughout) and *isotropic* (the same in all directions). This was a very significant discovery, for it suggested that we do not live in some unusual part of the universe, but rather that what we see from our location is typical of the entire universe. This observation formed the basis of an assumption which is at the heart of most modern cosmological models. It is called the *cosmological principle,* and it is stated as follows:

> The universe, on a large scale, appears the same from any location.

This suggests that the different parts of the universe may have had a common origin and lends hope that its history can be discovered.

By about 1950, this cosmological principle was expanded by a group at the University of Cambridge, first headed by Hermann Bondi and Thomas Gold, and later by Fred Hoyle. They suggested that not only does the universe appear the same from any location, but it also appears the same at any time (past, present, or future). This is referred to as the *perfect cosmological principle* and formed the basis for the "steady state" model. This theory does not deny the expansion of the universe, but rather it predicts its acceleration. In order to keep the distribution (density) of the universe constant, it suggests that as galaxies move apart, new matter comes into being to fill this space. Because it is assumed that the universe has always looked the same, there need be no creation event equivalent to the primordial fireball. The big bang theory and the steady state theory are illustrated in Figures 14.19 and 14.20. As we will see, there are several lines of evidence against the steady state theory and in favor of the big bang model. One of the most convincing is the discovery of a form of radiation which may be a consequence of the primordial fireball.

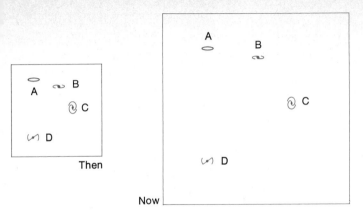

Figure 14.19 The big bang theory.

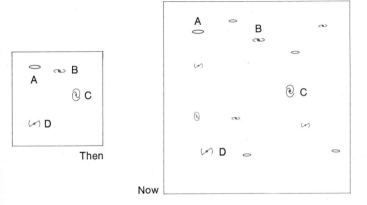

Figure 14.20 The steady state theory.

COSMIC BACKGROUND RADIATION

If the universe began as a gigantic fireball and if thermal equilibrium prevailed for even the first few seconds of that event, then the background radiation should be that of a *blackbody* (an ideal body that absorbs and radiates all radiant energy falling upon it). Because of the expansion of the universe that radiation would have cooled and should still exhibit itself as a background radiation equivalent to that of a very cold blackbody, one at $3°K$ ($-270°C$). If this radiation could be found, then it would be direct evidence of the fireball (Figure 14.21).

About 20 years after it was initially predicted, blackbody radiation was found quite accidentally by two astronomers of the Bell Telephone

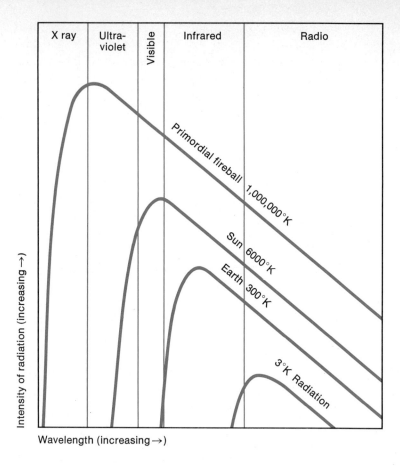

Figure 14.21 The black–body radiation curves for the primordial fireball and for 3°K radiation, the latter falling almost entirely in the radio portion of the spectrum.

Laboratory, Arno H. Penzias and Robert W. Wilson, who were testing certain very sensitive radio equipment. They experienced a form of radio noise which showed a very remarkable similarity to that of a blackbody at approximately 3°K. Normally radiation is detected because of an increase in energy received when the radio telescope (antenna) is pointed toward the source, but this 3°K radiation was thought to pervade space and thus would not be stronger in one direction than another, unless we were moving through it. In 1964, Robert H. Dicke devised twin receiving antennae—one of which was attached to a reference source that was known to radiate at 4.2°K, and the other was pointed skyward. When the sky radiation was compared to the reference source, it became evident that 3°K radiation can be received from any direction. In the years that have followed, measurements have been taken in a variety of wavelengths, and this background radiation appears to fit the predicted curve quite closely. Orbiting observatories will provide new data using wavelengths that are obscured by the earth's atmosphere, but sufficient evidence is now available to strongly suggest the existence of the fireball. The steady state theory provides no convincing explanation of this 3°K blackbody radiation.

CURVATURE OF SPACE

Within the two models of cosmology we have presented, there are variations. For instance the steady state model implies that the rate of expansion is speeding up (accelerating). On the other hand, all variations of the big bang model imply a slowing down (deceleration) of the rate of expansion, but different rates of deceleration are possible and this is significant. In order to visualize these various possibilities, let us suppose that a ball is tossed upward with varying forces that impart different initial velocities in each case. Our normal experience with such a toss suggests that the ball will decelerate (slow down) due to the force of gravity, eventually stop and then return to the earth only to bounce upward again and again [Figure 14.22(a)]. We might characterize its flight as an *oscillation*. On the other hand if it were possible to give the ball a higher initial velocity, it might just overcome the force of gravity and leave the earth forever [Figure 14.22(b)]. It too would experience deceleration, but its flight would be arrested only at some great distance from the earth (infinity). The physicist would describe the flight of the ball under such conditions as *parabolic*. If still a greater force were used, the flight of the ball would appear as in Figure 14.22(c), continually decelerating, yet climbing higher without limit. Such a flight is termed *hyperbolic*. A fourth possibility involves the continual application of a force, say by means of a rocket attached to the ball [Figure 14.22(d)]. The force of the rocket produces an *acceleration,* that is, the ball is carried upward at increasing speed.

These four cases are analagous to various ways in which the universe might be expanding. The explosive force of the "big bang" event may have sent the material of the universe outward at such a rate as to allow gravity to bring it to a halt and collapse upon itself—this is the *oscillating model*. A plot of the radius of the universe, as time goes by, would appear as in curve (a) in Figure 14.23. Had the outward force been just sufficient to overcome the force of gravity, the universe would continue to expand but would be slowing in its rate of expansion as shown in curve (b) in Figure 14.23. The shape of such a curve is said to be *parabolic*. Curve (c) of Figure 14.23 illustrates the expansion of the universe if still greater initial velocity had been imparted. This too represents a decelerating universe, but is said to be *hyperbolic*. Both

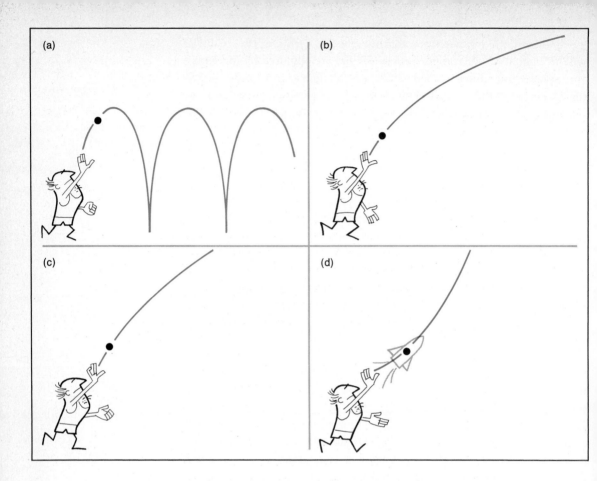

Figure 14.22 The flight of a ball (shotput) thrown upward may be described in various ways depending upon the force applied: (a) oscillating (bouncing), if only a small initial force is applied; (b) parabolic—continually rising but also slowing down; (c) hyperbolic—continually rising at a greater rate than in (b); (d) accelerating—continually rising and speeding up, due to an added propulsive force (here applied by a rocket).

the parabolic and hyperbolic models represent a universe which is infinite and in which radius has no meaning. The scaling factor in Figure 14.23 indicates only a change in the distance between galaxies when applied to these models.

The fourth model, that of an *accelerating expansion,* is illustrated by curve (d) in Figure 14.23. This represents a necessary condition of the steady state model; however, we have no indication that it is correct. Astronomers' best determination of the Hubble "constant" at the present time is represented by the straight (solid) line in Figure 14.23, and points on each curve having the same slope as that reference line have been made to coincide (see the point labeled "now"). As you can see, no

408

Plate 1 Eta Carinae (NGC 3372), an emission nebula seen in the southern sky, as photographed in 1974 by the 1.5-m Schmidt camera. This emission nebula resulted from the explosion of a supernova recorded in 1843. Embedded in this nebula are numerous hot, blue stars, and it is the ultraviolet radiation of these stars that excites the atoms of the nebula, causing it to emit light. (Cerro Tololo Inter-American Observatory)

Plate 2 The planet earth as seen from Apollo 11 at a distance of about 98,000 nautical miles, or 178,000 km. (NASA)

Plate 3 The Apollo 11 lunar module ascending from the moon to rendezvous with the command module. (NASA)

Plate 4 Jupiter as photographed from Pioneer 10. Clearly visible are the Great Red Spot and the shadow of Io, one of Jupiter's 13 moons. (NASA/Pioneer Project)

Plate 5 Comet Kohoutek (1973f) taken January 14, 1974, by R. B. Minton with the Catalina Schmidt camera. (Lunar and Planetary Laboratory)

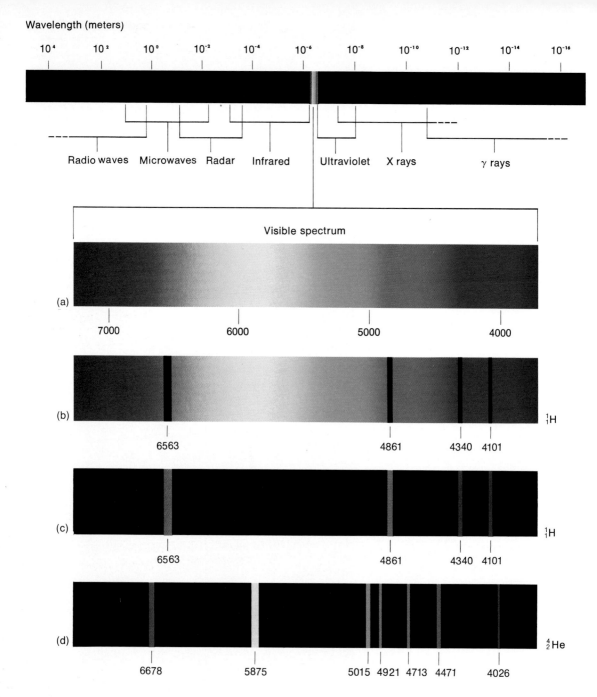

Plate 6 Spectrograms of (a) white light—a continuous spectrum; (b) hydrogen—an absorption spectrum; (c) hydrogen—an emission spectrum; (d) helium—an emission spectrum. Numbers on scale under the spectrograms indicate wavelengths corresponding to each color and are given in angstroms (Å); 1 Å equals 10^{-10} m. See pages 74 to 79 of the text.

Plate 7 An X-ray photograph of the sun taken aboard Skylab with the S-054 X-ray Spectrographic Telescope on May 28, 1973, revealing the corona with temperatures ranging upward to 1 million degrees Kelvin. The photo shows the whole range of coronal features in a broad spectral range. The active regions, bright points, interconnecting loops, filament cavities, coronal holes, and other features seen in the photograph are produced by the interaction of the sun's magnetic field and the ionized gas of the corona. (American Science and Engineering, Inc./NASA)

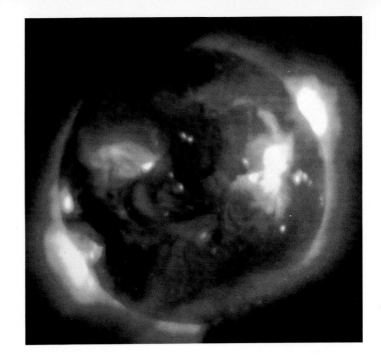

Plate 8 Large Magellanic Cloud, a galaxy neighboring our own Milky Way that may be seen in the southern sky. Photo taken with the 1.5-m Schmidt camera. (Cerro Tololo Inter-American Observatory)

◁ **Plate 9** The Trifid Nebula (M20; NGC 6514), a gaseous emission nebula in Sagittarius. A 4-m telescope photo taken in 1974. (Kitt Peak National Observatory)

Plate 10 Gaseous emission nebula and an associated galactic cluster in Serpens (M16; NGC 6611). Compact dust clouds, seen as dark globules, may be stars forming. Strong turbulence has been detected in the dark lanes. A 4-m telescope photo taken in 1974. (Kitt Peak National Observatory)

Plate 11 The Great Nebula (M42; NGC 1976), a gaseous emission nebula in Orion. Visible to the naked eye in Orion's sword, M42 has been known since the beginnings of recorded astronomy. Composed of mainly hydrogen gases, the Orion Nebula has a critical density about that required for star formation, and some star formation is believed to be occurring here. A 4-m telescope photo taken in 1974. (Kitt Peak National Observatory)

Plate 12 The Great Galaxy in   ▷
Andromeda (M31; NGC 224), with satellite galaxies NGC 205 and 221. (Hale Observatories)

model predicts that Hubble's "constant" is really constant, but rather that it is changing. If it is changing as in curve (a) in Figure 14.23, then the universe will oscillate; furthermore, projecting the curve backward into the past, we see that it has only been about 11 billion years since the last "big bang." If the change in the rate of expansion is more accurately described by curve (b), then we must look back in time about 13 billion years for the "big bang." Curve (c) indicates an even earlier beginning—about 15 billion years. If Hubble's "constant" were really constant, its straight-line graph would indicate an age for the universe of 20 billion years; and as you can see in curve (d), the accelerating universe would require a still earlier beginning.

But how do these models relate to Einstein's concept of the curvature of space-time? To describe the evolving universe mathematically, he introduced a constant k; depending upon the value of

Figure 14.23 The curves associated with the four models of the universe are shown with their present state made to coincide at the "now" point: (a) oscillating universe; (b) parabolic universe; (c) hyperbolic universe; and (d) accelerating universe. The straight reference line represents the best estimate of the Hubble "constant" at the present time. As is clear from this drawing, the "start-up" time of the universe is dependent upon the model which best describes its evolution.

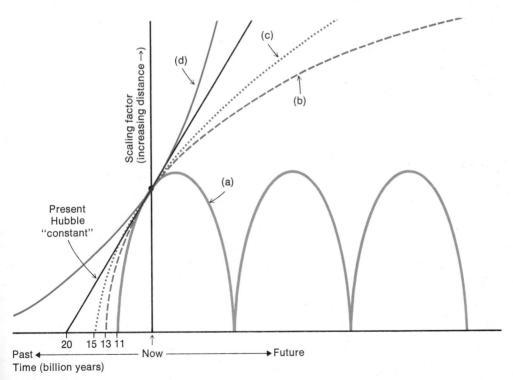

that constant, he termed the curvature of the universe as either positive (if k is positive), zero (if $k = 0$), or negative (if k is negative). Positive curvature of space-time correlates with the oscillating model, zero curvature with the parabolic model, and negative curvature with the hyperbolic and the accelerating model.

We might try to visualize each of these curvatures of space-time by considering models of one less dimension. A surface of zero curvature is a plane (a flat surface). If dots (which will represent galaxies) are distributed uniformly over such a surface, one may predict the ratio of numbers of dots in successive circles of radius 1, 2, 3, and so on. The area A of a circle is determined by the formula $A = r^2$, where r is the radius. Therefore, the areas of successively larger circles will have the ratio of $1:4:9:$ etc. (the squares of the corresponding radii). Likewise, we would expect the ratio of counts of dots (galaxies) in successive circles to be $1:4:9:$ etc. On the other hand, if dots are distributed uniformly over a surface of positive curvature, that of a sphere, then successive radii produce less than the expected ratio, say $1:3.6:8:$ etc. This is graphically demonstrated by the gaps which develop in the flattening process shown in Figure 14.24(b), resembling a flattened orange peel. Negative curvature produces just the opposite effect, namely, circles of successively larger radii produce more than the expected numbers of dots—for when a surface of negative curvature (hyperbolic, or saddle-shape) is flattened, wrinkles occur due to excess material. The ratio of dots may approach $1:4.5:10:$ etc. One would expect the density of galaxies to be uniform in the case of zero curvature; to thin out in the case of positive curvature; or to increase as in the case of negative curvature (Figure 14.24, bottom row). How can we possibly determine which model is correct?

TESTS FOR COSMOLOGICAL MODELS

The effect of space-time curvature does not become apparent merely by counting nearby galaxies. Therefore, the astronomer is concerned with galaxies which are beyond the reach of optical telescopes, namely, radio galaxies. Recently a number of astronomers on the staff of Ohio State University completed a survey of over 8000 radio sources. They assumed that the radio sources which are located billions of light-years away are just as bright as those which are nearer. Based upon that assumption, their plot showed a thinning out, somewhat resembling that of Figure 14.24(b), indicating positive curvature. We must be cautious at this point, however, for when we view very distant galaxies

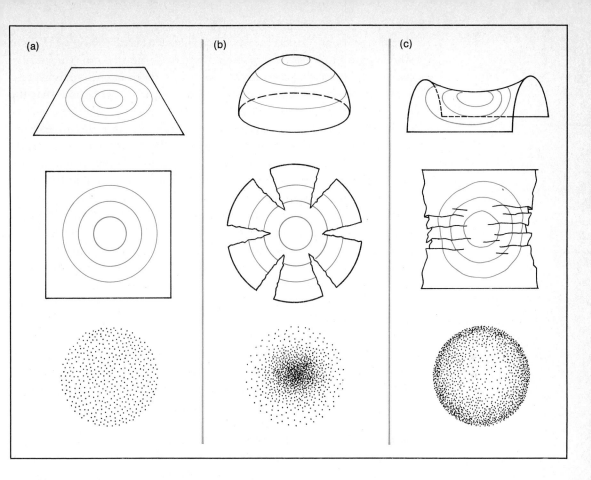

Figure 14.24 The curvature of space may be visualized as: (a) flat, wherein we would find a uniform distribution of galaxies; (b) positive, wherein galaxies would appear to thin out with greater distances; or (c) negative, wherein galaxies would appear to be more dense at greater distances.

we are also looking backward to the time when the light left those sources (billions of years ago), and perhaps galaxies were intrinsically brighter (or dimmer) in the early stages of the universe. The very fact that such an evolutionary factor must be considered illustrates the uncertainty with which the astronomer must regard this survey of radio sources. Perhaps we may confirm or deny the results of the Ohio survey by taking still another approach, one typified by the work of Allan Sandage and William A. Baum.

Let us recall how Hubble first recognized the relationship of red shift to distance. He plotted the red shift of galaxies against their apparent magnitude (see Figure 14.11). Extending this procedure to the more distant cluster of galaxies, astronomers have produced the plot shown in Figure 14.25. The four models of the universe (*oscillating, parabolic, hyperbolic,* and *accelerating*) have been interpreted by cosmologists as shown superimposed upon this plot. You can see that the plot of nearby galaxies (lower left-hand corner) is not sufficient to differentiate between the models. As more and more distant galaxies are being added, however, there appears to be a fairly close correlation with the oscillating universe (positive curvature). Is this evidence conclusive? Perhaps not, for there is a fair amount of scattering in the points and furthermore the location of the points on the graph is subject to correction with the advancement of techniques for measuring apparent magnitudes and correcting these measurements for various effects. There is little chance, however, that the plot will change sufficiently to correspond to the accelerating universe. This observation has virtually sounded the death knell for the steady state theory.

Figure 14.25 Hubble diagram—a plot of distant galaxies shows a fair amount of scattering among the four theoretical models of the universe: (a) oscillating; (b) parabolic; (c) hyperbolic; or (d) accelerating (steady state). Although there is some tendency at present to favor the oscillating model, more data is necessary for a conclusive decision.

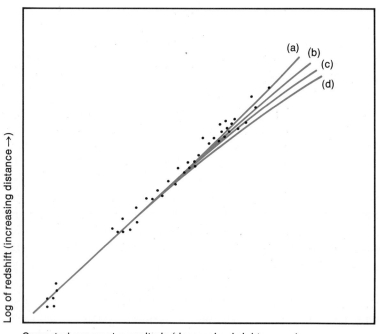

Table 14.3 Mass-energy density associated with various
models of the universe

COSMOLOGICAL MODEL	MASS-ENERGY DENSITY
Oscillating	More than 10^{-29} g/cm³
Parabolic	10^{-29} g/cm³
Hyperbolic	Less than 10^{-29} g/cm³

We may summarize the primary task of the cosmologist as that of finding two numbers: the Hubble "constant"; and the actual rate at which it is changing. This search is challenging the very limits of the art today. However, still one other test may be applied.

MASS-ENERGY DENSITY
OF THE UNIVERSE

Einstein predicted in his theory of relativity that the curvature of space-time is proportional to the mass-energy density of the universe. It is possible to compute the density associated with each model, and this is tabulated in Table 14.3.

At present, the best estimate of the density of the universe is 3×10^{-31} g/cm³, about $\frac{1}{30}$ of the mass-energy necessary to create an oscillating condition. This estimate is based upon the mass of all luminous material (stars, luminous nebulae, and the like), together with an estimate of nonluminous gas and dust in the galaxies and of all cosmic rays. Recent X-ray studies suggest a background of X-ray radiation which may be originating from nonluminous sources. Infrared astronomers are identifying large numbers of cool red dwarfs, unknown a few years ago, all of which may add to the known mass of the universe. One of the most significant sites of yet undetected mass may be the black hole (see Chapter 12). Astronomers are on the threshold of new techniques and new discoveries which may provide clues to enough mass-energy to close the universe, that is, to provide enough self-gravity to eventually stop the expansion and create the oscillating condition. More mass must be found if this test is to be reconciled to the indications set forth in Figure 14.25. The search goes on, and we can not say for sure which model represents the universe. For that matter, who is to say that any of the proposed models is correct?

CONCLUSION

We find ourselves not only in an expanding universe but also in the center of an explosion of ideas and techniques that are being applied in the field of astronomy. We have seen many questions answered and many more opened up. Man's concept of this universe is ever changing, ever enlarging. Surely the fascination of the unknown is endless.

QUESTIONS

1. Astronomers estimate that the Milky Way galaxy contains at least 100 billion stars. How many galaxies do they estimate exist in the universe?
2. Sketch the following types of galaxies: (a) Sa; (b) Sc; (c) SBb; (d) E3.
3. What distinguishes an S0-type galaxy from the highly flattened elliptical galaxy or the Sa-type spiral galaxy?
4. What general type of galaxy is most prevalent in our local group?
5. In order to use a Cepheid variable to find the distance to a galaxy, what must the observer be able to determine in relation to that Cepheid?
6. Under what conditions is it safe to assume that because a galaxy looks dimmer, it must be farther away?
7. What relationship did Edwin Hubble find between the distances to galaxies and the red shift in their spectra?
8. Can we apply the red-shift law which Hubble developed to every distant object in the universe without any question as to its validity?
9. Normal galaxies emit much less radio energy than light energy; however, certain types of galaxies have a very high output of radio energy. Name several of these types.
10. Is it possible for a radio galaxy to emit as much as one million times as much radio energy as a normal galaxy?
11. What does the contracted word *quasar* stand for in full?
12. What characteristics do all quasars have in common?
13. What evidence exists for the idea that the quasars are the most distant and therefore the brightest objects ever sensed by astronomers? What evidence is there that quasars are relatively nearby objects?
14. If the quasars are very distant objects, then what may be their source of energy?
15. In what sense is time related to distance in all astronomical observations?

16. Is there more evidence that elliptical galaxies evolve into spirals or that spirals evolve into ellipticals? Or do galaxies not evolve except in their earliest stage of formation? Substantiate your answer.

17. What factor probably determines the ultimate shape of a galaxy?

18. If our universe is expanding, as indicated by the fact that all distant objects have red shifts, are we necessarily at the center of that universe? Would you still see the same expansion from any point of view in the universe? See if you can prove your answer by a drawing.

19. What must be happening in the universe in order to satisfy the steady state theory?

20. Within which theories of cosmology does the density of the universe change?

21. What recent findings tend to substantiate the big bang theory?

SUGGESTED READINGS

Alfvén, Hannes, *Worlds–antiworlds*. San Francisco: Freeman, 1966.

Bondi, Hermann, *Relativity and common sense*. Garden City, N.Y.: Doubleday, 1964.

Kellerman, Kenneth I., Extragalactic radio sources. *Physics Today* **26** (10), 38–47 (1973).

Marder, L., *Time and the space-traveller*. Philadelphia: University of Pennsylvania Press, 1971.

Sandage, Allen R., Cosmology: A search for two numbers. *Physics Today* **23** (2), 34–41 (1970).

Schatzman, E. L., *The structure of the universe*. New York: World University Library/McGraw–Hill, 1968.

Schramm, David N., The age of the elements. *Scientific American* **230** (1), 69–77 (1974).

Sciama, D. W., *Modern cosmology*. New York: Cambridge University Press, 1972.

Woltjer, Lodewijk (ed.), *Galaxies and the universe*. New York: Columbia University Press, 1968.

Glossary

aberration of starlight The apparent displacement in the location of a star due to the orbital motion of the earth.

absolute magnitude The apparent magnitude of a star if viewed from a distance of ten parsecs.

absolute zero The temperature at which the linear motions of all molecules stop. A temperature of $0\,^{\circ}K$ (Kelvin), equivalent to $-273\,^{\circ}C$ (Celsius) and $-460\,^{\circ}F$ (Fahrenheit).

absorption spectrum Dark lines on the background of a continuous spectrum.

acceleration The change in velocity. It may be an increase or decrease in velocity, or a change in direction.

achromatic lens A lens system composed of two or more elements that are designed to correct for chromatic aberration.

active sun The sun during times of unusually large numbers of sunspots, flares, and other events.

albedo The percentage of light that a planet or moon reflects.

alpha particle A positively charged particle that consists of two protons and two neutrons; hence, a helium nucleus.

altitude The angle at which an object appears above the horizon as measured along its vertical circle.

angle of incidence The angle between the incoming ray and the normal (perpendicular) to the reflecting or refracting surface.

angstrom (Å) A unit of length equal to 10^{-10} m, used to measure very small wavelengths.

angular diameter The angle that the diameter of an object makes as measured at the observer's eye.

angular distance The angle between two objects as viewed on the celestial sphere.

annular eclipse An eclipse of the sun that occurs when the apparent diameter of the moon is not as great as the apparent diameter of the sun, thus leaving a ring of sunlight showing around the moon.

antimatter Particles that appear to possess properties opposite to those of matter.

aphelion A point in the orbit of a planet at which it is farthest from the sun. (*Helios* is a Greek word for sun.)

apogee A point in the orbit of an earth satellite at which it is farthest from the earth. (*Ge, gee,* and *geo* are combining forms—suffixes or prefixes—meaning earth.)

apparent magnitude A measure of the brightness of a star or other celestial object as seen from earth.

apparent solar day The interval be-

tween two successive transits of the sun's center across the observer's meridian.

Arctic Circle The parallel of latitude $66.5\,^{\circ}$ N. Within this circle the sun is not seen on the day of the winter solstice.

ascending node The point on the orbit of a body at which it crosses the celestial equator from south to north.

association A very loose cluster of stars that are thought to have a common origin.

asteroid A small body in orbit around the sun; a minor planet or planetoid.

astrology A study of the supposed influence of the positions of the sun, moon, planets, and stars upon human affairs.

astrometric binary A binary-star system in which only one component is visible but in which the presence of the second component is deduced from the perturbations (disturbances) that it produces upon the orbital motion of the first.

astrometry The branch of astronomy that is primarily concerned with the accurate measurement of positions and motions of stars.

astronomical unit (A.U.) The average distance between the earth and the sun. By international agreement, 1 A.U. = 92,870,000 miles, or approximately 149,790,000 km.

astronomy The science whereby celestial objects are described according to their location, motion, size, composition, and appearance.

astrophysics The branch of astronomy that applies the methods and tools of physics to the study of celestial objects.

atmospheric refraction The bending of light rays from celestial objects due to refraction by the earth's atmosphere. This phenomenon is most noticeable near the observer's horizon.

atom The smallest particle of an element that retains the properties which characterize that element.

atomic mass unit One-twelfth the mass of an atom of the most common form of carbon (^{12}C); approximately the mass of the hydrogen atom.

atomic number The number of protons in the nucleus of a given atom.

atomic weight The average mass of an atom of a given element as measured in atomic mass units.

aurora The light display that is produced by ionized atoms, usually in the polar regions; the northern and southern lights—*aurora borealis* and *aurora australis.*

autumn equinox The point on the celestial equator at which the sun crosses from north to south.

azimuth The angle measured eastward along the horizon from the north point to the vertical circle which passes through a given object.

Balmer lines The series of spectral lines, either bright or dark, that are produced by electron transitions up from energy level 2 or down to energy level 2, in the hydrogen atom. These lines lie in the visible portion of the spectrum.

barred spiral A galaxy characterized as having a "bar" (armlike extensions) through its nucleus. Spiral arms extend from the ends of the bar.

barycenter A point around which two objects that lie in each other's gravitational field seem to orbit. It constitutes a center of mass of the system.

beta particle A negatively charged particle; an electron.

"big bang" theory A theory concerning the evolution of the universe, which states that the expansion of the universe is the result of a primeval explosion.

binary star A double-star system in which the components revolve around a common point situated between them, their barycenter.

black body Theoretically, a body that is a perfect radiator, for instance, one that absorbs and reemits all radiation which falls on it.

black dwarf Thought to be the final stage in the evolution of some stars, a state in which all energy of the star has been exhausted and in which it no longer radiates.

black hole A star which has collapsed under the influence of gravity to such an extent that its surface gravity prevents further radiation of energy.

blink microscope An instrument in which two different photographs may be viewed alternately. If the two photographs represent the same region of the sky but were taken at differing times, then stars that have moved or changed in their apparent brightness may be easily recognized in the instrument. Stars that have moved will seem to jump back and forth. The image of stars that have varied in brightness will appear to change in size on the photograph.

Bode's law (More correctly called the *Bode-Titius relationship.*) A sequence of numbers that approximate the distances from the sun to the planets, measured in astronomical units.

Bohr atom A model of the atom, devised by Niels Bohr, that depicts the electrons in orbit around the nucleus.

bolide A very bright meteor or fireball, sometimes accompanied by a sound.

bolometric magnitude A measure of the total radiation of a star as received above the earth's atmosphere, measured in the full spectrum of electromagnetic radiation.

bright-line spectrum An array of colorful lines against a dark background, produced by an excited, low-pressure gas.

416

brightness A measure of the actual luminosity of an object.

calorie A unit of heat energy, the amount needed to raise the temperature of 1 g (1 cm^3) of water 1°C.

candlepower A unit of light intensity.

carbon cycle The series of nuclear reactions, involving carbon, that transforms hydrogen into helium.

cardinal points The four main points of the compass: north, east, south, and west.

Cassegrain reflector A telescope that utilizes a convex secondary mirror to bring the light rays to a focus near the primary lens. In order that the image formed at this point may be viewed, a hole is made in the primary mirror and an eyepiece inserted there.

Cassini's division A wide gap in the ring system of Saturn, between the outer and middle ring.

celestial equator The projection of the earth's equator onto the sky; hence a great circle that is 90° from each pole in the sky.

celestial mechanics A branch of astronomy that deals primarily with the motions and mutual gravitation of objects in space.

celestial meridian The great circle through the celestial poles and the observer's zenith.

celestial navigation The art of finding one's way from one point to another on the earth's surface by means of observation of the position of the sun, moon, planets, and stars.

celestial poles Extensions of the earth's axis of rotation; points on the celestial sphere about which the sky appears to rotate daily.

celestial sphere An apparent sphere of very large radius, centered on the observer, upon which the location of the stars may be specified.

center of gravity The point through which gravity seems to act no matter how the object is turned. The center of mass of the object.

centripetal force A force, directed toward the center of curvature, that diverts a body from a straight path into a curved one.

Cepheid variables A class of pulsating stars that vary in light output.

Ceres The first asteroid (minor planet) to be discovered; also the largest such body.

chromatic aberration A defect in a simple lens whereby light of different colors is brought to different focal points.

chromosphere That portion of the sun's atmosphere which lies directly above the photosphere.

circumpolar stars Those stars near the celestial poles which always appear above the observer's horizon.

cluster of galaxies A grouping of galaxies composed of hundreds or thousands of member galaxies.

cluster of stars A grouping of stars that is held together by mutual gravitation; they thus possess a common motion.

cluster variables A large class of pulsating variable stars that have a period of less than one day and are usually found in globular star clusters.

color index (C.I.) The difference between the photographic and the visual magnitudes of a star: C.I. = $m_p - m_v$.

coma A defect in a telescope by which the rays of light that enter the telescope at an angle to its axis are not brought to the same focal point but form *comma*-like (,) images.

coma (of a comet) The fuzzy, gaseous component of the comet's head.

comet A swarm of bodies composed of frozen gases with solid particles at their centers. Comets usually have very elongated orbits around the sun.

compound A substance composed of two or more elements.

concave lens or mirror A lens or reflecting surface curved somewhat like the inside of a sphere.

conduction The transfer of energy (usually heat energy) by the direct passing of energy from atom to atom.

configuration A particle form or arrangement of the sun, moon, planets, and/or stars.

conic section A curve formed by cutting a circular cone with a flat surface. Such a cut may produce a circle, ellipse, parabola, or hyperbola.

conjunction A lining up of celestial objects so that they appear to have the same right ascension.

constellation A group of stars that by its shape suggests an object, person, or animal. Today, a constellation includes a definite region of the sky around such a configuration.

continuous spectrum The uninterrupted band of color produced by a heated solid, liquid, or gas under pressure.

convection The transfer of energy (heat) by the motion of the medium that "carries" the energy.

convex lens A lens in which one or both surfaces are curved like the outside of a sphere and thus are thicker at the center than near the outside.

Copernican system A system of planets that revolve around the sun (heliocentric).

core The central portion of a planet or of any celestial body.

corona The outer atmosphere of the sun, seen only when the central disk of the sun is covered.

corona (of the galaxy) The halo or sphere of objects that surround the central nucleus of the Milky Way galaxy.

coronagraph An instrument for photographing the outer atmosphere of the sun by artificially covering the disk

of the sun's image at the focal plane of the telescope.

cosmic rays High-energy particles, largely protons, that strike the earth.

cosmogony The study of the origin and evolution of the material in the universe.

cosmological principle The assumption that, in general, the universe would appear the same from any location within itself.

cosmology The study of the organization and structure of the universe and its evolution.

cosmos The entire universe, seen as an orderly, self-inclusive system.

Coudé focus A system by which an arrangement of secondary mirrors directs the light gathered by the primary mirror along the polar axis of the telescope to the Coudé focal point. This point remains fixed as the telescope moves to follow a star.

crater A depression in the surface of the earth or moon.

crepe ring The innermost ring of Saturn; a dark ring.

crescent That phase of the moon which shows it less than half full; also applicable to Venus, or any planet when viewed from space.

crust The outer layer of the earth, moon, or other such body.

dark nebula A gas or dust cloud that obscures the light of stars and galaxies behind it.

declination The smallest angle between a given object and the equator.

deferent The larger orbit in the Ptolemaic system, along which the center of the epicycle of a planet supposedly moves.

deflection of starlight The bending of light as it passes close to a massive object; a bending due to gravity.

density The mass of an object divided by its volume and usually measured in grams per cubic centimeter.

descending node The point along the orbit of an object at which it passes from north to south of the celestial equator or of some other reference plane.

deuterium (Also called "heavy hydrogen.") A form of hydrogen in which the nucleus of each atom contains one proton and one neutron.

diffraction The spreading of light as it passes an object or passes through a small opening.

diffraction grating A system of finely ruled lines that diffract the light and by interference produce a spectrum.

diffraction pattern A series of bright and dark lines produced by the interference of light.

diffuse nebula A bright or dark nebula of irregular shape; not of the planetary form.

diffusion (of light) The scattering of light from an irregular surface.

direct motion The typical motion of

a planet—west to east—as seen against the background of stars.

disk (of a planet) The round shape of a planet as seen in a telescope; of measureable size.

disk (of our Galaxy) The flattened portion of the Milky Way galaxy; hence, the spiral arms.

dispersion The separation of white light into its component colors by means of refraction or diffraction.

diurnal circle The apparent path of an object in the sky during one day, due to the earth's rotation.

diurnal motion The daily apparent motion of all objects, due to the earth's rotation.

Doppler shift The change in observed wavelength of sound, radio, or light, due to the motion of the source, the observer, or both.

double star A star system that is composed of two stars, each influenced by the other's gravitational field. Their dual nature is revealed by telescopic or spectroscopic observation.

dwarf (star) A star of less than average mass and luminosity; a small star.

dyne A unit of force in the metric system—the force necessary to give a 1-g mass an acceleration of 1 cm/sec/sec.

earthquake A release of stresses that have been stored within the earth's crust, producing a movement of the crust.

earthshine (earthlight) That light which is reflected by the earth's atmosphere and which illuminates the dark portion of the moon.

eccentric A point within a circle but off-center.

eccentricity A measure of the degree to which an ellipse is elongated. It may be found by dividing the distance between the foci by the length of the major axis.

eclipse The partial or total darkening of an object that passes within the shadow of another object.

eclipse path The path on the earth's surface swept out by the shadow of the moon during a total eclipse of the sun.

eclipse season A period of time during which eclipses of the moon and sun may take place, approximately one month in duration and occurring approximately 6 months apart.

eclipsing binary (stars) A binary-star system in which the plane of revolution of the two stars is seen almost edge-on. The light of each star is periodically diminished by the passage of the other star in front of it.

ecliptic The plane of the earth's orbit projected onto the sky. The apparent path of the sun on the celestial sphere.

electromagnetic radiation A disturbance that is transmitted from its source to the observer by means of changing electrical and magnetic fields. Includes radio, infrared, visible light, ultraviolet, X rays, and gamma rays.

electromagnetic spectrum The full array of electromagnetic disturbances (radio, infrared, visible light, ultraviolet, X rays, gamma rays).

electron A subatomic particle that carries a negative charge and is thought to move about the nucleus of the atom.

element Any one of more than 100 fundamental substances that can not be broken down into simpler forms by chemical processes.

elements of an orbit Those particular quantities that describe the size, shape, and orientation of the orbit of a body in space. Such quantities are used to determine the location of the body at any given time.

ellipse A closed curve that may be obtained by passing a plane completely through a circular cone; a curve that describes the orbits of bodies in space.

elliptical galaxy A galaxy whose visible shape is that of an ellipse.

elongation The apparent angle between the sun and the specified object, measured at the observer's eye. (The *elongation* of Mercury is 14° when it appears in the sky 14° from the sun.)

emission line A bright spectral line produced by a downward transition of an electron.

emission nebula A bright cloud of gas that has been excited and is producing its own light.

emission spectrum A system of bright lines produced by an excited, low-pressure gas.

energy The capacity to do work.

energy level (in the atom) The possible energies that an electron may possess if excited by some external source such as light or an electrical current.

ephemeris A table that states the position of celestial bodies at various times.

epicycle In the Ptolemaic system, a small circle, the center of which moves along the deferent. The planet moves on the epicycle, thus the motion of the planet might be described as a circle moving on a circle.

equation of time The difference between the apparent solar time minus the average (mean) solar time; the amount of time by which the noonday sun appears on the observer's meridian, either ahead or behind the average noon time.

equator A great circle on the earth lying halfway between the poles of the earth.

equatorial mount A telescope mounting designed so that one axis is parallel to the earth's axis and hence only one motion is necessary to drive the telescope to compensate for the earth's rotation.

equinox Either of the two intersection points of the celestial equator and the ecliptic.

erg A unit of energy in the metric system; the amount of energy expended when a force of 1 dyne moves an object through a distance of 1 cm.

escape velocity The velocity at which a body overcomes the pull of gravity of another body and moves off into space.

evolution (of the cosmos) Progressive changes in the universe or in objects found in it.

excitation The process whereby the electrons of an atom are given greater energy than they normally possess.

extragalactic Beyond our own Milky Way galaxy.

eyepiece A lens system that magnifies the image formed by the objective lens at the prime focus.

filar micrometer A device attached to a telescope, at the eyepiece, to measure small angles between stars.

fireball A spectacular meteor usually visible for several seconds.

fission The breaking up of heavier atomic nuclei into two or more lighter atomic nuclei.

flare A sudden, temporary brightening of a given region on the sun's surface. It represents a tremendous outpouring of energy.

flare star A star that increases suddenly and unexpectedly in brightness.

flash spectrum A bright-line spectrum produced by the lower atmospheric "layers" of the sun and seen only for an instant before and after the total phase of a solar eclipse.

flocculi Bright regions usually just above sunspots and visible only in a spectroheliogram. (Also called *plages*.)

fluorescence Occurs when light of one wavelength is absorbed and then reemitted at another wavelength. Ultraviolet light may excite certain atoms to produce visible light.

focal length The distance from the center of a lens or mirror to the prime focus of the telescope.

focal ratio (*f*-number) The focal length of a lens or mirror divided by its diameter.

focus The point at which converging rays of light meet.

forbidden lines Spectral lines that are not usually produced under laboratory conditions but may be produced under certain conditions of space, for instance, very low pressure.

force The influence which can change the speed and/or direction of an object.

Foucault pendulum A device employing a swinging pendulum, used to prove the rotation of the earth.

Fraunhofer lines Absorption (dark) lines in the spectrum of the sun (or star).

frequency The number of waves that pass a given point per second.

fringes The alternate bright and dark regions produced by the interference of light.

full moon The phase of the moon that occurs when it is directly opposite the sun in the sky, revealing its fully lighted face.

fusion The process whereby heavier elements are created by means of nuclear reactions within lighter ones.

galactic center The point around which a given galaxy rotates. In the Milky Way galaxy, this point is located toward the constellation of Sagittarius.

galactic cluster An open cluster of stars situated in the spiral arms of the Galaxy.

galactic equator A great circle on the celestial sphere that indicates the plane of the Galaxy.

galactic poles Points on the celestial sphere 90° from the galactic equator.

galaxy (Capitalized when our own Galaxy, the Milky Way, is meant.) A fundamental collection of stellar material, usually containing millions to hundreds of billions of stars.

gamma rays Electromagnetic disturbances of wavelength shorter than X rays and carrying the most energy of all such disturbances.

gauss A unit of magnetic flux density; a measure of the strength of a magnetic field at a given point.

gegenschein (counterglow) A region directly opposite the sun that appears to glow, perhaps due to the reflection of sunlight from interplanetary particles.

geomagnetic field The earth's magnetic field.

geomagnetic poles The points on the earth's surface that seem to possess the same magnetic properties as the poles of a bar magnet.

giant (star) A star of very large radius.

gibbous The phase of the moon or a planet during which it appears more than half full but less than full.

globular cluster A large globe-shaped system of stars, usually found in the halo that surrounds the nucleus of the Galaxy.

globule A small, dense, dark nebula; possibly a cloud of gas that is in the process of forming a star.

granulation (of the photosphere) The mottled appearance of the visible ''surface'' of the sun, due to rising columns of hot gases.

gravitation The mutual force of attraction that masses exert on each other.

gravitational constant (G) A number that allows us to express the force of gravitational attraction in terms of the masses of the objects involved and the distance separating these objects.

When the mass is measured in grams and the distance in centimeters, then the force may be expressed in dynes; specifically $G = 6.668 \times 10^{-8}$ dyne-cm^2/gm^2.

gravitational energy The energy that may be released by the partial or total collapse of a system.

gravity (of the earth) The force of attraction that the earth exerts on a given object. The weight of an object.

great circle The largest circle that can be drawn on a sphere; a circle that divides a sphere into two equal parts.

greatest elongation The largest angle of separation between the sun and either Mercury or Venus.

Greenwich meridian A portion of a great circle on the earth that passes through the poles and through a given point at the Royal Greenwich Observatory in England. This meridian is also referred to as the ''prime meridian,'' from which the longitude of any point on the earth is measured.

Gregorian calendar The modern calendar, which was introduced by Pope Gregory XIII in the sixteenth century.

H I (hydrogen-one) region A region in space in which neutral hydrogen gas is found.

H II (hydrogen-two) region A region in space in which ionized hydrogen gas is found.

half-life The time required for one-half of the atoms in a sample of a radioactive element to change spontaneously into another element.

halo (of the Galaxy) System of globular clusters, stars, and gas that surrounds the nucleus of the Galaxy.

harmonic law Kepler's third law of planetary motion: *The cubes of the semimajor axes of the planetary orbits compare in the same way as the squares of the periods of the planets.*

harvest moon The full moon nearest the time of the autumn equinox.

head (of a comet) That portion of the comet, exclusive of any tail, which includes the nucleus and coma.

heavy elements Elements that have many protons and neutrons in their nuclei. (The term sometimes refers to any element other than hydrogen or helium.)

heliacal rising The simultaneous rising of any object with the sun.

heliocentric system A sun-centered system.

Hertzsprung-Russell (H-R) diagram A plot of a group of stars according to their absolute magnitude and spectral class (temperature).

horizon (celestial) A great circle 90° from the observer's zenith.

horizontal system A system by which the location of an object is specified in terms of its angle above the horizon (altitude) and the angle it makes relative to due north (azimuth).

Azimuth is measured in an easterly direction from due north along the horizon.

hour angle The angle between the zero hour circle and any given hour circle.

hour circle A great circle on the celestial sphere that runs through the celestial poles, hence is perpendicular to the celestial equator.

Hubble constant A number that expresses the apparent relationship between the distance to the galaxy and its speed of recession.

hydrostatic equilibrium A condition in which the inward gravitational attraction exactly balances the outward pressure force at every point within a star.

hyperbola A curve that may be produced by cutting a circular cone with a plane parallel to the axis of the cone. It may represent the path of certain comets.

hypothesis An idea that is assumed to be true and upon which a given theory is built.

ideal gas A gas that obeys certain laws that describe the relationships between pressure, volume, and temperature.

image A representation of an object that can be seen by the eye, usually because light rays are brought to a focus.

inclination (of an orbit) The angle between the plane of the orbit of a given body and another specified reference plane, such as that to the celestial equator or the galactic equator.

Index Catalogue (IC) A listing of star clusters, nebulae, and galaxies that supplements the New General Catalogue (NGC).

index of refraction A number found by dividing the speed of light in a vacuum by its speed in a given transparent substance. This number would then be the index of refraction of the transparent substance.

inertia The property of matter which resists any change in its velocity: an object at rest tends to remain at rest; an object in motion tends to remain in motion in a straight line.

inferior conjunction The configuration of Mercury or Venus when that planet is directly between the earth and the sun.

inferior planet A planet whose orbit lies between that of the earth and the sun: thus, Mercury and Venus.

infrared An electromagnetic radiation of wavelength just longer than red light.

intensity The brightness of a source of light.

interference The reinforcing or canceling of waves, as in light or water waves.

interferometer An optical device by

which the diameters of the largest nearby stars may be determined.

International Date Line A line opposite the prime (Greenwich) meridian, at approximately 180° longitude. When a traveller crosses this line, the date is changed by one day.

interstellar dust Microscopic dust-like grains that exist in the space between stars.

interstellar gas Very diffuse gas that exists in the space between stars.

interstellar lines Dark spectral lines that are due to absorption by interstellar gases. These lines are seen against the spectrum of the star itself.

interstellar matter Gas and dust in the space between stars.

ion An atom that has gained or lost one or more electrons; hence, a charged atom.

ionization The process whereby an atom gains or loses electrons.

ionosphere A region of the earth's upper atmosphere in which many atoms are ionized.

irregular galaxy A galaxy of irregular shape, neither spiral nor elliptical.

irregular variable A star whose variations in brightness do not occur at regular intervals.

island universe The name once given to galaxies.

isotope One of several forms that atoms of a given element may take, each varying in the number of neutrons contained in the atomic nucleus.

Jolly balance An apparatus used to measure the mass of the earth. (May also refer to an instrument used to determine the density of a given object.)

Jovian planet A Jupiter-like planet; hence, one of relatively low density—Jupiter, Saturn, Uranus, and Neptune.

Julian calendar A calendar based on the apparent motions of the sun, introduced by Julius Caesar.

Julian day The number assigned to a given day (in the Julian calendar) based on a starting time of January 1, 4713 B.C.

Jupiter The fifth planet from the sun and the largest in the solar system.

Kepler's laws Three basic statements that describe the motions of the planets.

kinetic energy The energy that a body possesses due to its motion.

Kirchhoff's laws Three statements that describe the formation of the continuous, the emission, and the absorption spectra.

Kirkwood's gaps Voids in the spacing of particles in the rings of Saturn or in the asteroid belt.

latitude An angular measure of a point on the surface of the earth that indicates its distance north or south of the equator.

law of areas Kepler's second law of planetary motion: A line joining any given planet with the sun sweeps out equal areas in equal times.

law of the red shift For distant galaxies, their recessional velocities are proportional to their distance. Their recessional velocities are measured by their red shift, hence the red shift becomes an indicator of distance.

law of reflection The angle of reflection is equal to the angle of incidence.

law of refraction A ray of light is bent toward the normal when passing from one medium to another in which it travels more slowly.

law of universal gravitation Any two objects in space experience a mutual and equal force of attraction. This force is proportional to the product of their masses and inversely proportional to the square of the distance separating the objects.

leap year A year containing 366 days; occurs once every four years.

librations (of the moon) Motions that over a period of time allow the observer to see more than one-half the moon's surface.

light An electromagnetic disturbance that is visible to the eye.

light curve A graph that indicates the variations in light output of a variable star or an eclipsing binary system as they occur over a period of time.

light-gathering power (of a telescope) A measure of the amount of light a telescope can collect.

light-year The distance light travels in one year—approximately 9.5 trillion kilometers (6 trillion miles).

limb The visible edge of a planet, the moon, or the sun.

limb darkening The phenomenon of decreased brightness of the sun near its edge.

limiting magnitude The dimmest magnitude observable in a given telescope under specified conditions.

line broadening Any phenomenon that results in the broadening of the spectral lines. (Pressure, for example, may cause line broadening.)

line of apsides Major axis of an ellipse.

line of nodes The line connecting two nodes of an orbit; hence, a line that lies both in the plane of the object's orbit and also in the plane of another's orbit.

local apparent noon The time at which the center of the sun is on the observer's meridian.

Local Group The cluster of galaxies to which the Milky Way galaxy belongs.

local mean noon The time at which the average sun is on the observer's meridian.

local mean time The hour angle of the average sun.

local meridian An imaginary line running north and south through the observer's zenith (in the sky) or through the observer's position (on earth).

longitude The angle between the prime meridian and a meridian through the point on the surface of the earth. This angle is measured along the equator.

long-period variable A variable star whose period of variation exceeds 100 days.

luminosity A measure of actual brightness; the sun may be used as a reference star and other stars compared to it.

lunar eclipse An eclipse of the moon, occurring when the moon passes within the earth's shadow.

lunar month A period of time ($29\frac{1}{2}$ days) based upon the cycle of phases of the moon, i.e. full moon to full moon.

Lyman series Those lines in the spectrum which occur in the ultraviolet portion, created by upward or downward electron transitions that originate or terminate with the first (lowest) energy level of the hydrogen atom.

magnetic field A region of space where magnetic forces may be detected.

magnetic pole One of two points on a magnet (or in a magnetic field) where the greatest density of lines of force exist.

magnifying power The number of times that the apparent size of an object is increased by viewing it through a telescope, as compared to naked-eye observation.

magnitude A number that is used to indicate the brightness of an object, either apparent or absolute, as specified.

main sequence A line on the H–R diagram that represents the majority of stars.

major axis (of an ellipse) A line drawn through the foci of an ellipse; also, the longest line that may be drawn joining two points of an ellipse. It may refer specifically to the length of such a line.

major planet One of the four largest planets (Jupiter, Saturn, Uranus, and Neptune).

mantle (of the earth) The layer of the earth that lies between the crust and the core.

maria Latin for "seas" (singular: *mare*); name of certain regions, once thought to be sealike, on the moon or Mars.

Mars The fourth planet from the sun.

maser Acronym for **m**icrowave **a**mplification by **s**timulated **e**mission, a device utilizing natural oscillations of atoms or molecules for amplifying electromagnetic waves in the microwave region of the spectrum.

mass A measure of the amount of atomic material in an object.

mass-luminosity relation The observed relationship that, in general, the more massive stars are, the brighter they are.

mean solar day The period of time between successive passages of the mean (average) sun across the observer's meridian; the average length of an apparent solar day.

mean sun An imaginary sun that moves at a constant speed along the celestial equator, making one circuit of the sky in one year.

Mercury The planet nearest the sun.

meridian A great circle on the earth that passes through a given point and both poles; a great circle on the celestial sphere that passes through the observer's zenith and both celestial poles.

Messier Catalogue (M) A listing of nebulae, star clusters, and galaxies compiled by Charles Messier in 1787.

meteor The bright streak of light that occurs when a particle from outside the earth's atmosphere enters that atmosphere and is heated due to friction.

meteor shower Numerous meteors that seem to radiate from a given point in the sky. Showers usually occur when the earth passes through collections of material left in the path of a comet.

meteorite That portion of a meteoroid which survives its flight through the earth's atmosphere and strikes the ground.

meteoroid A meteor particle while it is still in space, without relation to the phenomenon it causes once it has entered the earth's atmosphere.

micrometeorite A very small meteoroid which does not create friction sufficient to burn up in the atmosphere, but which falls to the earth.

micrometer (μm) A unit of length equal to 10^{-6} m.

Milky Way A diffuse band of light composed of millions of stars and nebulae. It encircles the sky and represents the flattened disklike portion of the Milky Way galaxy (our Galaxy).

minor axis (of an ellipse) The smallest diameter of an ellipse.

minor planet An asteroid, ranging in size from several hundred kilometers to less than 1 km in diameter.

Mohorovičić discontinuity The boundary between the crust and the mantle of the earth, named for the Yugoslav geologist Andrija Mohorovičić.

molecule A combination of two or more atoms; the smallest particle of a substance that still retains all the properties of that substance.

momentum Mass multiplied by the velocity of an object; a measure of the state of motion of an object.

monochromatic Limited to one color or wavelength.

moving cluster (of stars) A group of stars that are moving in the same direction and at the same speed.

n-body problem A problem that involves the gravitational effects of several bodies on each other.

nadir A point opposite the observer's zenith.

nautical mile The average length of an arc on the earth's surface that makes an angle of one minute (1/60 degree) at the center of the earth.

navigation The art of finding one's position on the earth by means of celestial observations.

neap tides The less extreme tides that occur when the moon is near first or third quarter phase.

nebula A cloud of gas or dust in space; the term may sometimes refer to galaxies or star clusters (because of their fuzzy appearance).

nebular hypothesis The theory that the solar system was formed from a nebula.

Neptune The eighth planet from the sun.

neutrino A neutral particle of very small mass that carries away energy from a nuclear reaction.

neutron A particle, within the nucleus of an atom, that has no charge but has mass approximately equal to that of a proton.

New General Catalogue (NGC) A listing of nebulae, star clusters, and galaxies that succeeded the one compiled by Charles Messier.

new moon That phase of the moon which occurs when it is between the earth and the sun.

Newtonian reflector A reflecting telescope that, by use of a flat diagonal mirror, brings the rays of light from a distant object to a focal point near the side of the tube.

Newton's laws The three statements set forth by Sir Isaac Newton regarding the motions of objects.

node The intersection points of the plane of the moon's or planet's orbit with another plane, such as that of the earth's orbit or the celestial equator.

north celestial pole The point on the celestial sphere that is determined by the extension of the earth's axis in a northerly direction.

north point A point on the observer's celestial horizon directly under the north celestial pole.

nova A star that suddenly brightens and then fades again, hence is seen as a "new" star.

nuclear Refers to the nucleus of the atom.

nuclear fission A process of nuclear change that results in lighter elements being formed from heavier ones.

nuclear fusion A process of nuclear change that results in heavier elements being formed from lighter ones.

nucleon A constituent of the nucleus of an atom: a neutron or proton.

nucleus (of an atom) The central portion of the atom, containing almost the entire mass of the atom.

nucleus (of a comet) The collection of solid (frozen) particles that compose the head of the comet.

nucleus (of a galaxy) The central, more dense portion of the galaxy.

nutation The small variations in the movements of the earth's poles. The principal movement is precession.

objective The main lens or mirror in a telescope, used to bring rays of light to a focal point.

oblate spheroid A sphere, such as the earth, that is flattened by rotation.

oblateness A measure of the degree to which a sphere is flattened; a number obtained by dividing the difference between the major and minor axes by the major axis itself.

obliquity of the ecliptic The angle between the ecliptic plane and that of the celestial equator.

obscuration The absorption of starlight by interstellar dust.

occular An eyepiece.

occultation The passing of one object behind a larger one, say, the passing of a moon behind Jupiter.

open cluster A loosely formed cluster of stars, usually found in the disk of the galaxy.

opposition The configuration of a planet when it is directly opposite the sun as seen from earth. The planet is seen 180° from the sun in the sky.

optical binary Two stars that merely appear close together because they happen to line up from the observer's point of view. They may actually be separated by a great distance and therefore they do not influence each other gravitationally.

optics A branch of physics that deals with light and its properties.

orbit A closed path along which a body moves as it revolves around a point in space.

orbital plane The plane in which a given body moves in its orbit; an imaginary flat surface that is determined by the motion of the body.

outer planet One of the planets beyond the asteroid belt (Jupiter, Saturn, Uranus, Neptune, and Pluto).

ozone layer A "layer" of the earth's atmosphere, composed of a special form of oxygen (^3O), which filters much of the ultraviolet radiation of the sun.

parabola A curve that is made by cutting a circular cone with a plane parallel to one of its elements (edges).

paraboloid A concave surface, the cross section of which is a parabola. The shape used for the primary mirror of most reflecting telescopes.

parallax The apparent shift in position of an object due to the motion of the observer.

parallax (stellar) The apparent shift of a star against the background of more distant stars due to the motion of the earth around the sun; the angle subtended (cut off) by the radius of the earth's orbit (1 A.U.) at the distance of the star.

parsec The distance to a star that exhibits 1 second of heliocentric parallax (1 parsec = 3.26 light-years).

partial eclipse An eclipse of the moon or sun in which the object is not completely obscured.

penumbra That portion of the shadow of an object in which the light for an extended source is not completely obscured.

penumbral eclipse An eclipse of the moon in which the moon merely passes through the penumbra of the earth's shadow.

perfect radiator A black body—a body that absorbs all radiation falling upon it and reemits all the radiation.

periastron That point in the orbit of a member of a binary star system at which it is nearest its companion star.

perigee The point in the orbit of an earth satellite at which it is nearest earth (*-gee*).

perihelion The point in the orbit of an object that revolves around the sun (*helios*) at which it is nearest the sun.

period The interval of time necessary to complete one rotation, one revolution, or one cycle.

period-luminosity relation The relationship between the period and the absolute magnitude of certain variable stars.

periodic comet A comet whose orbit is elliptical and hence one that returns to perihelion at regular intervals. A comet whose return is predictable.

perturbation Any gravitational disturbance that causes a body to deviate from its primary orbital path. Such disturbances may be caused by the presence of a third object.

phases (of the moon or planet) Changes in the portion of the illuminated "face" of the moon or planet that is visible from the earth.

photoelectric effect The emission of electrons from the surface of a substance caused by light striking it.

photoelectric magnitude A measure of the brightness of an object as indicated by a photomultiplier.

photographic magnitude A measure of the brightness of an object as indicated on a blue-sensitive photographic plate.

photometry The science of measuring the apparent brightness of celestial objects.

photomultiplier A light-sensitive cell in which the electric current generated by light is amplified so that it can be more easily and accurately measured.

photon A unit of electromagnetic energy; a certain quantity of light energy.

photosphere The apparent (visible) "surface" of the sun; the layer of the

sun from which light seems to radiate.

photovisual magnitude A measure of the apparent brightness of an object, using film that is sensitive to the same region of the spectrum as the human eye.

plage A bright region just above the sun's surface as seen in a spectroheliogram.

Planck's constant A number that relates the energy "carried" by a photon of light to its wavelength.

planet One of the nine main bodies that revolve around the sun and reflect its light; any similar body revolving around a star in another (possible) solar system.

planetarium A projection device that is capable of creating an artificial sky on a domed ceiling and showing the motions of celestial objects greatly speeded up in time.

planetary nebula A spherical shell of gas that surrounds a very hot star and is expanding relatively slowly.

planetoid A minor planet or asteroid.

Pluto The ninth planet from the sun.

polar axis (of a telescope) That axis, set parallel to the earth's axis, about which the telescope turns to compensate for the earth's rotation.

polarization A filtering process in which only those light rays whose disturbances lie in a given plane are allowed to pass.

Population I and II (stars) Two classes of stars that appear to be quite different in evolutionary state and in location within the Galaxy: type-I stars are found primarily in the spiral arms of the Galaxy, whereas type-II stars are found elsewhere in it.

positron A particle that has approximately the same mass as the electron but that carries a positive charge.

potential energy That type of energy which an object possesses because of its position; the capacity of an object to do work by reason of its position.

pound A unit of force (not mass) in the English system.

precession The slow gyration of the earth's axis, which sweeps out a circle in the sky over a 26,000-year period. This motion of the earth causes a continuous change of the polar positions in the sky.

precession of the equinoxes The slow westward shift of the equinoxes along the ecliptic due to the precession of the earth.

prime focus The point at which the objective of a telescope brings the light rays to a focus without the use of any secondary mirrors or lens.

prime meridian The meridian that runs through the Royal Observatory of Greenwich, England. The longitudes of points on the earth are measured from this meridian.

primeval atom A single mass com-

posed of all the matter of the universe.

primeval fireball The expanding ball of matter that resulted from the explosion of the primeval atom as depicted in the "big bang" theory of the origin of the universe.

Principia Newton's great work, in which he described the motions of objects under the influence of gravity: *Philosophiae Naturalis Principia Mathematica.*

prism A triangular shape (of glass or other transparent material) that is utilized to disperse light into its spectrum.

prominence A protrusion from the limb of the sun which appears as a flame or loop, best seen in the light of hydrogen.

proper motion The rate at which a star's position in the sky changes, measured in seconds of arc per year.

proton One of the basic subatomic particles that compose the nucleus, carrying a positive charge.

proton-proton cycle An atomic reaction that occurs in the core of a star whereby four hydrogen nuclei combine to form a helium nucleus. This reaction is the source of energy of the star (or sun).

protostar The mass of material that is in the process of forming a star.

pulsar An object that emits brief pulses of radio energy and that has also been observed optically by use of special photographic equipment; possibly a very dense (neutron) star that is spinning very rapidly.

pulsating variable A variable star that changes size at regular intervals, its variation in light output being directly related to its variation in size.

quadrature The configuration of a planet or moon as seen 90° from the sun.

quantum mechanics The study of the structure of atoms and how they interact with one another.

quarter moon A half-full moon as seen when it appears 90° from the sun, one-quarter or three-quarters the way around its orbit.

quasar Contraction of the term *quasi-stellar radio source;* a starlike object that has a very large red shift in its spectrum, hence is presumed to be very distant—perhaps the most distant object yet known—and probably a galaxy that is emitting much more energy than is normal.

quiet sun The sun at a time of very low activity.

R Corona Borealis variables The class of variable stars that exhibit irregular and sudden decreases in brightness.

RR Lyrae variables The class of variable stars that have periods of less than one day.

radar telescope A radio telescope that is also capable of sending a radio signal into space and then listening for its echo (reflection).

radial velocity That part of the velocity of an object which is measured along the observer's line of sight.

radiant (of a meteor shower) A point in the sky from which a number of meteors seem to originate during a meteor shower.

radiation The process whereby energy is transferred from one point to another through empty space.

radiation pressure The small force that electromagnetic radiation exerts on matter which it intercepts.

radio astronomy That branch of astronomy which is primarily concerned with receiving and analyzing the radio energy received from celestial objects.

radio telescopes A large parabolic reflector that collects the radio energy from one region of the sky and concentrates (focuses) that energy at a focal point. This energy is then amplified and recorded by electronic equipment.

radioactive element An element whose nucleus spontaneously disintegrates to produce a lighter element. Energy is also released in this process.

rays (lunar) A system of bright streaks that seem to radiate from certain craters on the moon.

reaction force The equal but opposite force that accompanies every force.

real image An image, formed at the focus of a telescope, that can be photographed; an image formed by light rays that converge after passing through a lens or after reflecting from a mirror.

red giant A very large, cool star.

red shift The shifting of spectral lines toward the red end of the spectrum due to the relative motion of the source away from the observer.

reddening (interstellar) The reddening of starlight as the result of the scattering of blue light when the light of a star passes through clouds of gas and dust in space.

reflecting telescope A telescope in which the primary objective is a concave mirror; a telescope that depends on the principle of reflection for its operation.

reflection The process whereby the direction of travel of light rays is changed by an optical surface.

reflection nebula A cloud of interstellar dust that is visible because it reflects starlight.

refracting telescope A telescope that depends on the principle of refraction for its operation, hence a telescope that has a lens or lens system as its objective.

refraction The bending of light as it passes from one transparent medium to another of different density.

relativity A theory formulated by Albert Einstein that deals with the measurement of various events as observed by two different observers, themselves in motion.

resolution The ability of a telescope to separate objects that appear close together; its ability to show detail.

retrograde motion (of a planet) The apparent westward motion of a planet as seen against the background of stars.

reversing layer (of the sun) A thin layer of solar atmosphere, just above the photosphere, that produces the dark-line spectrum of the sun.

revolution The motion of a body around a given point in space (for example, the earth's *revolution* around the sun).

right ascension The smallest angle between the zero hour circle and a given celestial object.

rill (or rille) A crevasse in the surface of the moon.

rotation The spinning of a body on its own axis.

saros An 18-year cycle during which the circumstances that produce similar eclipses recur.

satellite Any body that revolves around a larger body (the moon, for instance, is a satellite of the earth).

Saturn The sixth planet from the sun.

scale (of an image) The size of an extended image compared to its apparent size in the sky measured in centimeters (or inches) per degree.

Schmidt camera A telescope that utilizes both a spherical mirror and a weak refracting lens to produce a camera that is capable of photographing a wide field of stars.

science The branch of knowledge which seeks systematically to describe phenomena of nature.

scientific method An approach in which the researcher first observes certain pertinent phenomena, then formulates a theory that seems to be consistent with those observations, and finally tests his theory by determining whether it will accurately predict future events.

Sculptor-type system A very small elliptical galaxy similar to the galaxy in Sculptor.

secondary mirror A mirror that reflects the light gathered by the primary mirror; a mirror second in line.

"seeing" conditions Those conditions within the earth's atmosphere which affect the quality of image formed in the telescope.

seismic waves Vibrations that travel through the interior of the earth due to earthquakes.

seismograph An instrument that records the time, type, and strength of seismic (earthquake) waves.

seismology The science that deals

with the origin and transmission of seismic waves in the earth.

semimajor axis One-half the major axis of an ellipse. It represents the average distance from the sun to a given planet or comet.

separation The angular distance between two stars in a visual binary system.

shell star A star that is surrounded by a sphere or shell of gas.

shower (of meteors) Numerous meteors that seem to radiate from a given point in the sky. Such showers usually occur when the earth passes through collections of meteoric material left in the path of a comet.

sidereal day The length of a day as measured by the successive passages of any given star across the observer's meridian. A day as measured by the stars.

sidereal month The length of time required for the moon's revolution around the earth as measured by the stars.

sidereal revolution The period of revolution of one body around another with respect to the stars.

sidereal time Star time; the hour angle of the vernal equinox; the right ascension of the observer's meridian at the given time.

sidereal year The time required for the earth's revolution around the sun with respect to the stars.

siderite An iron-nickel meteorite.

singularity The central core of a black hole, characterized by infinite density and infinite tidal forces.

small circle Any circle on the surface of a sphere that is smaller than a great circle.

solar activity Prominences, sunspots, plages, flares, etc.; activities that occur on or above the photosphere of the sun.

solar apex The direction in which the sun is moving with respect to the average motion of the nearest stars.

solar constant The amount of solar radiation received at the distance of the earth, measured in ergs per square centimeters per second.

solar day The average time required for two successive passages of the sun across the observer's meridian.

solar eclipse An eclipse of the sun.

solar flare A sudden outburst of energy from the sun, causing a brightening of a given region, usually near a sunspot.

solar parallax The angle subtended (cut off) by the equatorial radius of the earth as seen from a distance of 1 A.U.

solar system the system of all objects that revolve around the sun: the planets, moons, comets, meteoroids, etc.

solar time Time as based on the sun; the hour angle of the sun plus 12 hr.

solar wind The outflow of particles from the sun.

solstices Either of the two points on the ecliptic where the sun reaches its maximum declination north or south of the equator; the longest and the shortest days of the year.

south celestial pole A point on the celestial sphere determined by extending the earth's axis southward until it intersects that sphere.

south point The point of intersection of the observer's meridian with his southern horizon.

space motion The velocity of a star with respect to the sun.

specific gravity The density of a given body or substance compared to that of water; numerically equal to the density of the body measured in grams per cubic centimeter.

spectral class The classification of a star with respect to characteristics of its spectrum.

spectrogram The photograph of a spectrum.

spectrograph The instrument used to photograph a spectrum.

spectroheliogram The photograph of the sun, taken in the light of a single spectral line of an element such as hydrogen.

spectroheliograph The instrument used to photograph the sun in the light of a single spectral line of an element such as hydrogen or calcium.

spectroscope An instrument in which an observer may view the spectrum of an element, a star, or the sun.

spectroscopic binary star A star system in which the true binary nature of the system is revealed by the periodic shifting of spectral lines. Such a system can not be separated optically.

spectroscopic parallax A method whereby the distance to a star is determined by observing its spectral characteristics, converting this to absolute magnitude by use of an H–R diagram, and comparing that to the star's apparent magnitude.

spectrum The rainbow of colors produced when light is dispersed by refraction or diffraction.

spectrum analysis The determination of such characteristics of a light source as velocity, temperature, and pressure by studying the spectrum of the source.

spectrum binary A system of stars whose true binary nature is revealed by the presence of spectral lines associated with two stars of different temperatures.

speed The rate at which the distance to an object changes without regard to its direction of travel.

spherical aberration A defect in a lens or mirror that is due to its incorrect shape. Light rays that pass near the center of the lens (or mirror) are brought to a different focus as compared to those which pass near the outer edge.

spicule A jet of hot material rising in the atmosphere of the sun.

spiral arms (of a galaxy) The curved, armlike structures that surround the nucleus of certain galaxies.

spiral galaxy A flattened galaxy composed of a central nucleus and a system of arms which spiral out from that nucleus.

sporadic meteor A meteor that does not appear to be associated with a known shower of meteors.

spring tides The most extreme tides produced when the moon, sun, and earth are aligned, that is, when the moon is new or full.

standard time The time used within a given time zone, computed as the average solar time for that zone.

star A spherical mass of gas that radiates various forms of energy owing to nuclear reactions within its core.

star cloud A region of the sky in which the stars are so close together that they appear as a luminous cloud.

star cluster A grouping of stars that is held together by mutual gravitation; the stars thus possess a common motion through space.

star map A map showing the positions and magnitudes of stars, designed to be held over the observer's head.

steady state theory The theory that the universe has always been as it is today, that matter is being continually created to replace matter which is converted into energy. The density of the universe would thus be maintained at the same level.

Stefan's law The assertion that the total amount of energy radiated from a body in a given time depends upon the absolute temperature of the body, raised to the fourth power.

stellar evolution The life cycle of a star. Stars change in size, pressure, luminosity, and structure.

stellar parallax The angle subtended (cut off) by the radius of the earth's orbit (1 A.U.) at the distance of the star.

stratosphere The layer of the earth's atmosphere between the troposphere and the ionosphere.

subdwarf star A star that, owing to its smaller size, is less luminous than a main-sequence star of the same spectral class.

subgiant star A star of luminosity between that of a normal giant and a main-sequence star of the same spectral class.

sublimate A process whereby a solid turns directly into a gaseous state without passing through a liquid state, for instance, Dry Ice.

summer solstice The point on the ecliptic where the sun appears farthest north of the equator; the longest day of the year.

sun The star about which the earth revolves.

sunspots Regions of the sun that appear dark because they are temporarily cooler than the surrounding region.

sunspot cycle The period over which both the number and location (latitude) of the sunspots vary (approximately 11 years).

supergiant A large star of very high luminosity.

superior conjunction A configuration that occurs when a planet appears to line up with the sun on its (the sun's) far side. This term is used only in reference to Mercury or Venus.

superior planet A planet whose orbit is beyond that of the earth.

supernova An exploding star that temporarily increases in luminosity, perhaps a million times brighter than it was before the eruption.

synchrotron radiation A type of radiation that results from charged particles being accelerated by a magnetic field.

synodic month The time required for the moon to complete its cycle of phases (29.5 days).

synodic period The time required for a planet (or moon) to move from a given configuration back to that same configuration again, as seen from earth; for example, the period between successive oppositions of a superior planet.

syzygy A lining up of any three celestial objects, as in a conjunction or opposition.

T Tauri stars A class of variable stars that show very rapid and irregular pulsations.

tail (of a comet) The gases that are forced away from the head of the comet by the solar wind.

tangential velocity That part of a star's space velocity which is perpendicular to its radial velocity; a measure of the speed with which a star crosses the observer's line of sight.

tektites Glasslike objects that have traveled in the earth's atmosphere. These objects are thought to have been formed by meteorite impact on either the earth or the moon.

telescope An optical instrument that makes possible the observation and photographing of objects too dim and/or too distant to be seen with the naked eye; hence, a light-gathering device.

telluric (spectral) lines Spectral lines that are produced by elements in the earth's atmosphere.

temperature A measure of the average speed with which the molecules of a substance (or atoms of a gas) are moving.

terminator The line between the sunlit and dark portion of the moon (or planet).

terrestrial planet An earthlike planet, similar to the earth in density (Mercury, Venus, Mars, and Pluto).

theory A set of ideas that are consistent with observed phenomena.

thermocouple A device for measuring the intensity of infrared radiation.

thermodynamics A branch of physical science that deals with the way in which heat moves from one body to another.

thermonuclear reactions Nuclear changes that result from high-temperature and high-pressure conditions.

tide The deformation of land and/or water masses by the differential gravitational attraction of another body. The moon and sun create tides on the earth; the earth and sun create tides on the moon.

time zone A zone on the earth's surface, approximately 15° wide, within which the hour used is uniform.

ton (English) A unit of force (weight) equivalent to 2000 pounds.

ton (metric) A unit of force (weight) equivalent to 1 million grams.

total eclipse (1) An eclipse of the sun during which the disk of the moon completely covers the photosphere of the sun. (2) An eclipse of the moon during which the moon lies completely within the umbra of the earth's shadow.

trail (of a meteor) The temporary luminous streak produced by the passage of a meteoroid through the earth's atmosphere.

transit (1) The passage of a body across the face of a larger body. (2) The passage of a body across a given meridian. (Mercury transits the sun. The sun transits the prime meridian.)

transverse wave A wave in which particles are disturbed in a direction perpendicular to the direction in which the wave is traveling.

triangulation A process whereby an inaccessible side of a triangle may be determined from the measurement of accessible sides and angles.

Trojan minor planet An asteroid that orbits the sun in approximately the same orbit as Jupiter but is located 60° ahead of or behind the planet as viewed from the sun.

Tropic of Cancer The parallel of latitude that lies 23.5° north of the equator, the limit of the sun's apparent travel in a northerly direction.

Tropic of Capricorn The parallel of latitude that lies 23.5° south of the equator, the limit of the sun's apparent travel in a southerly direction.

tropical year The time required for the earth to make one revolution around the sun as measured by the vernal equinox (approximately 365.25 days).

troposphere The layer of the earth's atmosphere just above the earth and extending to an elevation of about 15 km.

twinkle The apparent changes in the brightness and color of a star due to the motion of the earth's atmosphere.

ultraviolet radiation That part of the electromagnetic spectrum with wavelengths just shorter than visible light, approximately in the range of 100 to 4000 Å.

umbra (1) The completely dark central portion of a shadow. (2) The darkest portion of a sunspot.

Universal Time Average Greenwich time.

universe All of space that is occupied by matter and/or radiation.

Uranus The seventh planet from the sun.

Van Allen belts Regions that surround the earth consisting of high-energy charged particles whose motions are directed by the earth's magnetic field.

variable star A star that exhibits changes in luminosity and/or color; a pulsating star.

vector A quantity that has both magnitude and direction.

velocity A vector quantity that denotes both the speed and direction of motion.

velocity of escape The velocity at which a body overcomes the pull of gravity of another body and moves off into space.

Venus The second planet from the sun.

vernal equinox The point on the celestial equator at which the sun crosses on its way northward; an intersection of the celestial equator and the ecliptic; the position of the sun on March 21.

vertical circle A great circle that passes through the zenith of the observer and is perpendicular to the horizon.

visual binary A binary system in which the two components are visible as separate stars in a telescope.

volume A measure of the amount of space occupied by an object.

Vulcan An imaginary planet once thought to orbit between Mercury and the sun.

walled plain (of the moon) A very large crater on the moon.

wandering of the poles A shifting of the body of the earth in relation to its axis of rotation.

watt A unit of power, equivalent to 10 million ergs of energy used up in 1 sec.

wavelength The distance from any point on a wave to the next similar point on the succeeding wave, as crest to crest.

weight A measure of the force exerted on one object by another due to gravity; specifically, the gravitational force exerted by the earth on a given mass.

west point A point on the celestial horizon that is located 270° from the north point, measured in a clockwise direction.

white dwarf An old star that has collapsed due to its exhausted fuel supply and yet has a large portion of its original mass; hence, a very dense, hot star.

Widmanstätten figures A definite pattern of crystal formations often seen in the interior of a polished meteorite.

Wien's law A statement relating T, the temperature of a body (in degrees Kelvin), to λ, the wavelength of its maximum radiation: $\lambda = 3000 \, \mu m / T$.

winter solstice A point on the ecliptic at which the sun reaches its maximum distance south of the celestial equator; the shortest day of the year.

Wolf-Rayet stars A class of very hot stars that eject shells of gas at high velocity.

X rays Electromagnetic radiation of short wavelength between that of ultraviolet rays and of gamma rays.

year The time required for one revolution of the earth around the sun.

Zeeman effect The splitting or broadening of spectral lines, which indicates the presence and strength of magnetic fields at the source.

zenith A point on the celestial sphere directly over the head of the observer.

zodiac A band on the celestial sphere that is centered on the ecliptic and contains the twelve constellations usually associated with astrology.

zodiacal light A faint light seen along the ecliptic, possibly due to sunlight being scattered by interplanetary dust.

zone of avoidance A region toward the center of the Milky Way galaxy where few—if any—other galaxies are seen, since they are obscured by clouds of gas and dust.

Appendixes

Appendix 1 Temperature conversion charts

FAHRENHEIT	CELSIUS	KELVIN	EXAMPLES
	Approximately		
27 million °F	15 million °C	15 million °K	Core of the sun
10,337°F	5727°C	6000°K	Surface temperature of the sun
700°F	371°C	644°K	Probable maximum temperature of Venus
212°F	100°C	373°K	Boiling point of water
100°F	38°C	311°K	Normal body temperature
68°F	20°C	293°K	Normal room temperature
32°F	0°C	273°K	Freezing point of water
0°F	−18°C	255°K	
−100°F	−73°C	200°K	Minimum temperature on the earth's surface
−198°F	−128°C	145°K	Polar cap of Mars
−230°F	−146°C	127°K	Average temperature of Saturn
−297°F	−183°C	90°K	Dark side of Mercury
−459°F	−273°C	0°K	Absolute zero; all translational molecular motion stops

Appendix 2 International System of Units (SI) with English equivalents

INTERNATIONAL SYSTEM	ENGLISH SYSTEM
Length (units most commonly used):	
1 micrometer (μm) = 0.000001 m	
1 millimeter (mm) = 0.001 m	= 0.03937 in.
1 centimeter (cm) = 0.01 m	= 0.3937 in.
1 meter (m) = 1.00 m	= 39.37 in.
1 kilometer (km) = 1000 m	= 0.6214 mile
1 megameter (Mm) = 1,000,000 m	
1.6093 km	= 1 mile
2.5400 cm	= 1 in.

Note: SI units are based on powers of ten (see Appendix 3), and the prefix indicates the power to be taken. The following list of prefixes may be used with any unit [for instance, *kilo*gram (kg), a unit of mass; or *nano*second (nsec), a unit of time]:

INTERNATIONAL SYSTEM	ENGLISH SYSTEM
Mass:	
1 milligram (mg) = 0.001 g	
1 gram (g) = 1.000 g	= 0.0022046 lb
1 kilogram (kg) = 1000 g	= 2.2046 lb
453.6 g	= 1 lb = 16 oz
28.3495 g	= 1 oz
Time:	
1 nanosecond (nsec) = 0.000000001 sec	
1 microsecond (μsec) = 0.000001 sec	
1 millisecond (msec) = 0.001 sec	
1 second (sec) = 1.0 sec	

pico (p)	= 10^{-12}	centi (c)	= 10^{-2}	kilo (k)	= 10^{3}
nano (n)	= 10^{-9}	deci (d)	= 10^{-1}	mega (m)	= 10^{6}
micro (μ)	= 10^{-6}	deka (da)	= 10^{1}	giga (g)	= 10^{9}
milli (m)	= 10^{-3}	hecto (h)	= 10^{2}	tera (t)	= 10^{12}

Appendix 3 Powers-of-ten notation

In writing very large or very small numbers, it is convenient to use the following system of notation:

$10^1 = 10$

$10^2 = 10 \times 10 = 100$

$10^3 = 10 \times 10 \times 10 = 1000$

$10^4 = 10 \times 10 \times 10 \times 10 = 10{,}000$

Following this pattern:

$10^{12} = 1{,}000{,}000{,}000{,}000$

A light-year is approximately equivalent to 6,000,000,000,000 miles, which could be written $6 \times 1{,}000{,}000{,}000{,}000$ miles, or 6×10^{12} miles—a much simpler notation.

In a very similar way:

$10^{-1} = 0.1 = 1/10$

$10^{-2} = 0.01 = 1/100$

$10^{-3} = 0.001 = 1/1000$

Following this pattern:

$10^{-7} = 0.0000001$

The wavelength of blue light is approximately 0.0000005 m, but this number is equal to 5×0.0000001, therefore it may be written 5×10^{-7} m.

Summary:

If given 7×10^9, move the decimal nine places to the right, which produces 7,000,000,000.

If given 7×10^{-9}, move the decimal nine places to the left, which produces 0.000000007.

Appendix 4 Constants with useful approximations[a]

Pi (π) = 3.14159 = 22/7

Velocity of light, $c = 2.99793 \times 10^{10}$ cm/sec $\cong$ 300,000 km/sec $\cong$ 186,000 miles/sec

Constant of gravitation, $G = 6.67 \times 10^{-8}$ dyne-cm^2/g^2

Mass of the hydrogen atom, $m_h = 1.673 \times 10^{-24}$ g

Angstrom, Å = 10^{-10} m

Astronomical unit, A.U. = 1.49598×10^{11} m $\cong$ 150,000,000 km $\cong$ 93,000,000 miles

Parsec = 206,265 A.U. = 3.262 light-years

Light-year = 9.4605×10^{15} m $\cong 9.5 \times 10^{12}$ km $\cong 6 \times 10^{12}$ miles

Mass of the earth, $m_e = 5.98 \times 10^{27}$ g

Mass of the sun, $m_s = 1.991 \times 10^{33}$ g

Radius of earth (at the equator), $r_e = 6378.24$ km $\cong$ 4000 miles

Solar constant, $S = 1.97$ cal/cm^2-min

Precession along the ecliptic, $p = 50.26''$ per year

[a] Round-number approximations are indicated by $\cong$.

Appendix 5 Orbital data of the planets

PLANET	SYMBOL	SEMIMAJOR AXIS (A.U.)	SIDEREAL PERIOD	SYNODIC PERIOD	ECCENTRICITY OF ORBIT	INCLINATION OF ORBIT	AVERAGE ORBITAL SPEED (km/sec)
Mercury	☿	0.387	87.97 days	116 days	0.2056	7.0°	47.8
Venus	♀	0.723	224.7 days	584 days	0.0068	3.4°	35.0
Earth	⊕	1.000	365.26 days	—	0.0167	0.0°	29.8
Mars	♂	1.524	687.0 days or 1.88 years	780 days	0.0934	1.8°	24.2
(Ceres[a])	①	2.77	4.60 years	467 days	0.0765	10.6°	17.9
Jupiter	♃	5.20	11.86 years	399 days	0.0484	1.3°	13.1
Saturn	♄	9.54	29.46 years	378 days	0.0557	2.5°	9.7
Uranus	⛢ or ♅	19.18	84.01 years	370 days	0.0472	0.8°	6.8
Neptune	♆	30.06	164.79 years	367.5 days	0.0086	1.8°	5.4
Pluto	♇	39.44	248 years	366.5 days	0.2502	17.2°	4.7

[a] An asteroid.

Appendix 6 Physical and rotational data for the planets

PLANET	DIAMETER km	DIAMETER E^a = 1	MASS (E^a = 1)	DENSITY (WATER = 1)	PERIOD OF ROTATION	INCLINATION OF EQUATOR TO ECLIPTIC^b	ALBEDO	SURFACE GRAVITY (E^a = 1)	VELOCITY OF ESCAPE (km/sec)
Mercury	4,880	0.38	0.05	5.2	58^d 15^h	7°	0.07	0.39	4.3
Venus	12,108	0.95	0.82	5.3	243^d 4^h	176°	0.76	0.90	10.3
Earth	12,750	1.00	1.00	5.52	23^h 56^m	23°27′	0.39	1.00	11.2
Mars	6,800	0.53	0.11	3.82	24^h 37^m	25°	0.18	0.38	5.1
Jupiter	143,200	11.23	317.9	1.33	9^h 50^m	3°	0.45(?)	2.58	59.5
Saturn	120,000	9.41	95.2	0.69	10^h 2^m	26°45′	0.61(?)	1.11	35.6
Uranus	50,800	3.98	14.6	1.3	10^h 49^m	98°	0.35(?)	1.07	21.4
Neptune	49,500	3.88	17.2	1.7	15^h 40^m	29°	0.62	1.40	23.6
Pluto	6,400	0.5	0.1	0.5	6^d 9^h 17^m	?	0.15	?	5.3

^{a} E is the earth.
^{b} An inclination greater than 90° indicates retrograde rotation.

Appendix 7 Satellites of planets

PLANET	SATELLITE	DISCOVERER	MEAN DISTANCE FROM PLANET (km)	SIDEREAL PERIOD (DAYS)^a	INCLINATION OF ORBIT TO PLANET'S EQUATOR	DIAMETER OF SATELLITE (km)	APPROXIMATE MAGNITUDE AT OPPOSITION
Earth	Moon	—	384,405	27.322	23.5°	3476	−12.5
Mars	Phobos	A. Hall (1877)	9,380	0.319	1°	16	11.5
	Deimos	A. Hall (1877)	23,500	1.262	2°	8	12.0
Jupiter^b	V	Barnard (1892)	180,500	0.498	27.3°	160	13.0
	I Io	Galileo (1610)	421,800	1.769	1.6°	3658	5.5
	II Europa	Galileo (1610)	671,400	3.551	28.1°	3100	5.7
	III Ganymede	Galileo (1610)	1,070,000	7.155	11.0°	5500	5.0
	IV Callisto	Galileo (1610)	1,884,000	16.689	15.2°	5000	6.3
	VI	Perrine (1904)	11,470,000	250.57	27.6°	120	14.0
	VII	Perrine (1905)	11,800,000	260.10	24.8°	40	17.5
	X	Nicholson (1938)	11,850,000	263.55	29.0°	20	19.0
	XII	Nicholson (1951)	21,200,000	617.0r	147.0°	20	18.5
	XI	Nicholson (1938)	22,600,000	692.5r	164.0°	24	19.0
	VIII	Melotte (1908)	23,500,000	735.0r	145.0°	40	17.5
	IX	Nicholson (1914)	23,700,000	758.0r	153.0°	22	19.0
Saturn	Janus	A. Dollfus (1966)	168,700	0.749	~0°	350	14.0
	Mimas	W. Herschel (1789)	185,800	0.942	~0°	520	12.0
	Enceladus	W. Herschel (1789)	238,300	1.370	~0°	600	12.0
	Tethys	Cassini (1684)	294,900	1.888	~1°	1200	10.5
	Dione	Cassini (1684)	377,900	2.737	~0°	800	11.0
	Rhea	Cassini (1672)	527,600	4.518	~0°	1300	10.0

^{a} The notation "r" indicates that the satellite orbits the planet in retrograde motion.
^{b} A thirteenth moon of Jupiter was discovered on September 14, 1974, by Charles T. Kowal at Hale Observatories, Mt. Palomar, having an estimated diameter of 8 km and a magnitude of 20.

PLANET	SATELLITE	DISCOVERER	MEAN DISTANCE FROM PLANET (km)	SIDEREAL PERIOD (DAYS)[a]	INCLINATION OF ORBIT TO PLANET'S EQUATOR	DIAMETER OF SATELLITE (km)	APPROXIMATE MAGNITUDE AT OPPOSITION
Saturn	Titan	Huygens (1655)	1,222,600	15.945	~0°	4800	8.3
(cont.)	Hyperion	Bond (1848)	1,484,100	21.277	~0°	400	13.0
	Iapetus	Cassini (1671)	3,562,900	79.331	14.7°	1300	11.0
	Phoebe	W. Pickering (1898)	12,960,000	550.45r	150.1°	300	14.0
Uranus	Miranda	Kuiper (1948)	130,000	1.414r	0°	—	19.0
	Ariel	Lassell (1851)	191,000	2.520r	0°	600	15.0
	Umbriel	Lassell (1851)	266,000	4.144r	0°	400	16.0
	Titania	W. Herschel (1787)	436,000	8.706r	0°	1000	14.0
	Oberon	W. Herschel (1787)	583,400	13.463r	0°	800	14.0
Neptune	Triton	Lassell (1846)	355,500	5.877r	160°	4000	14.0
	Nereid	Kuiper (1949)	5,567,000	359,881	27.7°	320	19.0

Appendix 8   The twenty brightest stars

STAR	RIGHT ASCENSION (1950) (h) (m)	DECLI-NATION (1950) (°) (')	DIS-TANCE (PARSECS) (pc)	PROPER MOTION ('')	SPECTRA OF COMPONENTS[a,c] A	B	C	VISUAL MAGNITUDES OF COMPONENTS[b,c] A	B	C	ABSOLUTE VISUAL MAGNITUDES OF COMPONENTS[c] A	B	C
Sirius	6 42.9	−16 39	2.7	1.32	A1V	wd	—	−1.47	+7.1	—	+1.4	+10.5	—
Canopus	6 22.8	−52 40	30	0.03	F0Ib	—	—	−0.72	—	—	−3.1	—	—
α Centauri	14 36.2	−60 38	1.3	3.68	G2V	K5V	M5V	−0.01	+1.5	+10.7	+4.4	+5.8	+15
Arcturus	14 13.4	+19 27	11	2.28	K2III	—	—	−0.06	—	—	−0.3	—	—
Vega	18 35.2	+38 44	8.0	0.34	A0V	—	—	+0.04	—	—	+0.5	—	—
Capella	5 13.0	+45 57	14	0.44	G0II	M1V	M5V	+0.09	+10.2	+13.7	−0.7	+9.5	+13
Rigel	5 12.1	−8 15	250	0.00	B8Ia	B9	—	+0.10	+6.6	—	−6.8	−0.4	—
Procyon	7 36.7	+5 21	3.5	1.25	F5IV-V	wd	—	+0.38	+10.7	—	+2.7	+13.1	—
Betelgeuse	5 52.5	+7 24	200	0.03	M2Iab	—	—	+0.41v	—	—	−5.5	—	—
Achernar	1 35.9	−57 29	20	0.10	B5V	—	—	+0.47	—	—	−1.6	—	—
β Centauri	14 00.3	−60 08	90	0.04	B1III	—	—	+0.63	—	—	−4.1	—	—
Altair	19 48.3	+8 44	5.1	0.66	A7IV,V	—	—	+0.77	—	—	+2.2	—	—
α Crucis	12 23.8	−62 49	120	0.04	B1IV	B3	—	+1.39	+1.9	—	−4.0	−3.5	—
Aldebaran	4 33.0	+16 25	16	0.20	K5III	M2V	—	+0.86v	+13	—	−0.2	+12	—
Spica	13 22.6	−10 54	70	0.05	B1V	—	—	+0.91	—	—	−3.6	—	—
Antares	16 26.3	−26 19	120	0.03	M1Ib	B4V	—	+0.92v	+5.1	—	−4.5	−0.3	—
Pollux	7 42.3	+28 09	12	0.62	K0III	—	—	+1.16	—	—	+0.8	—	—
Fomalhaut	22 54.9	−29 53	7.0	0.37	A3V	K4V	—	+1.19	+6.5	—	+2.0	+7.3	—
Deneb	20 39.7	+45 06	430	0.00	A2Ia	—	—	+1.26	—	—	−6.9	—	—
β Crucis	12 44.8	−59 24	150	0.05	B0.5IV	—	—	+1.28	—	—	−4.6	—	—

[a] The Roman numerals after the spectral classifications have the following meanings: Ia or Ib, *supergiant*; II or III, *giant*; IV, *subgiant*; V, *main-sequence star* (see pages 229–230). The notation "wd" indicates *white dwarf.*
[b] The notation "v" following the magnitude indicates a *variable star.*
[c] When entries are shown in both A and B columns, the star is known to be a binary system. When an entry is also shown in the C column, the system is known to have three components.

Appendix 9 The Messier Catalogue of nebulae and star clusters

M	NGC	RIGHT ASCENSION (1950)		DECLI-NATION (1950)		APPARENT VISUAL MAGNITUDE	DESCRIPTION
		(h)	(m)	(°)	(')		
1	1952	5	31.5	+21	59	8.4	Crab Nebula in Taurus; remains of supernova
2	7089	21	30.9	−1	02	6.4	Globular cluster in Aquarius
3	5272	13	39.8	+28	38	6.3	Globular cluster in Canes Venatici
4	6121	16	20.6	−26	24	6.5	Globular cluster in Scorpius
5	5904	15	16.0	+2	16	6.1	Globular cluster in Serpens
6	6405	17	36.8	−32	10	5.3	Open cluster in Scorpius
7	6475	17	50.7	−34	48	4.1	Open cluster in Scorpius
8	6523	18	00.1	−24	23	6.0	Lagoon Nebula in Sagittarius
9	6333	17	16.3	−18	28	7.3	Globular cluster in Ophiuchus
10	6254	16	54.5	−4	02	6.7	Globular cluster in Ophiuchus
11	6705	18	48.4	−6	20	6.3	Open cluster in Scutum
12	6218	16	44.7	−1	52	6.6	Globular cluster in Ophiuchus
13	6205	16	39.9	+36	33	5.9	Globular cluster in Hercules
14	6402	17	35.0	−3	13	7.7	Globular cluster in Ophiuchus
15	7078	21	27.5	+11	57	6.4	Globular cluster in Pegasus
16	6611	18	16.1	−13	48	6.4	Open cluster with nebulosity in Serpens
17	6618	18	17.9	−16	12	7.0	Swan or Omega Nebula in Sagittarius
18	6613	18	17.0	−17	09	7.5	Open cluster in Sagittarius
19	6273	16	59.5	−26	11	6.6	Globular cluster in Ophiuchus
20	6514	17	59.4	−23	02	9.0	Trifid Nebula in Sagittarius
21	6531	18	01.6	−22	30	6.5	Open cluster in Sagittarius
22	6656	18	33.4	−23	57	5.6	Globular cluster in Sagittarius
23	6494	17	54.0	−19	00	6.9	Open cluster in Sagittarius
24	6603	18	15.5	−18	27	11.4	Open cluster in Sagittarius
25	(4725)[a]	18	28.7	−19	17	6.5	Open cluster in Sagittarius
26	6694	18	42.5	−9	27	9.3	Open cluster in Scutum
27	6853	19	57.5	+22	35	7.6	Dumbbell Planetary Nebula in Vulpecula
28	6626	18	21.4	−24	53	7.6	Globular cluster in Sagittarius
29	6913	20	22.2	+38	21	7.1	Open cluster in Cygnus
30	7099	21	37.5	−23	24	8.4	Globular cluster in Capricornus
31	224	0	40.0	+41	00	4.8	Andromeda galaxy
32	221	0	40.0	+40	36	8.7	Elliptical galaxy; companion to M31
33	598	1	31.0	+30	24	6.7	Spiral galaxy in Triangulum
34	1039	2	38.8	+42	35	5.5	Open cluster in Perseus
35	2168	6	05.7	+24	21	5.3	Open cluster in Gemini
36	1960	5	33.0	+34	04	6.3	Open cluster in Auriga
37	2099	5	49.1	+32	33	6.2	Open cluster in Auriga
38	1912	5	25.3	+35	47	7.4	Open cluster in Auriga
39	7092	21	30.4	+48	13	5.2	Open cluster in Cygnus
40	—	12	20	+58	20	—	Close double star in Ursa Major
41	2287	6	44.9	−20	41	4.6	Loose open cluster in Canis Major
42	1976	5	32.9	−5	25	4.0	Orion Nebula

[a] Index Catalogue (IC) number.

M	NGC	RIGHT ASCENSION (1950)		DECLI-NATION (1950)		APPARENT VISUAL MAGNITUDE	DESCRIPTION
		(h)	(m)	(°)	(')		
43	1982	5	33.1	−5	19	9.0	Northeast portion of Orion Nebula
44	2632	8	37	+20	10	3.7	Praesepe; open cluster in Cancer
45	—	3	44.5	+23	57	1.6	The Pleiades; open cluster in Taurus
46	2437	7	39.5	−14	42	6.0	Open cluster in Puppis
47	2422	7	34.3	−14	22	5.2	Loose group of stars in Puppis
48	2458	8	11	−5	38	5.5	Open cluster in Hydra
49	4472	12	27.3	+8	16	8.5	Elliptical galaxy in Virgo
50	2323	7	00.6	−8	16	6.3	Loose open cluster in Monoceros
51	5194	13	27.8	+47	27	8.4	Whirlpool spiral galaxy in Canes Venatici
52	7654	23	22.0	+61	20	7.3	Loose open cluster in Cassiopeia
53	5024	13	10.5	+18	26	7.8	Globular cluster in Coma Berenices
54	6715	18	51.9	−30	32	7.3	Globular cluster in Sagittarius
55	6809	19	36.8	−31	03	7.6	Globular cluster in Sagittarius
56	6779	19	14.6	+30	05	8.2	Globular cluster in Lyra
57	6720	18	51.7	+32	58	9.0	Ring Nebula; planetary nebula in Lyra
58	4579	12	35.2	+12	05	8.2	Barred spiral galaxy in Virgo
59	4621	12	39.5	+11	56	9.3	Elliptical spiral galaxy in Virgo
60	4649	12	41.1	+11	50	9.0	Elliptical galaxy in Virgo
61	4303	12	19.3	+4	45	9.6	Spiral galaxy in Virgo
62	6266	16	58.0	−30	02	6.6	Globular cluster in Ophiuchus
63	5055	13	13.5	+42	17	10.1	Spiral galaxy in Canes Venatici
64	4826	12	54.2	+21	57	6.6	Spiral galaxy in Coma Berenices
65	3623	11	16.3	+13	22	9.4	Spiral galaxy in Leo
66	3627	11	17.6	+13	16	9.0	Spiral galaxy in Leo; companion to M65
67	2682	8	48.4	+12	00	6.1	Open cluster in Cancer
68	4590	12	36.8	−26	29	8.2	Globular cluster in Hydra
69	6637	18	28.1	−32	24	8.9	Globular cluster in Sagittarius
70	6681	18	40.0	−32	20	9.6	Globular cluster in Sagittarius
71	6838	19	51.5	+18	39	9.0	Globular cluster in Sagitta
72	6981	20	50.7	−12	45	9.8	Globular cluster in Aquarius
73	6994	20	56.2	−12	50	9.0	Open cluster in Aquarius
74	628	1	34.0	+15	32	10.2	Spiral galaxy in Pisces
75	6864	20	03.1	−22	04	8.0	Globular cluster in Sagittarius
76	650	1	38.8	+51	19	11.4	Planetary nebula in Perseus
77	1068	2	40.1	−0	12	8.9	Spiral galaxy in Cetus
78	2068	5	44.2	+0	02	8.3	Small reflection nebula in Orion
79	1904	5	22.1	−24	34	7.5	Globular cluster in Lepus
80	6093	16	14.0	−22	52	7.5	Globular cluster in Scorpius
81	3031	9	51.7	+69	18	7.9	Spiral galaxy in Ursa Major
82	3034	9	51.9	+69	56	8.4	Irregular galaxy in Ursa Major
83	5236	13	34.2	−29	37	10.1	Spiral galaxy in Hydra
84	4374	12	22.6	+13	10	9.4	S0 type galaxy in Virgo
85	4382	12	22.8	+18	28	9.3	S0 type galaxy in Coma Berenices
86	4406	12	23.6	+13	13	9.2	Elliptical galaxy in Virgo

M	NGC	RIGHT ASCENSION (1950) (h) (m)	DECLI-NATION (1950) (°) (')	APPARENT VISUAL MAGNITUDE	DESCRIPTION
87	4486	12 28.2	+12 40	8.7	Elliptical galaxy in Virgo
88	4501	12 29.4	+14 42	10.2	Spiral galaxy in Coma Berenices
89	4552	12 33.1	+12 50	9.5	Elliptical galaxy in Virgo
90	4569	12 34.3	+13 26	9.6	Spiral galaxy in Virgo
91[b]	4571(?)	— —	— —	—	
92	6341	17 15.6	+43 12	6.4	Globular cluster in Hercules
93	2447	7 42.4	−23 45	6.0	Open cluster in Puppis
94	4736	12 48.6	+41 24	8.3	Spiral galaxy in Canes Venatici
95	3351	10 41.3	+11 58	9.8	Barred spiral galaxy in Leo
96	3368	10 44.1	+12 05	9.3	Spiral galaxy in Leo
97	3587	11 12.0	+55 17	12.0	Owl Nebula; planetary nebula in Ursa Major
98	4192	12 11.2	+15 11	10.2	Spiral galaxy in Coma Berenices
99	4254	12 16.3	+14 42	9.9	Spiral galaxy in Coma Berenices
100	4321	12 20.4	+16 06	10.6	Spiral galaxy in Coma Berenices
101	5457	14 01.4	+54 36	9.6	Spiral galaxy in Ursa Major
102[b]	5866(?)	— —	— —	—	
103	581	1 29.9	+60 26	7.4	Open cluster in Cassiopeia
104	4594	12 37.4	−11 21	8.3	Spiral galaxy in Virgo
105	3379	10 45.2	+13 01	9.7	Elliptical galaxy in Leo
106	4258	12 16.5	+47 35	8.4	Spiral galaxy in Canes Venatici
107	6171	16 29.7	−12 57	9.2	Globular cluster in Ophiuchus

[b] Items of doubtful identification.

Appendix 10 The Greek alphabet

A	α	alpha	H	η	eta	N	ν	nu	T	τ	tau
B	β	beta	Θ	θ	theta	Ξ	ξ	xi	Υ	υ	upsilon
Γ	γ	gamma	I	ι	iota	O	o	omicron	Φ	ϕ	phi
Δ	δ	delta	K	κ	kappa	Π	π	pi	X	χ	chi
E	ϵ	epsilon	Θ	λ	lambda	P	ρ	rho	Ψ	ψ	psi
Z	ζ	zeta	M	μ	mu	Σ	σ	sigma	Ω	ω	omega

CONSTELLATION NAME[a]	DESCRIPTION	POSITION IN SKY R.A.[b]	DEC.[b]
Andromeda	Princess of Ethiopia	1^h	+40°
Antlia	The Air Pump	10^h	−35°
Apus	The Bird of Paradise	16^h	−75°
Aquarius	The Water Bearer	23^h	−15°
Aquila	The Eagle	20^h	+5°
Ara	The Altar	17^h	−55°
Aries	The Ram	3^h	+20°
Auriga	The Charioteer	6^h	+40°
Boötes	The Bear Driver	15^h	+30°
Caelum	The Sculptor's Chisel	5^h	−40°
Camelopardus	The Giraffe	6^h	−70°
Cancer	The Crab	9^h	+20°
Canes Venatici	The Hunting Dogs	13^h	+40°
Canis Major	The Greater Dog	7^h	−20°
Canis Minor	The Lesser Dog	8^h	+5°
Capricornus	The Sea Goat	21^h	−20°
Carina	The Keel (of Argo Navis)	9^h	−60°
Cassiopeia	Queen of Ethiopia	1^h	+60°
Centaurus	The Centaur	13^h	−50°
Cepheus	King of Ethiopia	22^h	+70°
Cetus	The Sea Monster	2^h	−10°
Chamaeleon	The Chameleon	11^h	−80°
Circinus	The Compasses	15^h	−60°
Columba	The Dove (of Noah)	6^h	−35°
Coma Berenices	Berenice's Hair	13^h	+20°
Corona Austrina	The Southern Crown	19^h	−40°
Corona Borealis	The Northern Crown	16^h	+30°
Corvus	The Crow (or Raven)	12^h	−20°
Crater	The Cup	11^h	−15°
Crux	The Southern Cross	12^h	−60°
Cygnus	The Swan	21^h	+40°
Delphinus	The Dolphin	21^h	+10°
Dorado	The Swordfish	5^h	−65°
Draco	The Dragon	17^h	+65°
Equuleus	The Foal	21^h	+10°
Eridanus	The River	3^h	−20°
Fornax	The Laboratory Furnace	3^h	−30°
Gemini	The Twins	7^h	+20°
Grus	The Crane	22^h	−45°
Hercules	Hercules	17^h	+30°
Horologium	The Clock	3^h	−60°
Hydra	The Water Serpent	10^h	−20°
Hydrus	The Water Snake	2^h	−75°
Indus	The American Indian	21^h	−55°
Lacerta	The Lizard	22^h	+45°
Leo	The Lion	11^h	+15°
Leo Minor	The Lion Cub	10^h	+35°
Lepus	The Hare	6^h	−20°
Libra	The Beam Balance	15^h	−15°
Lupus	The Wolf	15^h	−45°
Lynx	The Lynx	8^h	+45°
Lyra	The Lyre	19^h	+40°
Mensa	The Table Mountain	5^h	−80°
Microscopium	The Microscope	21^h	−35°
Monoceros	The Unicorn	7^h	−5°
Musca	The Fly	12^h	−70°
Norma	The Carpenter's Square	16^h	−50°
Octans	The Octant	22^h	−85°
Ophiuchus	The Serpent Holder	17^h	0°
Orion	The Great Hunter	5^h	+5°
Pavo	The Peacock	20^h	−65°
Pegasus	The Winged Horse	22^h	+20°
Perseus	The Hero	3^h	+45°
Phoenix	The Phoenix	1^h	−50°
Pictor	The Painter's Easel	6^h	−55°
Pisces	The Fishes	1^h	+15°
Piscis Austrinus	The Southern Fish	22^h	−30°
Puppis	The Stern (of Argo Navis)	8^h	−40°
Pyxis	The Compass Box (of Argo)	9^h	−30°
Reticulum	The Net	4^h	−60°
Sagitta	The Arrow	10^h	+10°
Sagittarius	The Archer	19^h	−25°
Scorpius	The Scorpion	17^h	−40°
Sculptor	The Sculptor's Workshop	0^h	−30°
Scutum (Sobieski)	The Shield (of John Sobieski[c])	19^h	−10°
Serpens	The Serpent	17^h	0°
Sextans	The Sextant	10^h	0°
Taurus	The Bull	4^h	+15°
Telescopium	The Telescope	19^h	−50°
Triangulum	The Triangle	2^h	+30°
Triangulum Australe	The Southern Triangle	16^h	−65°
Tucana	The Toucan	0^h	−65°
Ursa Major	The Greater Bear	11^h	+50°
Ursa Minor	The Lesser Bear	15^h	+70°
Vela	The Sail (of Argo Navis)	9^h	−50°
Virgo	The Maiden	13^h	0°
Volans	The Flying Fish	8^h	−70°
Vulpecula	The Fox	20^h	+25°

[a] Constellations with declinations between −50° and −90° are difficult or impossible to see from the United States.
[b] R.A., right ascension; Dec., declination.
[c] King John III of Poland (1624–1697).

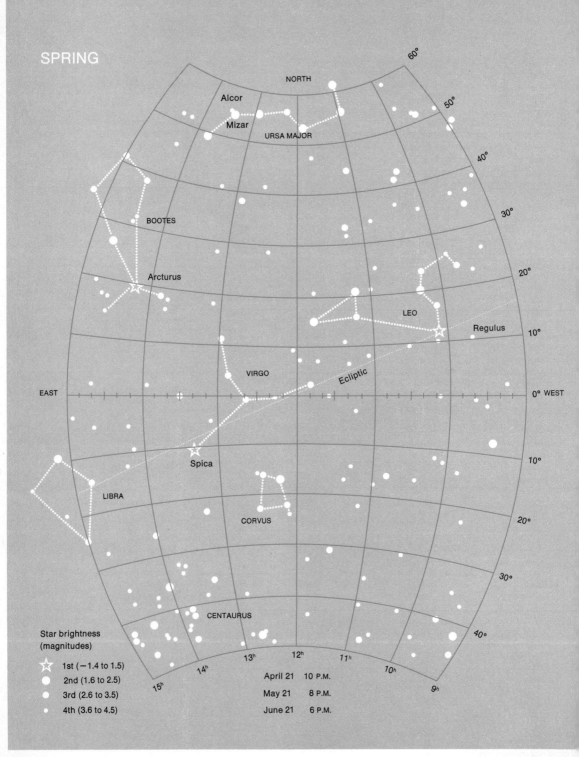

SPRING

These star maps show the brighter stars and the prominent constellations as they appear on the dates and at the times indicated. To use these maps, face the south and hold the book overhead with top of the map toward the north and the right-hand edge toward the west. The brightest stars are indicated by the star symbol (☆) and the names are indicated. (Star maps were designed by the author.)

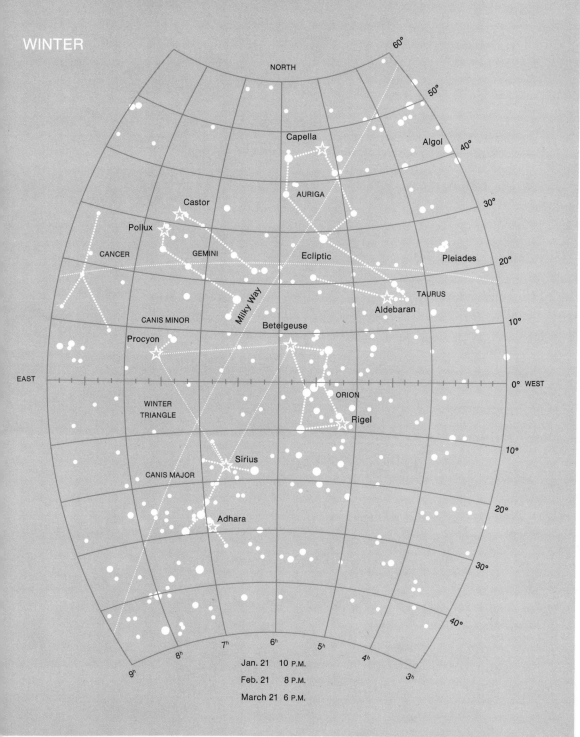

WINTER

NORTH

60°
50°
Capella
Algol
40°
AURIGA
30°
Castor
Pollux
GEMINI
Ecliptic
Pleiades
20°
CANCER
TAURUS
Aldebaran
Milky Way
10°
CANIS MINOR
Betelgeuse
Procyon
ORION
EAST
0° WEST
WINTER
TRIANGLE
Rigel
10°
Sirius
CANIS MAJOR
20°
Adhara
30°
40°

9ʰ   8ʰ   7ʰ   6ʰ   5ʰ   4ʰ   3ʰ

Jan. 21   10 P.M.

Feb. 21   8 P.M.

March 21   6 P.M.

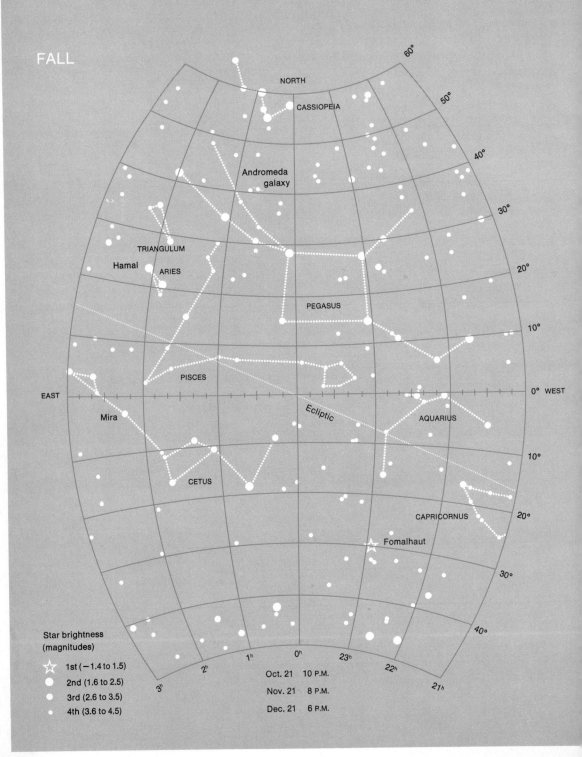

FALL

NORTH

CASSIOPEIA

Andromeda galaxy

TRIANGULUM

Hamal

ARIES

PEGASUS

PISCES

EAST

0° WEST

Mira

Ecliptic

AQUARIUS

CETUS

CAPRICORNUS

Fomalhaut

60°
50°
40°
30°
20°
10°
0° WEST
10°
20°
30°
40°

3ʰ 2ʰ 1ʰ 0ʰ 23ʰ 22ʰ 21ʰ

Star brightness (magnitudes)

☆ 1st (−1.4 to 1.5)
● 2nd (1.6 to 2.5)
○ 3rd (2.6 to 3.5)
· 4th (3.6 to 4.5)

Oct. 21   10 P.M.

Nov. 21   8 P.M.

Dec. 21   6 P.M.

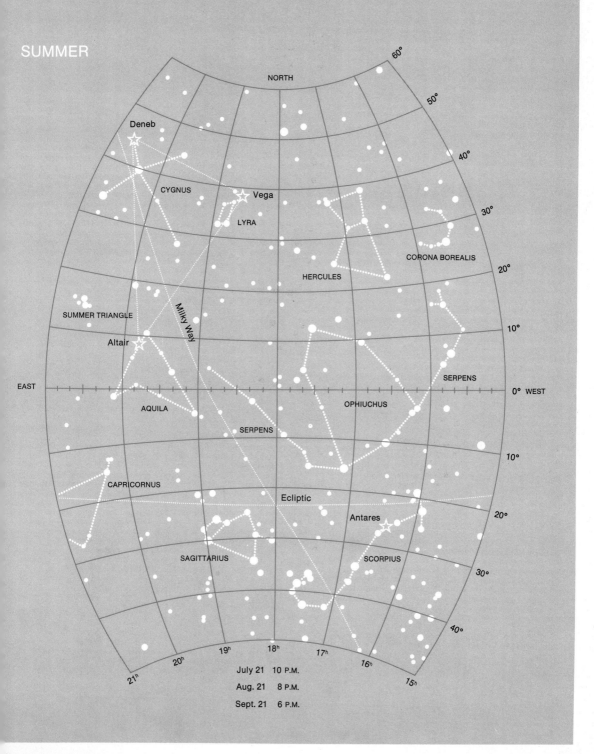

SUMMER

NORTH

60°
50°
40°
30°
20°

Deneb

CYGNUS

Vega

LYRA

HERCULES

CORONA BOREALIS

SUMMER TRIANGLE

Milky Way

Altair

10°

SERPENS

EAST

0° WEST

AQUILA

OPHIUCHUS

SERPENS

CAPRICORNUS

10°

Ecliptic

20°

Antares

SAGITTARIUS

SCORPIUS

30°

40°

21ʰ   20ʰ   19ʰ   18ʰ   17ʰ   16ʰ   15ʰ

July 21   10 P.M.

Aug. 21   8 P.M.

Sept. 21   6 P.M.

Index